SYMBIOSIS

the pearson custom library for the biological sciences

Biology Department
Middlesex County College
General Biology I
BIO 123

Pearson Learning Solutions

New York Boston San Francisco
London Toronto Sydney Tokyo Singapore Madrid
Mexico City Munich Paris Cape Town Hong Kong Montreal

Senior Vice President, Editorial and Marketing: Patrick F. Boles
Senior Sponsoring Editor: Natalie Danner
Development Editor: Annette Fantasia
Editorial Assistant: Jill Johnson
Executive Marketing Manager: Nathan L. Wilbur
Operations Manager: Eric M. Kenney
Database Production Manager: Jennifer Berry
Art Director: Renée Sartell
Cover Designer: Kristen Kiley

Cover Art: Courtesy of Michael R. Martin, Darryl Johnson, Photodisk, DK Images, and Prentice-Hall, Inc.

This special edition published in cooperation with Pearson Learning Solutions.

Printed in the United States of America.

Please visit our web site at *www.pearsoncustom.com/*.

Attention bookstores: For permission to return unused stock, contact us at *pe-uscustomreturns@pearson.com*.

Pearson Learning Solutions, 501 Boylston Street, Suite 900, Boston, MA 02116
A Pearson Education Company
www.pearsoned.com

ISBN 10: 0-536-94368-0
ISBN 13: 978-0-536-94368-2

49 2019

Laboratory Safety: General Guidelines

1. Notify your instructor immediately if you are pregnant, color blind, allergic to any insects or chemicals, taking immunosuppressive drugs, or have any other medical condition (such as diabetes, immunologic defect) that may require special precautionary measures in the laboratory.
2. Upon entering the laboratory, place all books, coats, purses, backpacks, etc. in designated areas, not on the bench tops.
3. Locate and, when appropriate, learn to use exits, fire extinguisher, fire blanket, chemical shower, eyewash, first aid kit, broken glass container, and cleanup materials for spills.
4. In case of fire, evacuate the room and assemble outside the building.
5. Do not eat, drink, smoke, or apply cosmetics in the laboratory.
6. Confine long hair, loose clothing, and dangling jewelry.
7. Wear shoes at all times in the laboratory.
8. Cover any cuts or scrapes with a sterile, waterproof bandage before attending lab.
9. Wear eye protection when working with chemicals.
10. Never pipet by mouth. Use mechanical pipeting devices.
11. Wash skin immediately and thoroughly if contaminated by chemicals or microorganisms.
12. Do not perform unauthorized experiments.
13. Do not use equipment without instruction.
14. Report *all* spills and accidents to your instructor immediately.
15. Never leave heat sources unattended.
16. When using hot plates, note that there is no visible sign that they are hot (such as a red glow). Always assume that hot plates are hot.
17. Use an appropriate apparatus when handling hot glassware.
18. Keep chemicals away from direct heat or sunlight.
19. Keep containers of alcohol, acetone, and other flammable liquids away from flames.
20. Do not allow any liquid to come into contact with electrical cords. Handle electrical connectors with dry hands. Do not attempt to disconnect electrical equipment that crackles, snaps, or smokes.
21. Upon completion of laboratory exercises, place all materials in the disposal areas designated by your instructor.
22. Do not pick up broken glassware with your hands. Use a broom and dustpan and discard the glass in designated glass waste containers; never discard with paper waste.
23. Wear disposable gloves when working with blood, other body fluids, or mucous membranes. Change gloves after possible contamination and wash hands immediately after gloves are removed.
24. The disposal symbol indicates that items that may have come in contact with body fluids should be placed in your lab's designated container. It also refers to liquid wastes that should not be poured down the drain into the sewage system.
25. Leave the laboratory clean and organized for the next student.
26. Wash your hands with liquid or powdered soap prior to leaving the laboratory.
27. The biohazard symbol indicates procedures that may pose health concerns.

The caution symbol points out instruments, substances, and procedures that require special attention to safety. These symbols appear throughout this manual.

Measurement Conversions

Metric to American Standard	American Standard to Metric

Length

1 mm = 0.039 inches	1 inch = 2.54 cm
1 cm = 0.394 inches	1 foot = 0.305 m
1 m = 3.28 feet	1 yard = 0.914 m
1 m = 1.09 yards	1 mile = 1.61 km

Volume

1 mL = 0.0338 fluid ounces	1 fluid ounce = 29.6 mL
1 L = 4.23 cups	1 cup = 237 mL
1 L = 2.11 pints	1 pint = 0.474 L
1 L = 1.06 quarts	1 quart = 0.947 L
1 L = 0.264 gallons	1 gallon = 3.79 L

Mass

1 mg = 0.0000353 ounces	1 ounce = 28.3 g
1 g = 0.0353 ounces	1 pound = 0.454 kg
1 kg = 2.21 pounds	

Temperature

To convert temperature:

$°C = \frac{5}{9}(F - 32)$ $°F = \frac{9}{5}C + 32$

°F °C

100 Water boils

98.6°F Normal human body temperature

37.0°C Normal human body temperature

0 Water freezes

Centimeters Inches

Contents

Microscopes and Cells

Laboratory Objectives

After completing this lab topic, you should be able to:

1. Identify the parts of compound and stereoscopic microscopes and be proficient in their correct use in biological studies.
2. Describe procedures used in preparing materials for electron microscopy and compare these with procedures used in light microscopy.
3. Identify cell structures and organelles from electron micrographs and state the functions of each.
4. Describe features of specific cells and determine characteristics shared by all cells studied.
5. Discuss the evolutionary significance of increasing complexity from unicellular to multicellular organization and provide examples from the lab.

Introduction

According to cell theory, the *cell* is the fundamental biological unit, the smallest and simplest biological structure possessing all the characteristics of the living condition. All living organisms are composed of one or more cells, and every activity taking place in a living organism is ultimately related to metabolic activities in cells. Thus, understanding the processes of life necessitates an understanding of the structure and function of the cell.

The earliest known cells found in fossilized sediments 3.5 billion years old (called **prokaryotic** cells) lack nuclei and membrane-bound organelles. Cells with a membrane-bound nucleus and organelles (**eukaryotic** cells) do not appear in the fossil record for another 2 billion years. But the eventual evolution of the eukaryotic cell and its internal compartmentalization led to enormous biological diversity in single cells. The evolution of loose aggregates of cells ultimately to colonies of connected cells provided for specialization, so that groups of cells had specific and different functions. This early division of labor included cells whose primary function was locomotion or reproduction. The evolution of multicellularity appears to have originated more than once in eukaryotes and provided an opportunity for extensive adaptive radiation as organisms specialized and diversified, eventually giving rise to fungi, plants, and animals. This general trend in increasing complexity and specialization seen in the history of life will be illustrated in this lab.

Given the fundamental role played by cells in the organization of life, one can readily understand why the study of cells is essential to the study of life. Cells, however, are below the limit of resolution of the human eye. We cannot study them without using a microscope. The microscope has probably contributed more than any other instrument to the development of biology as a science. Two types of microscopes are named according to the source of illumination used: light microscopes and electron microscopes. We will be using light microscopes exclusively in our study of cells, and we will view electron micrographs of cell structures not visible with the light microscope.

Microscopes of one kind or another are used by all biologists in numerous subdisciplines: genetics, molecular biology, neurobiology, cell biology, evolution, and ecology. The knowledge and skills you develop today will be used and enhanced throughout this course and throughout your career in biology. It is important, therefore, that you take the time to master these exercises thoroughly.

EXERCISE 1

Parts of the Microscope

Materials

compound microscope

Introduction

The microscope is designed to make objects visible that are too difficult or too small to see with the unaided eye. There are many different kinds of light microscopes, including phase-contrast, darkfield, polarizing, and UV. These differ primarily in the source and manner in which light is passed through the specimen to be viewed.

The microscopes in biology lab are usually compound binocular or monocular light microscopes, some of which may have phase-contrast attachments. **Compound** means that the scopes have a minimum of two magnifying lenses (the ocular and the objective lenses). **Binocular microscopes** have two eyepieces, **monoculars** have only one eyepiece, and **light** refers to the type of illumination used, that is, visible light from a lamp.

Your success in and enjoyment of a large portion of the laboratory work in introductory biology will depend on how proficient you become in the use of the microscope. When used and maintained correctly, these precision instruments are capable of producing images of the highest quality.

Although there are many variations in the features of microscopes, they are all constructed on a similar plan (Figure 1). In this exercise you will be introduced to the common variations found in different models of compound microscopes and asked to identify those features found on your microscope.

Please treat these microscopes with the greatest care!

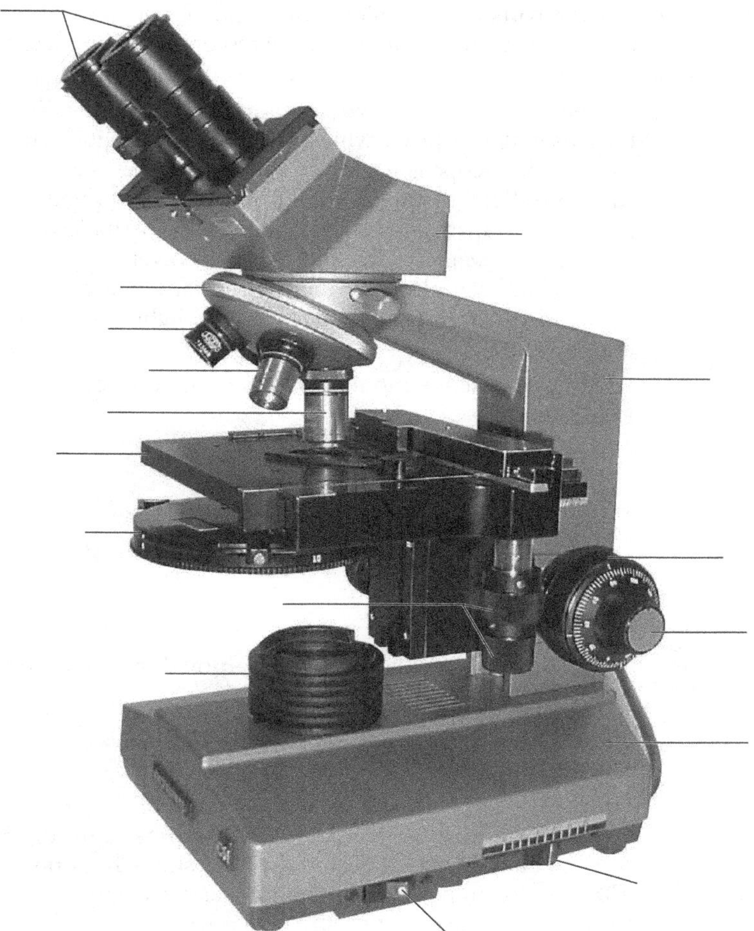

a.

b.

Figure 1.

a. **The compound binocular light microscope.** Locate the parts of your microscope described in Exercise 1 and label this photograph. Indicate in the margin of your lab manual any features unique to your microscope.

b. **Enlarged photo of compound light microscope as viewed from under the stage.** This microscope is equipped with phase-contrast optics. Locate the condenser, condenser adjustment knob, phase-contrast revolving turret, and iris diaphragm on your microscope (if present) and label them on the diagram.

Procedure

1. Obtain a compound light microscope, following directions from your instructor. To carry the microscope correctly, hold the arm with one hand, and support the base with your other hand. Remove the cover, but do not plug in the microscope.

2. Locate the parts of your microscope, and label Figure 1. Refer to the following description of a typical microscope. In the spaces provided, indicate the specific features related to your microscope.

   a. The **head** supports the two sets of magnifying lenses. The **ocular** is the lens in the eyepiece, which typically has a magnification of 10X. If your microscope is binocular, the distance between the eyepieces (**interpupillary distance**) can be adjusted to suit your eyes. Move the eyepieces apart, and look for the scale used to indicate the distance between the eyepieces. Do not adjust the eyepieces at this time. A pointer has been placed in the eyepiece and is used to point to an object in the **field of view**, the circle of light that one sees in the microscope.

      Is your microscope monocular (one eyepiece) or binocular (two eyepieces)?

      What is the magnification of your ocular(s)?

Although the eyepiece may be removable, it should not be removed from the microscope.

   b. **Objectives** are the three lenses on the **revolving nosepiece.** The shortest lens is typically 4X and is called the **scanning lens.** The **intermediate lens** is 10X, and the longest, the **high-power lens,** is 40X (the fourth position on the nosepiece is empty). It is important to clean both the objective and ocular lenses before each use. Dirty lenses will cause a blurring or fogging of the image. Always use lens paper for cleaning! Any other material (including Kimwipes®) may scratch the lenses.

      What is the magnification of each of your objectives? List them in order of increasing magnification.

   c. The **arm** supports the stage and condenser lens. The **condenser lens** is used to focus the light from the **lamp** through the specimen to be viewed. The height of the condenser can be adjusted by an **adjustment knob.** The **iris diaphragm** controls the width of the circle of light and, therefore, the amount of light passing through the specimen.

      If your microscope has phase-contrast optics, the condenser may be housed in a **revolving turret.** When the turret is set on 0, the normal optical arrangement is in place. This condition is called **bright-field microscopy.** Other positions of the turret set phase-contrast optics in place. To use phase-contrast, the turret setting must correspond to the magnifying power of the objective being used.

      Is your microscope equipped with phase-contrast optics?

The **stage** supports the specimen to be viewed. A mechanical stage can be moved right and left and back and forth by two **stage adjustment knobs.** With a stationary stage, the slide is secured under **stage clips** and moved slightly by hand while viewing the slide. The distance between the stage and the objective can be adjusted with the **coarse** and **fine focus adjustment knobs.**

Does your microscope have a mechanical or stationary stage?

d. The **base** acts as a stand for the microscope and houses the lamp. In some microscopes, the intensity of the light that passes through the specimen can be adjusted with the **light intensity lever.** Generally, more light is needed when using high magnification than when using low magnification. Describe the light system for your microscope.

EXERCISE 2
Basic Microscope Techniques

Materials

clear ruler
coverslips
prepared slides: letter and crossed thread
lens paper
blank slides
Kimwipes®
dropper bottle with distilled water

Introduction

In this exercise, you will learn to use the microscope to examine a recognizable object, a slide of the letter *e*. Recall that microscopes vary, so you may have to omit steps that refer to features not available on your microscope. Practice adjusting your microscope to become proficient in locating a specimen, focusing clearly, and adjusting the light for the best contrast.

Procedure

1. Clean microscope lenses.

   Each time you use the microscope, you should begin by cleaning the lenses. Using lens paper moistened with a drop of distilled water, wipe the ocular, objective, and condenser lenses. Wipe them again with a piece of dry lens paper.

Use only lens paper on microscope lenses. Do not use Kimwipes®, tissues, or other papers.

2. Adjust the focus on your microscope:

   a. Plug your microscope into the outlet.

   b. Turn on the light. Adjust the light intensity to mid-range if your microscope has that feature.

c. Rotate the 4X objective into position using the revolving nosepiece ring, not the objective itself.

d. Take the letter slide and wipe it with a Kimwipe® tissue. Each time you study a prepared slide, you should first wipe it clean. Place the letter slide on the stage, and center it over the stage opening.

Slides should be placed on and removed from the stage only when the 4X objective is in place. Removing a slide when the higher objectives are in position may scratch the lenses.

e. Look through the ocular and bring the letter into rough focus by slowly focusing upward using the coarse adjustment.

f. For binocular microscopes, looking through the oculars, move the oculars until you see only one image of the letter *e*. In this position, the oculars should be aligned with your pupils. In the margin of your lab manual, make a note of the **interpupillary distance** on the scale between the oculars. Each new lab day, before you begin to use the microscope, set this distance.

g. Raise the condenser to its highest position, and fully close the iris diaphragm.

h. Looking through the ocular, slowly lower the condenser just until the graininess disappears. Slowly open the iris diaphragm just until the entire field of view is illuminated. This is the correct position for both the condenser and the iris diaphragm.

i. Rotate the 10X objective into position.

j. Look through the ocular and slowly focus upward with the coarse adjustment knob until the image is in rough focus. Sharpen the focus using the fine adjustment knob.

Do not turn the fine adjustment knob more than two revolutions in either direction. If the image does not come into focus, return to 10X and refocus using the coarse adjustment.

k. For binocular microscopes, cover your left eye and use the fine adjustment knob to focus the fixed (right) ocular until the letter *e* is in maximum focus. Now cover the right eye and, using the diopter ring on the left ocular, bring the image into focus. The letter *e* should now be in focus for both of your eyes. Each new lab day, as you begin to study your first slide, repeat this procedure.

l. You can increase or decrease the contrast by adjusting the iris diaphragm opening. Note that the maximum amount of light provides little contrast. Adjust the aperture until the image is sharp.

m. Move the slide slowly to the right. In what direction does the image in the ocular move?

n. Is the image in the ocular inverted relative to the specimen on the stage?

o. Center the specimen in the field of view; then rotate the 40X objective into position while watching from the side. *If it appears that the objective will hit the slide, stop and ask for assistance.*

Most of the microscopes have **parfocal** lenses, which means that little refocusing is required when moving from one lens to another. If your scope is *not* parfocal, ask your instructor for assistance.

p. After the 40X objective is in place, focus using the fine adjustment knob.

Never focus with the coarse adjustment knob when you are using the high-power objective.

q. The distance between the specimen and the objective lens is called the **working distance.** Is this distance greater with the 40X or the 10X objective?

3. Compute the total magnification of the specimen being viewed. To do so, multiply the magnification of the ocular lens by that of the objective lens.

a. What is the total magnification of the letter as the microscope is now set?

b. What would be the total magnification if the ocular were 20X and the objective were 100X (oil immersion)? This is the magnification achieved by the best light microscopes.

4. Measure the diameter of the field of view. Once you determine the size of the field of view for any combination of ocular and objective lenses, you can determine the size of any structure within that field.

a. Rotate the 4X objective into position and remove the letter slide.

b. Place a clear ruler on the stage, and focus on its edge.

c. The distance between two lines on the ruler is 1 mm. What is the diameter (mm) of the field of view?

d. Convert this measurement to micrometers, a more commonly used unit of measurement in microscopy (1 mm = 1,000 μm).

e. Measure the diameters of the field of view for the 10X and 40X objectives, and enter all three in the spaces below to be used for future reference.

4X ≈ ________ 10X ≈ ________ 40X ≈ ________

f. What is the relationship between the size of the field of view and magnification?

5. Determine spatial relationships. The **depth of field** is the thickness of the specimen that may be seen in focus at one time. Because the depth of focus is very short in the compound microscope, focus up and down to clearly view all planes of a specimen.

   a. Rotate the 4X objective into position and remove the ruler. Take a slide of crossed threads, wipe it with a Kimwipe, and place the slide on the stage. Center the slide so that the region where the two threads cross is in the center of the stage opening.

   b. Focus on the region where the threads cross. Are both threads in focus at the same time?

   c. Rotate the 10X objective into position and focus on the cross. Are both threads in focus at the same time?

   Does the 4X or the 10X objective have a shorter depth of field?

   d. Focus upward (move the stage up) with the coarse adjustment until both threads are just out of focus. Slowly focus down using the fine adjustment. Which thread comes into focus first? Is this thread lying under or over the other thread?

   e. Rotate the 40X objective into position and slowly focus up and down, using the fine adjustment only. Does the 10X or the 40X objective have a shorter depth of field?

6. At the end of your microscope session, use these procedures to store your microscope:

   a. Rotate the 4X objective into position.

   b. Remove the slide from the stage.

c. Return the phase-contrast condenser to the 0 setting if you have used phase-contrast.
d. Set the light intensity to its lowest setting and turn off the power.
e. Unplug the cord and wrap it around the base of the microscope.
f. Replace the dust cover.
g. Return the microscope to the cabinet using two hands; one hand should hold the arm, and the other should support the base.

These steps should be followed every time you store your microscope.

EXERCISE 3
The Stereoscopic Microscope

Materials

stereoscopic microscope
dissecting needles
living *Elodea*
microscope slides
droppers of water
coverslips

Introduction

The stereoscopic (dissecting) microscope has relatively low magnification, 7× to 30×, and is used for viewing and manipulating relatively large objects. The binocular feature creates the stereoscopic effect. The stereoscopic microscope is similar to the compound microscope except in the following ways: (1) The depth of field is much greater than with the compound microscope, so objects are seen in three dimensions, and (2) the light source can be directed down onto as well as up through an object, which permits the viewing of objects too thick to transmit light. Light directed down on the object is called **reflected** or **incident light.** Light passing through the object is called **transmitted light.**

Procedure

1. Remove your dissecting microscope from the cabinet and locate the parts labeled in Figure 2. Locate the switches for both incident and transmitted light. In the margin of your lab manual, note any features of your microscope that are not shown in the figure. What is the range of magnification for your microscope?

2. Prepare a wet mount of *Elodea*. Living material is often prepared for observation using a wet mount. (The material is either in water or covered with water prior to adding a coverslip.) You will use this technique to view living material under the dissecting and compound microscopes (Figure 3).
   a. Place a drop of water in the center of a clean microscope slide.
   b. Remove a single leaf of *Elodea,* and place it in the drop of water.
   c. Using a dissecting needle, place a coverslip at a 45° angle above the slide with one edge of the coverslip in contact with the edge of the water droplet, as shown.

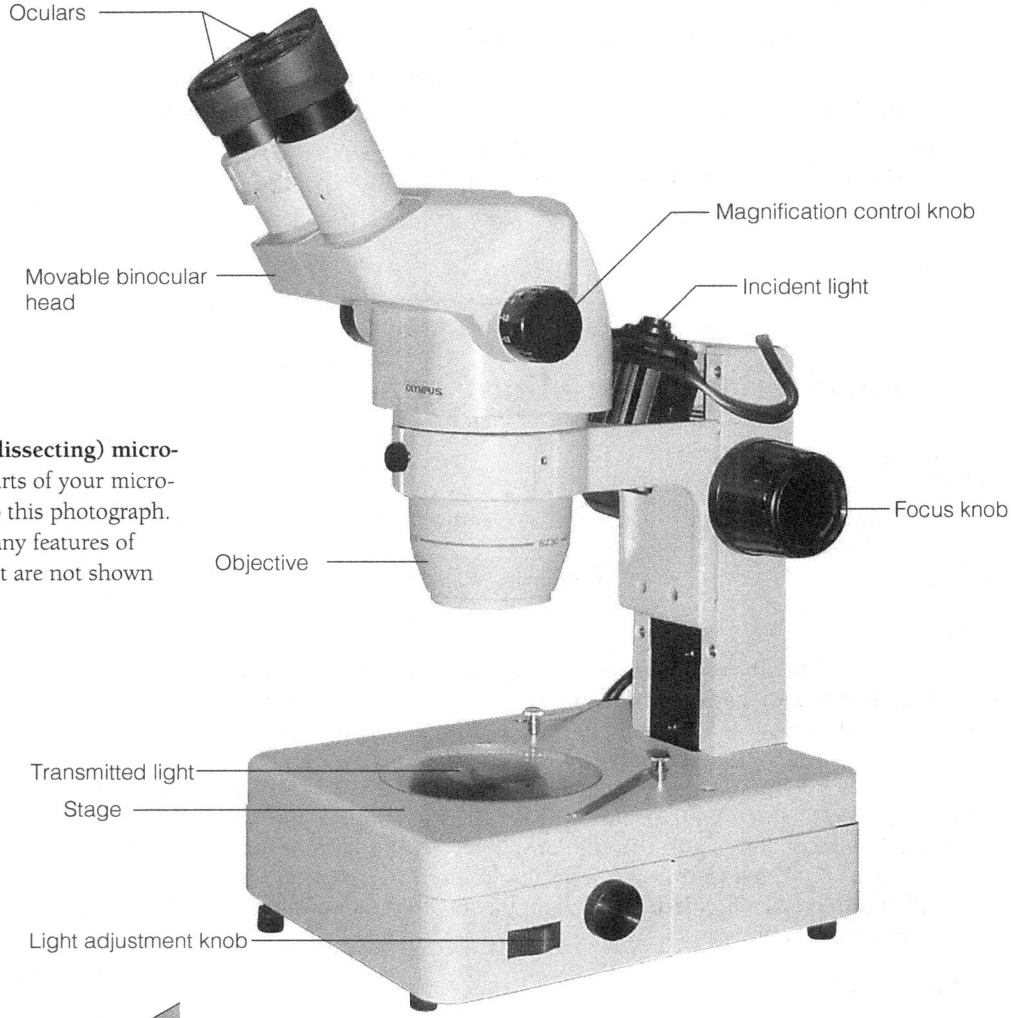

Figure 2.
The stereoscopic (dissecting) microscope. Locate the parts of your microscope by referring to this photograph. Note in the margin any features of your microscope that are not shown in the photograph.

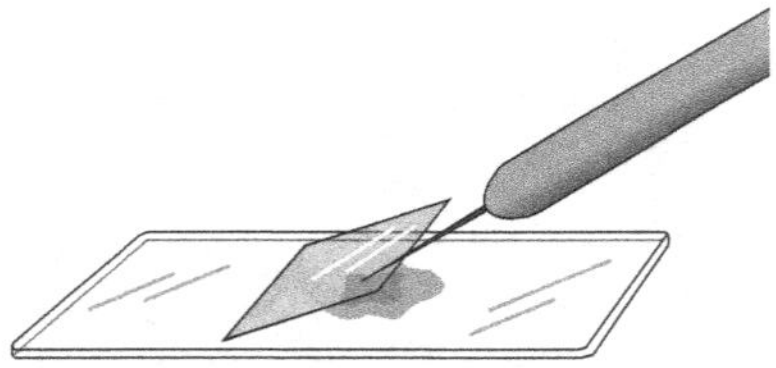

Figure 3.
Preparation of a wet mount. Place a drop of water and your specimen on the slide. Using a dissecting needle, slowly lower a coverslip onto the slide, being careful not to trap air bubbles in the droplet.

d. Lower the coverslip slowly onto the slide, being careful not to trap air bubbles in the droplet. The function of the coverslip is threefold: (1) to flatten the preparation, (2) to keep the preparation from drying out, and (3) to protect the objective lenses. Over long periods of time, the preparation may dry out, at which point water can be added to one edge of the coverslip.

Specimens can be viewed without a coverslip using the stereoscopic microscope, but a coverslip must always be used with the compound microscope.

3. Observe the structure of the *Elodea* leaf at increasing magnification.
   a. Place the leaf slide on the stage, and adjust the interpupillary distance (distance between the oculars) by gently pushing or pulling the oculars until you can see the object clearly as a single image.
   b. Change the magnification and note the three-dimensional characteristic of the leaf.
   c. Sketch the leaf in the margin of your lab manual and list, in the space below, the structures that are visible at low and high magnification.

      Low:

      High:

      Is it possible to see cells in the leaf using the stereoscopic microscope?

      Organelles?

   d. Save your slide for later study. In Exercise 5, Lab Study C, you will be asked to compare these observations of *Elodea* with those made while using the compound microscope.

EXERCISE 4
The Electron Microscope

Materials

demonstration resources for the electron microscope
electron micrographs

Introduction

The electron microscope magnifies objects approximately 1,000× larger than a light microscope can (up to 1,000,000×). This difference depends on the **resolving power** of the electron microscope, which allows the viewer to see two objects of comparable size that are close together and still be able to recognize that they are two objects rather than one. Resolving power, in turn, depends on the wavelength of light passed through the specimen: the shorter the wavelength, the greater the resolution. Because electron microscopes use electrons as a source of illumination and electrons have a much shorter wavelength than does visible light, the resolving power of electron microscopes is much greater than that of light microscopes. Both the electron and light microscopes can be equipped with lenses that allow for tremendous magnification, but only the electron microscope has sufficient resolving power to make these lenses useful.

Procedure

1. Compare the features of the light and electron microscopes (Figure 4).
   a. Name three structures found in both microscopes.

   b. What is the energy source for the electron microscope?

   For the compound microscope?

   c. Describe how the lenses differ for the two microscopes.

2. Using the resources provided by your instructor, review the procedures and materials for preparing a specimen for electron microscopy.

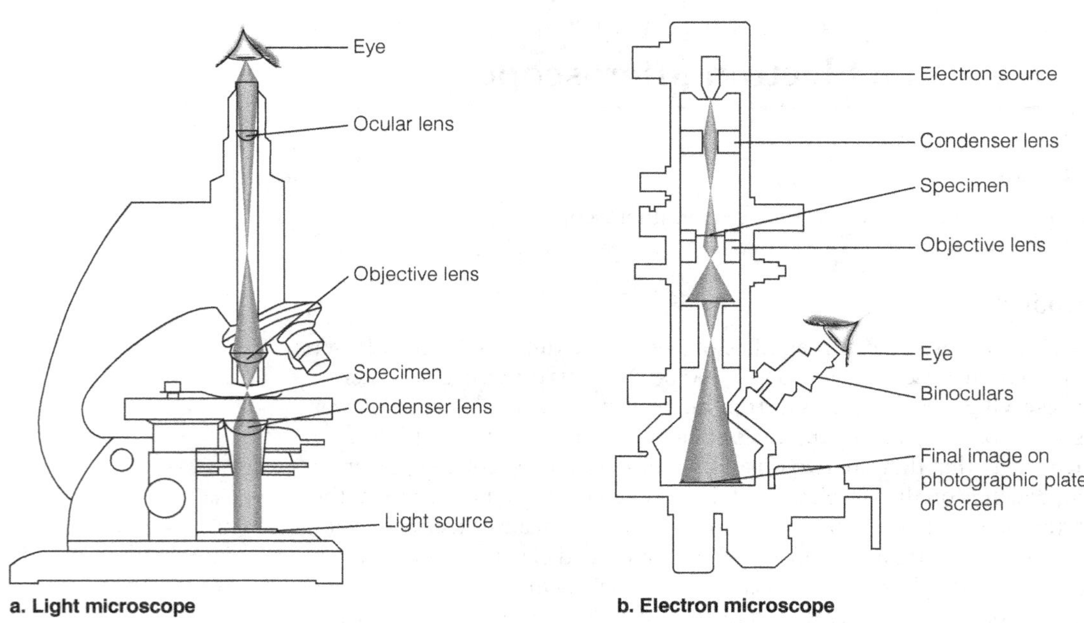

Figure 4.
Comparison of light microscope and electron microscope. The source of illumination is light for the light microscope and electrons for the electron microscope. The image is magnified by glass objectives in light microscopy and by electromagnets in electron microscopy.

3. Define the following terms on separate paper or in the margin of your lab manual:

fixation	*staining with heavy metals*
embedding	*electromagnetic lenses*
ultramicrotome	*fluorescent screen*
boat on diamond or glass knife	*vacuum*
copper grids	*electron micrographs*

4. Observe the electron micrographs on demonstration in the laboratory. Use these and your textbook to complete Table 1.

EXERCISE 5
The Organization of Cells

In this exercise, you will examine the features common to all eukaryotic cells that are indicative of their common ancestry. However, you will observe that all cells are not the same. Some organisms are **unicellular** (single-celled), with all living functions (respiration, digestion, reproduction, and excretion) handled by that one cell. Others form random, temporary **aggregates,** or clusters, of cells. Clusters composed of a consistent and predictable number of cells are called **colonies.** Simple colonies have no physiological connections but maintain a predictable multicellular structure. Complex colonies have physiological connections and specialization of groups of cells. **Multicellular** organisms have large numbers of cells with specialized structure and function, and no one cell can exist successfully by itself.

In this exercise, you will examine selected unicellular, aggregate, colonial, and multicellular organisms.

Lab Study A. Unicellular Organisms

Materials

microscope slides	coverslips
culture of *Amoeba*	dissecting needles
living termites	insect Ringers
forceps	

Introduction

Unicellular eukaryotic organisms may be **autotrophic** (photosynthetic) or **heterotrophic** (deriving food from other organisms or their by-products).

Table 1
Characteristics of Cellular Organelles; EM = Electron Microscope, LM = Light Microscope

Organelle	Size (μm); Visualization	Function	Where Present: Plants and Autotrophic Protists	Where Present: Animals and Heterotrophic Protists
Plasma membrane	7–9 × 10^{-3} (thickness); EM			
Cell wall	Variable; a single fibril is as thick as the plasma membrane; LM, EM			
Nucleus	4–10 (diameter); LM, EM			
Chloroplast	8 (length); LM, EM			
Mitochondria	0.5–10 (diameter); EM			
Vacuole	Variable; LM, EM			
Golgi apparatus	Variable; EM			
Peroxisomes	0.2–1.5 (diameter); EM			
Lysosomes	0.2–0.5 (diameter); EM			
Endoplasmic reticulum	0.005–0.01 (tube diameter); EM			
Ribosomes	1.7–2.3 × 10^{-3} (diameter); EM			
Flagella, cilia	0.2 (diameter); 2–150 (length); LM, EM			

Procedure

1. Examine a living *Amoeba* (Figure 5) under the compound microscope. Amoebas are aquatic organisms commonly found in ponds. To transfer a specimen to your slide, follow these procedures:
   a. Place the culture dish containing the amoeba under the dissecting microscope, and focus on the bottom of the dish. The amoeba will appear as a whitish, irregularly shaped organism attached to the bottom.
   b. Using a clean pipette (it is important not to interchange pipettes between culture dishes), transfer a drop with several amoebas to your microscope slide. To do this, squeeze the pipette bulb *before* you place the tip under the surface of the water. Disturbing the culture as little as possible, pipette a drop of water with debris from the *bottom* of the culture dish. You may use your stereoscopic microscope to scan the slide to locate amoebas before continuing.
   c. Cover your preparation with a clean coverslip.
   d. Under low power on the compound scope, scan the slide to locate an amoeba. Center the specimen in your field of view; then switch to higher powers.
   e. Identify the following structures in the amoeba:

      Cell membrane is the boundary that separates the organism from its surroundings.

      Ectoplasm is the thin, transparent layer of cytoplasm directly beneath the cell membrane.

      Endoplasm is the granular cytoplasm containing the cell organelles.

      The **nucleus** is the grayish, football-shaped body that is somewhat granular in appearance. This organelle, which directs the cellular activities, will often be seen moving within the endoplasm.

      Contractile vacuoles are clear, spherical vesicles of varying sizes that gradually enlarge as they fill with excess water. Once you've located a vacuole, watch it fill and then empty its contents into the surrounding environment. These vacuoles serve an excretory function for the amoeba.

      Food vacuoles are small, dark, irregularly shaped vesicles within the endoplasm. They contain undigested food particles.

      Pseudopodia ("false feet") are fingerlike projections of the cytoplasm. They are used for locomotion as well as for trapping and engulfing food in a process called **phagocytosis.**

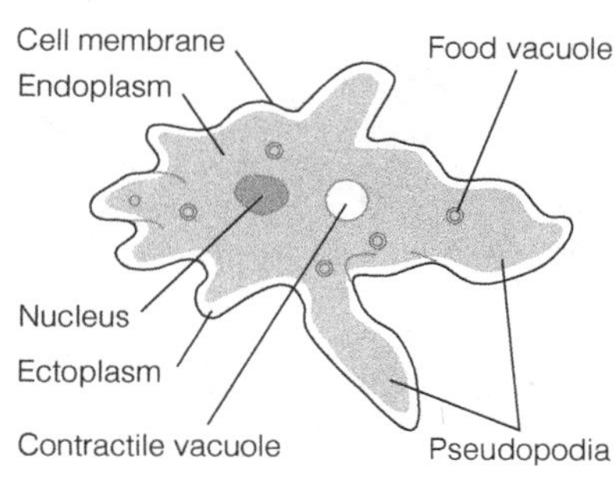

Figure 5.
Amoeba. An *Amoeba* moves using pseudopodia. Observe the living organisms using the compound microscope.

2. Examine *Trichonympha* under a compound microscope. You will first have to separate the *Trichonympha* (Figure 6) from the termite with which it lives in a symbiotic relationship. *Trichonympha* and other organisms occupy the gut of the termites, where they digest wood particles eaten by the insect. Termites lack the enzymes necessary to digest wood and are dependent on *Trichonympha* to make the nutrients in the wood available to them. *Trichonympha* has become so well adapted to the environment of the termite's gut that it cannot survive outside of it.

   To obtain a specimen:
   a. Place a couple of drops of **insect Ringers** (a saline solution that is isotonic to the internal environment of insects) on a clean microscope slide.
   b. Using forceps or your fingers, transfer a termite into the drop of Ringers.

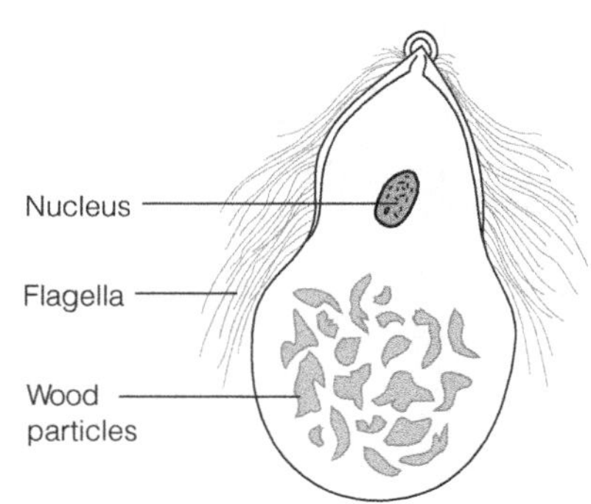

Figure 6.
Trichonympha. A community of microorganisms, including *Trichonympha,* inhabits the intestine of the termite. Following the procedure in Exercise 5, Lab Study A, disperse the microorganisms and locate the cellular structures in *Trichonympha.*

c. Place the slide under the dissecting microscope.
d. Place the tips of dissecting needles at either end of the termite and pull in opposite directions.
e. Locate the long tube that is the termite's intestine. Remove all the larger parts of the insect from the slide.
f. Using a dissecting needle, mash the intestine to release the *Trichonympha* and other protozoa and bacteria.
g. Cover your preparation with a clean coverslip.
h. Transfer your slide to the compound microscope and scan the slide under low power. Center several *Trichonympha* in the field of view and switch to higher powers.

Several types of protozoans and bacteria will be present in the termite gut.

i. Locate the following structures under highest power:

Flagella are the long, hairlike structures on the outside of the organism. The function of the flagella is not fully understood. Within the gut of the termite, the organisms live in such high density that movement by flagellar action seems unlikely and perhaps impossible.

The **nucleus** is a somewhat spherical organelle near the middle of the organism.

Wood particles may be located in the posterior region of the organism.

Lab Study B. Aggregate and Colonial Organisms

Materials

microscope slides
dissecting needles
forceps
coverslips
broken glass chips
cultures of *Protococcus*, *Scenedesmus*, and *Volvox*

Introduction

Unlike unicellular organisms, which live independently of each other, colonial organisms are cells that live in groups and are to some degree dependent on one another. The following organisms show an increasing degree of interaction among cells.

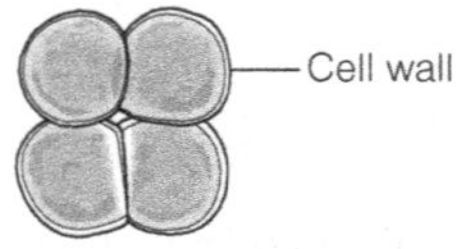

Figure 7.
Protococcus. *Protococcus* is a terrestrial green alga that forms loose aggregates on the bark of trees.

Procedure

1. Examine *Protococcus* under the compound microscope. *Protococcus* (Figure 7) is a terrestrial green alga that grows on the north sides of trees and is often referred to as "moss."

a. To obtain a specimen, use a dissecting needle to brush off a small amount of the green growth on the piece of tree bark provided into a drop of water on a clean microscope slide. Avoid scraping bark onto the slide. Cover the preparation with a clean coverslip.

b. Observe at highest power that these cells are **aggregates:** The size of the cell groupings is random, and there are no permanent connections between cells. Each cell is surrounded by a cell membrane and an outer **cell wall.**

c. Observe several small cell groupings and avoid large clumps of cells. Cellular detail may be obscure.

2. Examine living *Scenedesmus* under the compound microscope. *Scenedesmus* (Figure 8) is an aquatic green alga that is common in aquaria and polluted water.

   a. To obtain a specimen, place a drop from the culture dish (using a clean pipette) onto a clean microscope slide, and cover it with a clean coverslip.

   b. Observe that the cells of this organism form a **simple colony:** The cells always occur in groups of from four to eight cells, and they are permanently united.

   c. Identify the following structures:

   The **nucleus** is the spherical organelle in the approximate middle of each cell.

   Vacuoles are the transparent spheres that tend to occur at either end of the cells.

   Spines are the transparent projections that occur on the two end cells.

   Cell walls surround each cell.

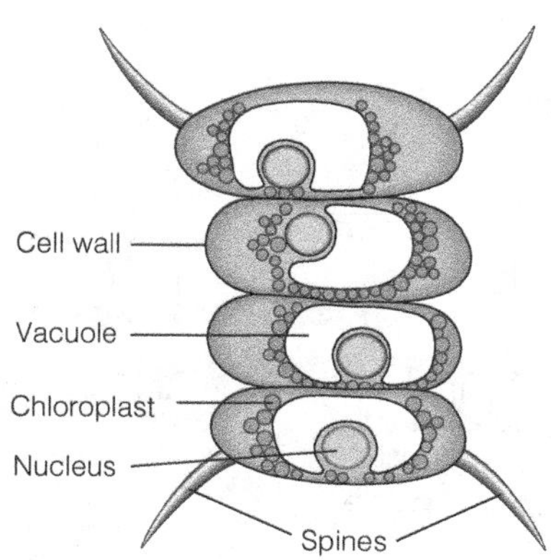

Figure 8.
Scenedesmus. *Scenedesmus* is an aquatic alga that usually occurs in simple colonies of four cells connected by an outer cell wall.

3. Examine living *Volvox* under the compound microscope. *Volvox* (Figure 9) is an aquatic green alga that also is common in aquaria, ponds, and lakes.

   a. To obtain a specimen, prepare a wet mount as you did for *Scenedesmus* with the following addition: Before placing a drop of the culture on your slide, place several glass chips on the slide. This will keep the coverslip from crushing these spherical organisms.

   b. Observe that the cells of this organism form a large **complex colony.** Approximately 500 to 50,000 cells (depending on the species) are permanently united, there are cytoplasmic connections between cells, and some cells are specialized for reproduction.

   c. Identify the following structures:

   Individual cells all possess the following structures: **cell wall, nucleus, vacuole, chloroplasts, flagella** (two per cell).

   Cytoplasmic strands form connections between adjacent cells.

   Daughter colonies are smaller spheres within the larger colony. These are produced asexually, and when they are large enough, they will be discharged from the parent colony into the surrounding environment.

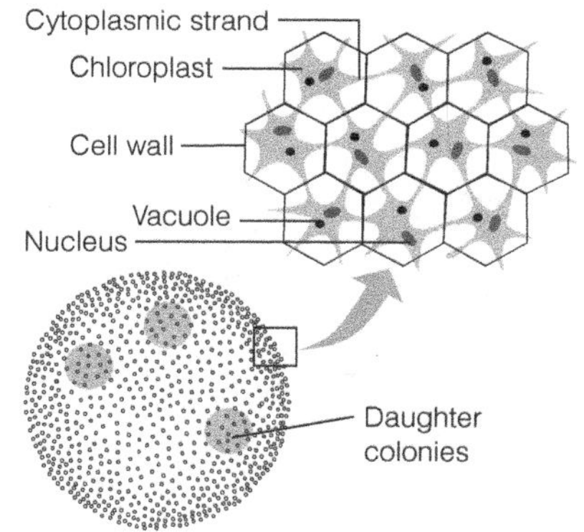

Figure 9.
Volvox. In this complex colony, the individual cells are interconnected by cytoplasmic strands to form a sphere. Small clusters of cells, called daughter colonies, are specialized for reproduction.

Lab Study C. Multicellular Organisms

Materials

microscope slides
dropper bottles of water
toothpicks
coverslips
Elodea
methylene blue
finger bowl with disinfectant

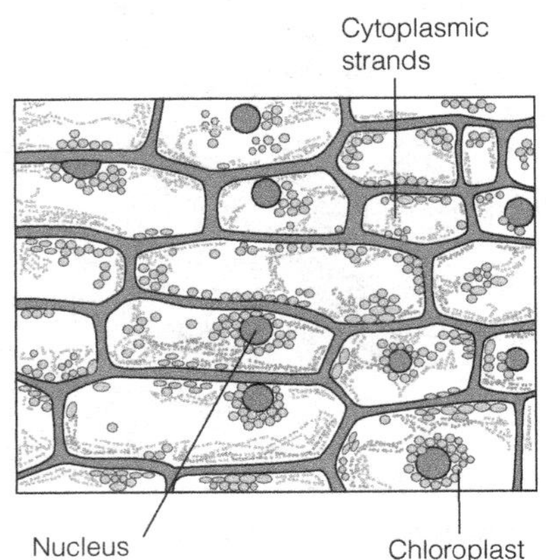

Figure 10.
Elodea. *Elodea* is an aquatic plant commonly grown in freshwater aquaria. The cell structures may be difficult to see because of the three-dimensional cell shape and the presence of a large central vacuole.

Introduction

Multicellular organisms are composed of groups of specialized cells, called **tissues,** that together perform particular functions for the organism. Tissues, in turn, may be grouped to form **organs,** and organs may be grouped into **organ systems.** In this lab study, you will examine some of the cells that compose the basic tissue types of plants and animals.

Procedure

Plant Cells

1. The major characteristics of a typical plant cell are readily seen in the leaf cells of *Elodea,* a common aquatic plant (Figure 10). Prepare a wet mount and examine one of the youngest (smallest) leaves from a sprig of *Elodea* under the compound microscope.
2. Identify the following structures:

   The **cell wall** is the rigid outer framework surrounding the cell. This structure gives the cell a definite shape and support. It is not found in animal cells.

   Protoplasm is the organized contents of the cell, exclusive of the cell wall.

   Cytoplasm is the protoplasm of the cell, exclusive of the nucleus.

   The **central vacuole** is a membrane-bound sac within the cytoplasm that is filled with water and dissolved substances. This structure serves to store metabolic wastes and gives the cell support by means of turgor pressure. Animal cells also have vacuoles, but they are not as large and conspicuous as those found in plants.

   Chloroplasts are the green, spherical organelles often seen moving within the cytoplasm. These organelles carry the pigment chlorophyll that is involved in photosynthesis. As the microscope light heats up the cells, cytoplasm and chloroplasts may begin to move around the central vacuole in a process called *cytoplasmic streaming,* or *cyclosis.*

   The **nucleus** is the usually spherical, transparent organelle within the cytoplasm. This structure controls cell metabolism and division.
3. What three structures observed in *Elodea* are unique to plants?

4. Compare your observations of *Elodea* using the compound scope with those made in Exercise 3 using the stereoscopic scope. List the structures seen with each:

   Stereoscopic:

   Compound:

Animal Cells

1. Animals are multicellular heterotrophic organisms that ingest organic matter. They are composed of cells that can be categorized into four major tissue groups: epithelial, connective, muscle, and nervous tissue. In this lab study, you will examine epithelial cells. Similar to the epidermal cells of plants, **epithelial cells** occur on the outside of animals and serve to protect the animals from water loss, mechanical injury, and foreign invaders. In addition, epithelial cells line interior cavities and ducts in animals. Examine the epithelial cells (Figure 11) that form the lining of your inner cheek. To obtain a specimen, follow this procedure:
   a. With a clean toothpick, gently scrape the inside of your cheek several times.
   b. Roll the scraping into a drop of water on a clean microscope slide, add a small drop of methylene blue, and cover with a coverslip. Discard the used toothpick in disinfectant.
   c. Using the compound microscope, view the cells under higher powers.
2. Observe that these cells are extremely flat and so may be folded over on themselves. Attempt to locate several cells that are not badly folded, and study their detail.
3. Identify the following structures:

   The **cell membrane** is the boundary that separates the cell from its surroundings.

   The **nucleus** is the large, circular organelle near the middle of the cell.

   Cytoplasm is the granular contents of the cell, exclusive of the nucleus.

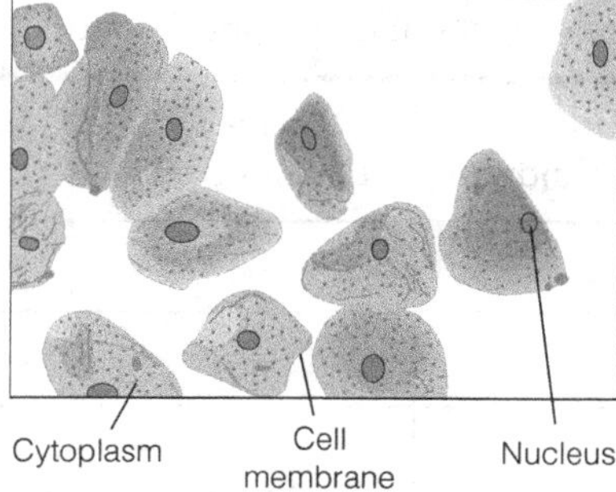

Figure 11.
Human epithelial cells. The epithelial cells that line your cheek are thin, flat cells that you can remove easily from your cheek by scraping it with a toothpick.

Lab Study D. Unknowns

Materials

microscope slides
coverslips
pond water or culture of unknowns

Introduction

Use this lab study to see if you have met the objectives of this lab topic. As you carry out this lab study, (1) think carefully about using correct microscopic techniques; (2) distinguish organisms with different cellular organization or configuration; (3) note how the different organisms are similar yet different; and (4) note cell differences.

Procedure

1. Examine several drops of the culture of pond water that you collected, or examine the unknown culture provided by the instructor.
2. Record in Table 2 the characteristics of at least four different organisms.

Table 2
Characteristics of Organisms Found in Pond Water

Tube Unknown	Means of Locomotion	Cell Wall (+/–)	Chloroplasts (+/–)	Organization
1				
2				
3				
4				
5				

Questions for Review

1. List several organelles that are visible with the electron microscope but that were not visible with your microscope.

2. Describe at least two types of materials or observations that would necessitate the use of the stereoscopic microscope.

3. What characteristics do all eukaryotic cells have in common?

4. a. What cellular features differentiate plants from animals?

   b. How are the structures that are unique to plants important to their success?

Applying Your Knowledge

1. In your own words, describe the evolutionary trend for increasing organismal complexity, using examples from this lab to illustrate your answer.

2. We often imply that multicellular organisms are more advanced (and therefore more successful) than unicellular or colonial organisms. Explain why this is not true, using examples from this lab or elsewhere.

3. Following is a list of tissues that have specialized functions and demonstrate corresponding specialization of subcellular structure. Match the tissue with the letter of the cell structures and organelles listed to the right that would be abundant in these cells. (Refer to Table 1.)

Tissues

- Enzyme (protein)-secreting cells of the pancreas
- Insect flight muscles
- Cells lining the respiratory passages
- White blood cells that engulf and destroy invading bacteria
- Leaf cells of cacti

Cell Structures and Organelles

a. plasma membrane
b. mitochondria
c. Golgi apparatus
d. chloroplast
e. endoplasmic reticulum
f. cilia and flagella
g. vacuole
h. ribosome
i. lysosome
j. peroxisomes

4. One organism found in a termite's gut is *Mixotricha paradoxa.* This strange creature looks like a single-celled swimming ciliate under low magnification. However, the electron microscope reveals that it contains spherical bacteria rather than mitochondria and has on its surface, rather than cilia, hundreds of thousands of spirilla and bacilla bacteria. You are the scientist who first observed this organism. How would you describe this organism—single-celled? aggregate? colony? multicellular? Review definitions of these terms. Can the structure of this organism give you any insight into the evolution of eukaryotic cells? (*Hint:* See the discussion of the endosymbiosis hypothesis in your text.)

References

Alberts, B., D. Bray, J. Lewis, M. Raff, K. Roberts, and J. Watson. *Molecular Biology of the Cell,* 3rd ed. New York: Garland, 1994.

Becker, W. M., J. B. Reece, and M. F. Poenie. *The World of the Cell,* 3rd ed. Redwood City, CA: Benjamin/Cummings, 1996.

Cooper, G. M. *The Cell: A Molecular Approach,* 2nd ed. Sunderland, MA: ASM Press/Sinauer Associates, 2000.

Margulis, L., and D. Sagan. "The Beast with Five Genomes," *Natural History,* 2001, vol. 110, pp. 38–41.

Website

Cells Alive:
http://www.cellsalive.com

Photo Credits

1: Eloise Carter. 2: Judith Morgan.

Art Credits

4: Adapted from Neil Campbell, *Biology,* 3rd ed. (Redwood City, CA: Benjamin/Cummings, 1993), ©1993 The Benjamin/Cummings Publishing Company.

Microbial Ecology

Acne, spoiled milk, polluted water. What do these have in common? They are caused by living organisms. Usually when we think of organisms, most of us can point to things we can see, things that have definite color and shape. We think of plants and animals that consume, prey upon each other or in some way interact to change the environment. Yet an entire world exists in biology that cannot be seen by our eyes—the microbial world. This consists of organisms that are invisible to us except with the microscope.

These organisms that include bacteria, microscopic algae and fungi, and protozoa inhabit the earth in vast numbers and are responsible for some of the principle life processes that occur in the biosphere. Most of the photosynthesis that supplies us with oxygen is done by microscopic algae and bacteria rather than by plants. Bacteria and fungi decompose large amounts of organic waste through fermentation and respiration. Their activities convert many substances back to minerals and elements essential to the survival of plants and animals and therefore contribute to the cycling of matter through communities of living things. If it were not for this vital recycling, material would "pile up" and be excluded from the food chain and mineral cycling to the detriment of all life forms.

It is this study of the interrelationships of microorganisms and their interactions with other organisms and the physical environment that is known as "Microbial Ecology." This series of labs explores the many different niches that these tiny organisms occupy including the hostile environments of the desert and tundra to the relatively benign (and potentially damaging to us) environments of the human digestive system. The labs also examine the ways in which microorganisms feed and grow and how they may compete and change over time.

Part 1: Where Are Microorganisms Found?

Introduction

What do microorganisms need to survive and grow? How can you collect microorganisms? Where would you find them? Actually, you would not have to look far. Microorganisms inhabit virtually every niche on this planet from hot springs and geysers to the hot desert, to the cold tundra, to the deep ocean trenches, to the high atmospheric thermals.

Microorganisms will grow anywhere that a suitable substrate exists. A substrate might include materials necessary for their growth and successful reproduction. Actually they require no more to live than we do ourselves—a source of food, some minerals and vitamins and energy. The old meatloaf in the refrigerator or the sour milk on the shelf fill this criteria. This substrate can be simulated in an algal extract called nutrient agar. This gel material is supplemented with beef extract as a source of protein and some minerals. A sterile nutrient agar plate is a suitable and convenient way to grow and study microorganisms. A plate cover keeps the organisms inside safe from contamination by other organisms.

Purpose:

To investigate where microorganisms grow.

Materials:

sterile cotton swabs
nutrient agar plates
wax marking pencil
beaker with disinfectant

Procedure:

1. Determine two locations where you would like to test for the presence of microorganisms.
2. All labels should be written on the bottom of the petri dish—not on the lid. Draw a line through the diameter of the petri dish and label each half of the petri dish with the source of the sample. Also put your name on the dish.
3. Rub a sterile cotton swab on the area to be sampled.
4. Streak the swab on half of the nutrient agar as demonstrated by your instructor.
5. Repeat the transfer of a second sample with another sterile swab to the other half of the petri dish.
6. Dispose of the swabs in the disinfectant.
7. Incubate for several days at room temperature.

The visible growth on the nutrient agar are piles of bacteria or fungal cells. Under the right conditions, a single cell will multiply quickly to form a colony. Although some of the growth in your dishes may be mixed groups of cells, you may see some isolated individual colonies.

It is possible that in addition to bacteria, you may have collected some fungi. Fungi usually look fuzzy, and may be light colored around the edges with darker areas in the center. Figure 1 shows some examples of the differents forms, margins and elevations of bacterial colonies.

Carefully look at the colonies in your dishes with a stereomicroscope.

Questions

1. Describe the different types of colonies that you see. What are their sizes, shapes, colors, margins and elevation?
2. Do you have any isolated colonies?
3. What is the difference between bacterial and fungal colonies?
4. Did all your samples grow? Why or why not?
5. What is the benefit of covering a cut on your skin?
6. Do microorganisms live in the air?
7. From what kind of sample did you find the most variety of colonies?
8. How can you tell if there is more than one type of microbe in your colonies?

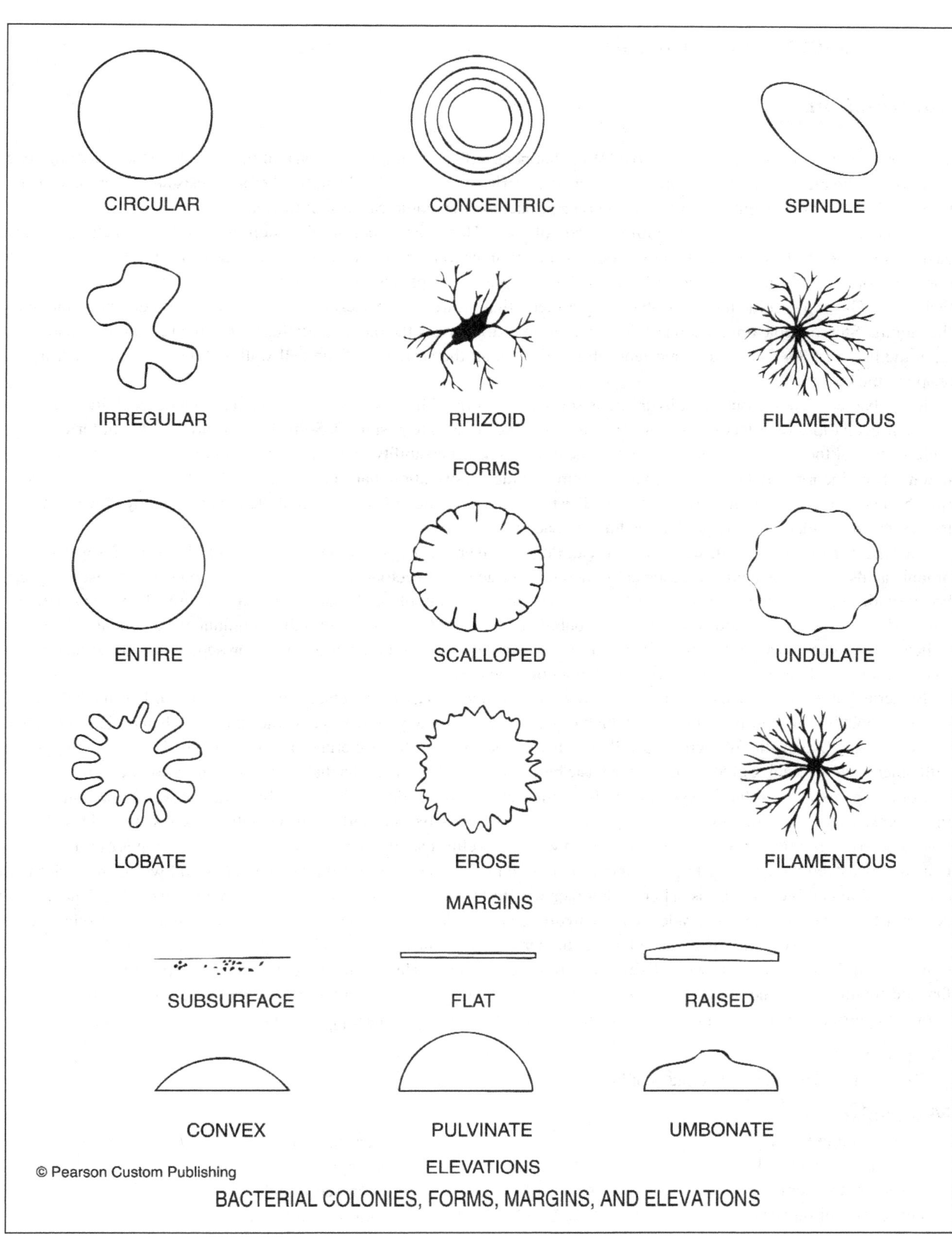

Figure 1. Colony Morphology

Part 2: Bacterial Identification

Introduction

Why does the doctor swab your sore throat? What happens with this sample? The task of the pathologist is to identify bacteria so that the proper treatments can be prescribed. A series of observational and biochemical tests are undertaken. These tests can be used to "key out" or narrow the choice of bacteria that could cause an infection.

You have been given agar plates with isolated colonies. This is an important first step in identifying bacteria because each colony formed from one cell that reproduced many times to form millions of identical cells. Furthermore, each plate contains colonies of only one kind of bacteria. The sample was kept free of contamination by a technique called aseptic technique. This is a specific method of handling bacteria that insures that bacteria from the environment do not contaminate the culture. Stereoscopic observation of the colonies helps to identify the bacteria. In this part of the lab you will also Gram stain the bacteria. This gives us important information about the structure of the cell wall and also helps us identify the shape of the bacteria.

Many bacteria use various carbohydrates as sources of energy. These carbohydrates include monosaccharides (e.g. glucose), disaccharides (e.g. lactose and sucrose), and polysaccharides (e.g. starch). Some bacteria are capable of fermenting a wide variety of these carbohydrates, others ferment only a few. The ability of a bacterial cell to break down a carbohydrate that has been incorporated into the growth medium provides information that can be used to identify the bacterium in question. You will perform a number of biochemical tests to determine the kind of carbohydrate metabolized by inoculating lactose broth and oxidation/fermentation media with bacteria.

Bacteria vary in the way in which they break down a given carbohydrate. Different end products are formed such as organic acids (e.g. lactic acid and acetic acid), neutral products (e.g. acetone and ethyl alcohol), and various gases (e.g. carbon dioxide and hydrogen). Gas production can be observed as a bubble in the lactose broth medium when the bacteria are cultured under anaerobic conditions. Since the bubble is often hard to observe with the technique we are using, phenol red indicator was also added to the broth. Phenol red is an indicator which turns yellow in the presence of acid. Observance of a color change indicates that the bacteria are fermenting lactose.

Bacteria that ferment glucose to acid end products can be detected as a color change in the O/F media. This media contains brom thymol blue, an acid-base indicator, which is green when neutral, yellow when acidic and blue when basic. A change in the color of the O/F media from green to yellow indicates the ability of the bacteria growing in that media to ferment glucose. Still other bacteria oxidize glucose and make basic by-products in the O/F media that change the green color to blue.

Some organisms must have oxygen to perform their chemical reactions. These aerobic microorganisms will grow only in the presence of oxygen. Other microorganisms are poisoned by oxygen and can grow only in its absence. These "anaerobic" bacteria will grow only in the media layered with oil to eliminate the presence of oxygen. Many types of microorganisms have evolved the capacity to grow under either condition. These are facultative anaerobes and will grow under both aerobic and anaerobic conditions. There is another way to test to see if an organism is aerobic or anaerobic. The aerobic cells must have an enzyme to degrade the toxic hydrogen peroxide that is made as a by-product of chemical reactions in the presence of oxygen. Catalase is the enzyme that all aerobic cells must contain to break down the poisonous hydrogen peroxide to harmless oxygen and water. Even your cells have catalase. Have you ever put hydrogen peroxide onto a cut for a first aid treatment? Remember how it fizzes? The fizzing comes from the catalase from the cut cells breaking down the hydrogen peroxide. The fizzing is caused by the bubbles of oxygen which are produced as the reaction proceeds.

Purpose:

To identify the unknown specimens of bacteria.

Materials:

Gram staining kit
staining trays and racks
sterile light mineral oil
sterile Pasteur pipettes
bacteria cultures of unknowns
3% hydrogen peroxide
microscope slides
stereo microscope

- mini-wells with lids
- nutrient broth
- lactose phenol red broth
- oxidation/fermentation broth with 1% glucose
- microscope with oil immersion lens
- immersion oil
- wax pencils
- colored tape

Procedures:

A. Observation Of Colony Morphology

Examine the colony morphology of the pure cultures. Record their size, whole colony shape, margin, and color characteristics on the data table. (Refer to Figure 1)

B. Gram Staining

1. Label a clean glass slide with the culture number and your initials.
2. Apply a drop of water to the slide with a sterile inoculating loop. Touch a sterile inoculating loop to one colony then stir the culture into the water on the slide to disperse the cells. Sterilize the loop before putting it down.
3. Set the slide aside to air dry. Make smears of all cultures on separate slides using this same technique.
4. When the smear is completely dry, heat-fix the cells to the slide by holding the slide against opening of the incinerator for about 15 seconds. This will kill the bacteria and fix them to the slide so that they do not wash off during staining. **Caution**—the incinerators are hot. Hold the slide with a slide holder or clothes pin.
5. The slide is ready to stain. This can be done immediately or the slides can be stored to be stained during the next lab period.
6. Place the prepared slide on a staining rack or tray and cover the smear with a drop or two of the Crystal Violet stain and stain for 20 seconds.
7. Wash gently in a stream of water for 2 seconds. Now all the cells are purple.
8. Cover the smear with Gram's Iodine for one minute, then wash it off with water. The iodine is a mordant which increases the affinity of the dye for the cell by forming a complex with the Crystal Violet. This complex is not easily removed from Gram Positive cells.
9. De-colorize the cells with alcohol by flushing the smear with the mixture for 15 seconds. Wash with water for 2 seconds. At this point Gram Positive cells continue to retain the Crystal Violet-Iodine complex and the Gram Negative cells are transparent. But be careful not to de-colorize too much, or even the Gram Positive cells will lose the stain. If you do not de-colorize enough then the Gram Negative cells will appear purple.
10. Flood the smear with safranin, the counterstain, for 20 seconds, wash and blot dry with bibulous paper. The red safranin dye will stain the cells so that Gram Negative cells will now appear red. Gram Positive cells remain purple because they retained the Crystal Violet stain.
11. Record on the data sheet whether each specimen was Gram Positive or Gram Negative on the data table.
12. Record on the data table the shape and arrangement of the cells using Figure 3 as a guide.
13. Look for the presence of endospores using Figure 3 as a guide. Record the presence/absence of endospores on the data sheet.

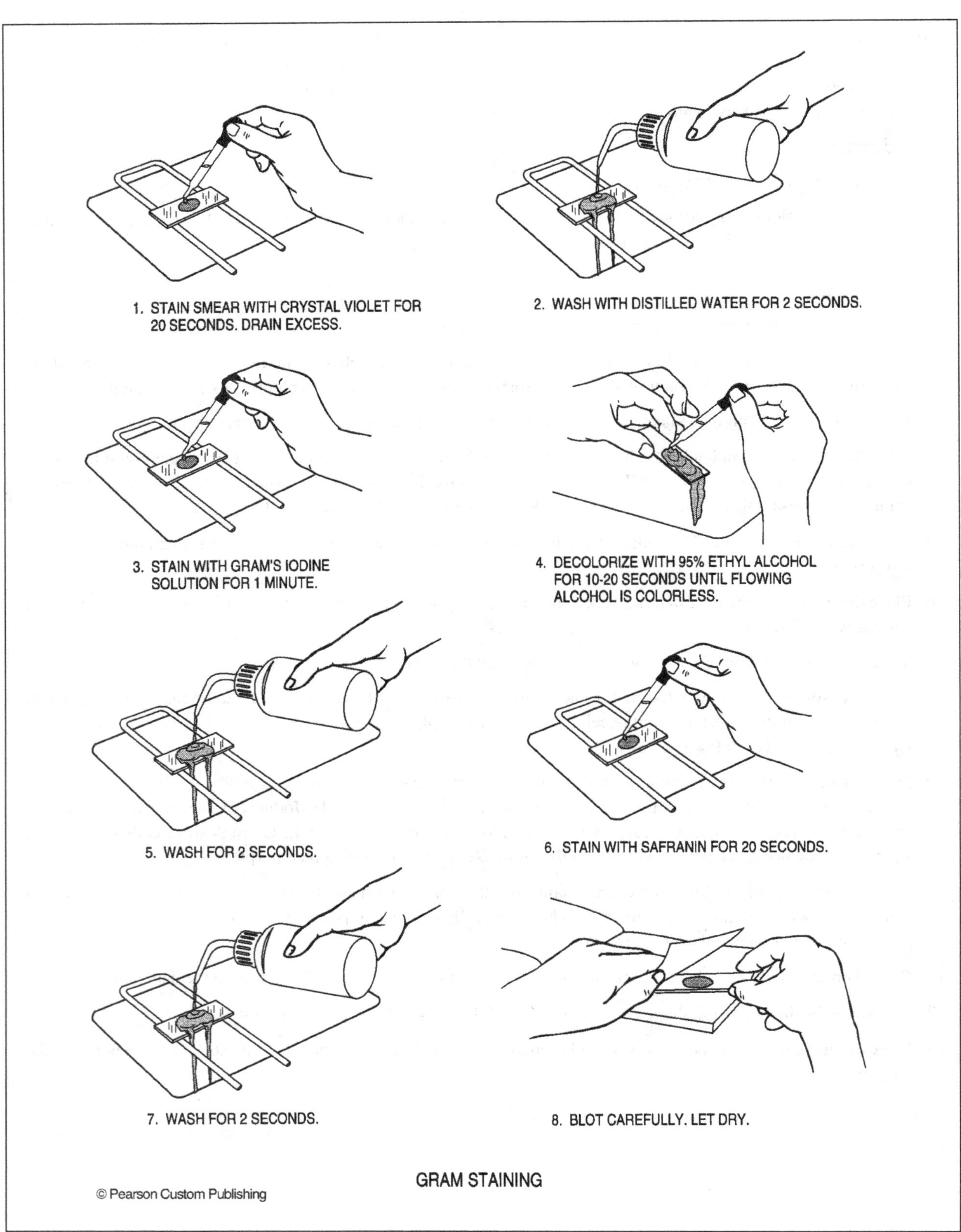

Figure 2. Procedure for Gram Staining

Questions:

1. What is the structural difference between Gram+ and Gram– bacteria?

C. Catalase Test

1. Place a drop of hydrogen peroxide on a microscope slide.
2. Scrape some of the culture from the nutrient agar dish with a sterile inoculating loop and mix it in the peroxide.
3. Look for the presence of bubbles with the aid of a stereomicroscope.
4. Record your results on the data table. Repeat procedure for each culture.

D. Metabolic Tests

1. Set up the mini-well matrix using Figure 4 as a guide. Assign each bacterial strain a letter that corresponds to the letters on the rows of the grid. (A row runs horizontally on the matrix.) Skip a row in between each unknown (i.e. assign unknowns to rows A, C, E and G). Set up row H as the control. No bacteria will be placed in the wells of this row. You will be sharing the mini-well apparatus with the other team at your lab table. Assign the row numbers to each team and record which numbers you are using for your two bacterial samples.
2. The odd numbered columns will be used to perform the biochemical tests. (The columns run vertically on the matrix.) Using a sterile Pasteur pipette, fill the wells of columns #1 and #3 with the O/F media. The even numbered columns will remain empty.
3. Using a different sterile Pasteur pipette, fill columns #5 and #7 with Phenol red lactose broth.
4. Fill column #9 with nutrient broth using a third sterile Pasteur pipette.
5. Label a tube of sterile nutrient broth with the letter of your unknown. **Using aseptic technique**, transfer one loop of bacteria from a colony on the agar plate to the broth. **Thoroughly mix the cells with the broth** so that they are evenly distributed. Use this mixture to inoculate the mini-wells as described below.
6. Inoculate the odd number wells of Row A with one loop of the appropriate bacterial strain using **aseptic technique**. Use a different disposable loop for each transfer. Row A will contain the first unknown bacteria strain. Skip Row B and inoculate Row C with the second unknown bacteria strain, etc.
7. Using a sterile pipette cover the wells in columns #3 and #7 with a few drops of sterile mineral oil to create anaerobic conditions. **The wells must be inoculated with the bacteria before the oil is added.**
8. Seal the edge of the mini-well with parafilm to prevent evaporation. Make sure the wells are labeled with your name.
9. During the next lab period observe the results and record observations on the data table.
10. Your data table should now be complete and you can now use the dichotomous key provided to identify your bacteria.

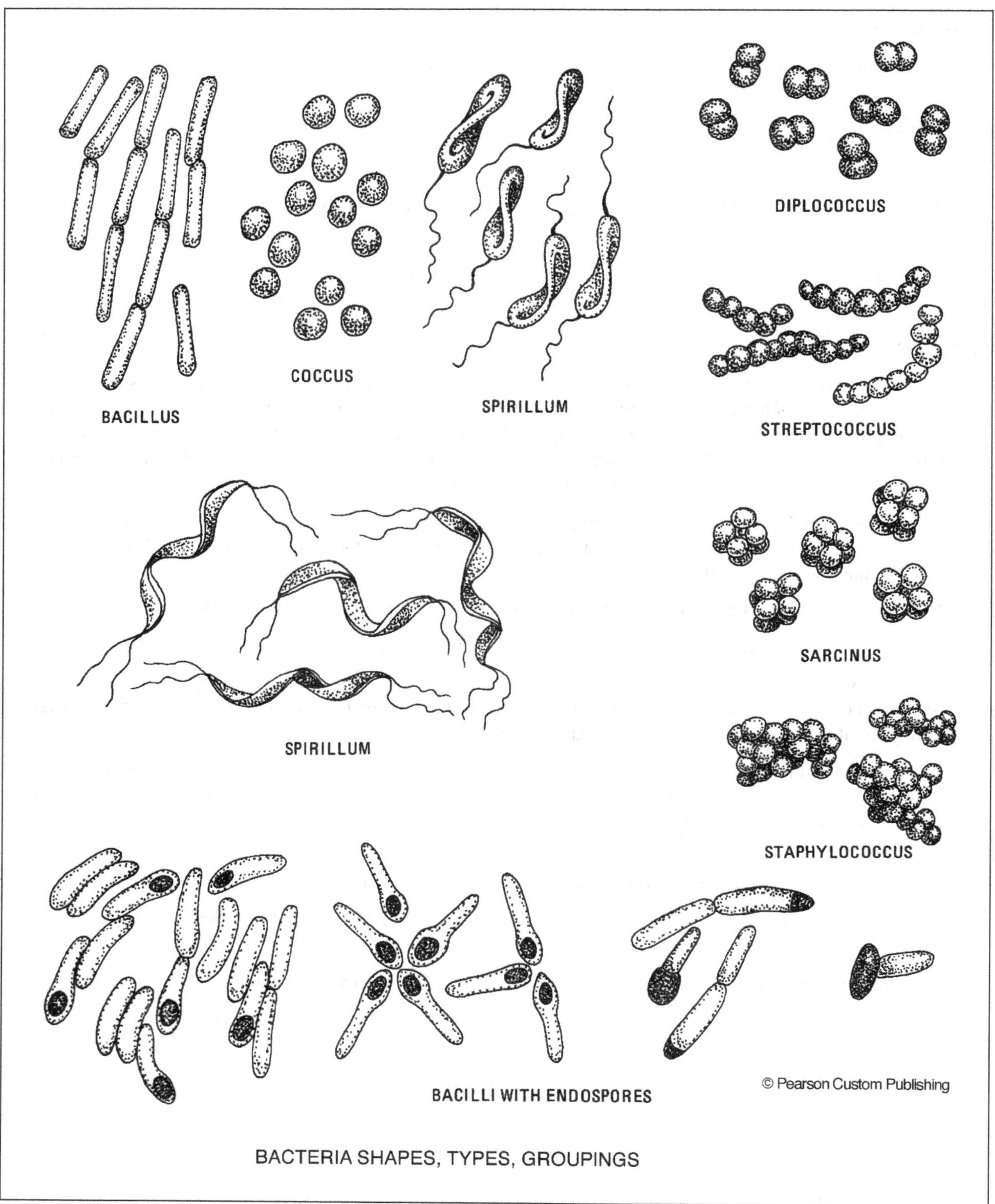

Figure 3. Cell Morphology

Acknowledgements

We wish to thank the Rutgers/Industry Science Modules Program for the use of this material.

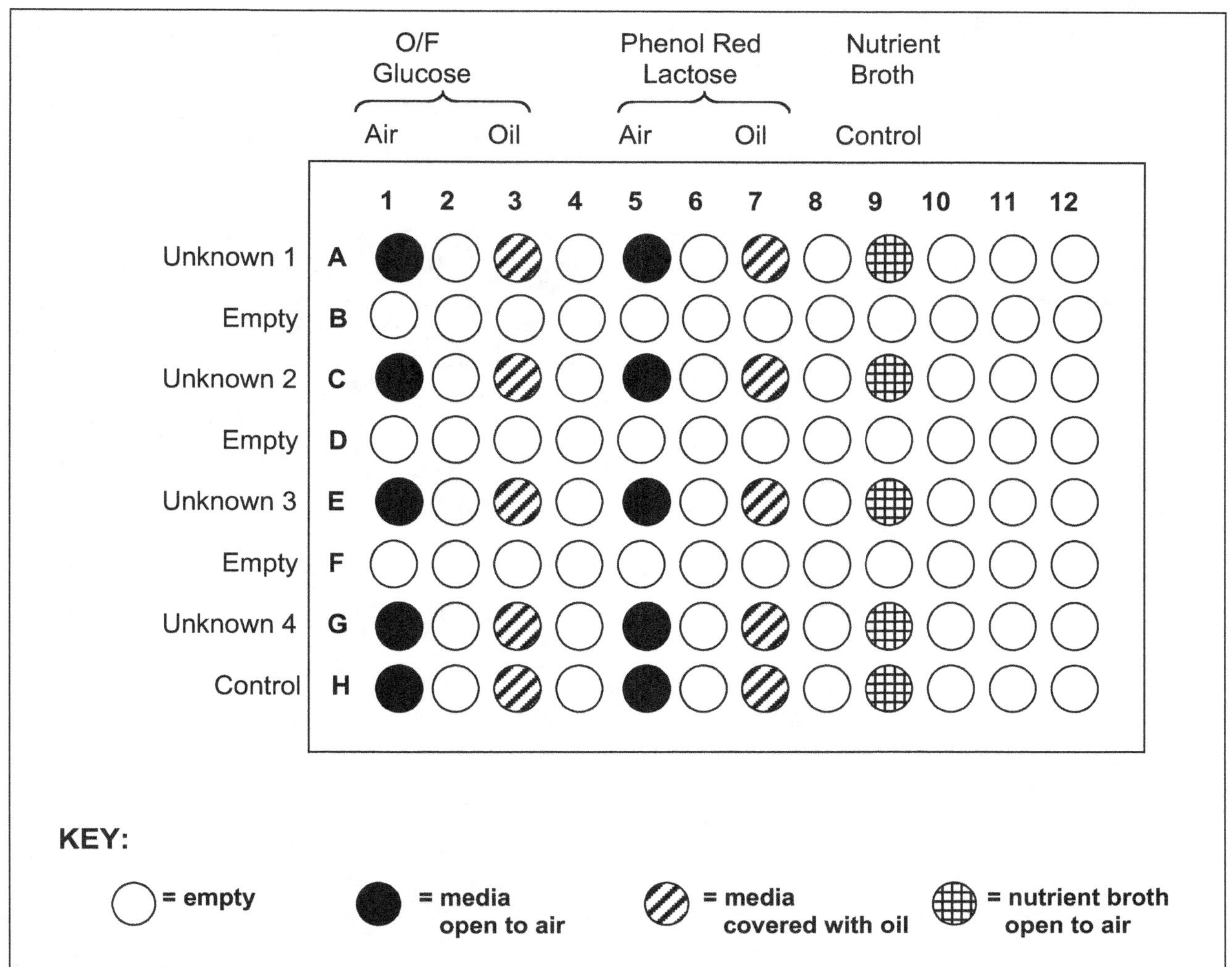

Figure 4. Set up for Mini-wells

Lab Team Names ______________________________

____

DATA

CULTURE CODE LETTER		
TESTS		
Gram Stain Reaction: purple=gram+ pink=gram-		
Cell Shape: rod or coccus		
Spore Formation: clear sphere inside cell		
Colony Morphology		
Catalase Test: fizzing = +		
Ferments Glucose: green=neutral or no growth yellow=ferments blue=oxidizes		
Ferments Lactose: bubbles or yellow= ferments		
Name of Bacteria		

Table 1. Data Table for Identification of Bacterial Cultures

DICHOTOMOUS KEY	
1. Gram Reaction	
purple, Gram+, go to	2
pink, Gram–, go to	6
2. Cell Morphology	
coccus, go to	3
bacillus (rod), go to	5
3. Colony Morphology	
large & opaque, go to	4
small & transparent	4
4. Catalase Reaction	
fizzing, catalase+	*Staphlococcus*
no fizzing, catalase–	*Streptococcus*
5. Formation of Spores	
non-spore formers	*Lactobacillus*
spore formers	*Bacillus*
6. Cell Morphology	
coccus	*Neisseria*
bacillus (rods), go to	7
7. Fermentation/Oxidation of Glucose	
fermentation (yellow), go to	8
no fermentation (blue)	*Alcaligenes*
8. Fermentation of Lactose	
Lactose+ (gas bubble or yellow)	*Escherichia*
Lactose– (no gas bubble or color change)	*Proteus*

Table 2. Dichotomous Key for Identification of Bacterial Cultures

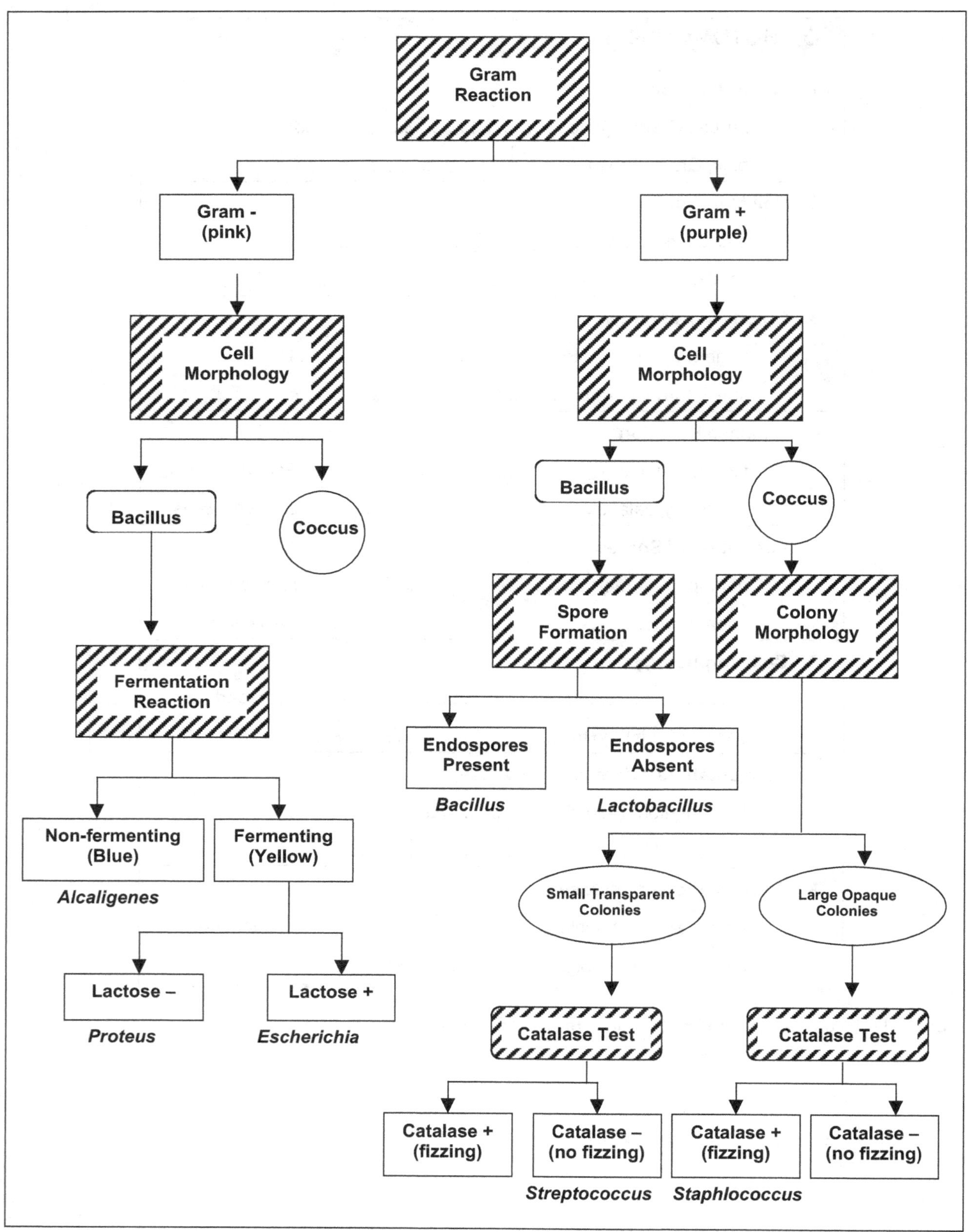

Figure 5. Flow Chart for Identification of Bacterial Cultures

Protists and Fungi

This lab topic gives you the opportunity to practice the scientific process. Before going to lab, carefully read through this lab exercise. Be prepared to use this information to design an experiment with protists or fungi.

Laboratory Objectives

After completing this lab topic, you should be able to:

1. Discuss the diversity of protists and fungi, and the current interest in their phylogenetic relationships.
2. Describe the diversity of protists, explaining the means of obtaining nutrition and method of locomotion for each group.
3. Identify representative organisms in several major protistan phyla.
4. Discuss the ecological role and economic importance of protists.
5. Describe the characteristics and representative organisms of the green algae and their relationship to land plants.
6. Describe the divisions of the kingdom Fungi, recognizing and identifying representative organisms in each.
7. Describe differences in reproduction in fungal phyla.
8. Discuss the ecological role and economic importance of fungi.
9. Design and perform an independent investigation of a protist or an organism in the kingdom Fungi.

Introduction

Unicellular eukaryotic organisms originated over 2 billion years ago, and today they are found in every habitable region of Earth. The enormous diversity of organisms, their numerous adaptations, and their cellular complexity reflect the long evolutionary history of eukaryotes. For almost 30 years, scientists placed these diverse groups of unicellular organisms into the kingdom Protista. The Protista usually included all organisms not placed in the other eukaryotic kingdoms of Plants, Animals, and Fungi. This catchall kingdom included not only the unicellular eukaryotes, but also their multicellular relatives, like the giant kelps and seaweeds. However, most scientists now agree that the kingdom Protista should be divided into several kingdoms within the domain Eukarya, each reflecting a single evolutionary origin. Some propose six eukaryotic kingdoms, others propose more. In this lab topic we will refer to this diverse group as **protists** (a general term, not a taxonomic category), leaving open the final designation of kingdoms.

The most familiar protists, algae and protozoans, have been well studied since the earliest development of the microscope. Therefore, one might assume that the taxonomic relationships among the various protistans are well understood. However, the phylogeny (evolutionary history) of these groups has been difficult to determine from comparisons of cell structure and function, nutrition, and reproduction. Evolutionary biology and taxonomy are branches of science in which many of the interesting "experiments" occurred millions or even billions of years ago. Scientists cannot repeat these evolutionary "experiments," but they can use multiple sources of evidence to determine which groups of organisms have features in common and therefore represent a single phylogenetic group. Recent molecular and biochemical research, particularly the ability to sequence ribosomal and transfer RNA genes, has provided strong new evidence for reconstructing the relationships of the protists. The results of this work have challenged not only the five-kingdom classification scheme, but also our definition of a kingdom. Some of the evidence is contradictory, requiring further testing. These investigations into the nature of eukaryotic diversity demonstrate the process of scientific inquiry. New technologies, new ideas, and novel experiments are used to test hypotheses, and the resulting evidence must be consistent with the existing body of knowledge and our classification scheme. The results lead to modification of our hypotheses and further research.

Some students may find the changing classification within the protists frustrating, but you should try to view this as the hallmark of science. Even the concept of the kingdom can be challenged and changed in response to new evidence. No matter how many kingdoms are proposed, remember that this is a reflection of the evolution of eukaryotes over the rich history of the earth. It is not surprising that the diversity of life does not easily fit into our constructed categories.

If you complete all of the lab topics in this laboratory manual, you will have studied examples of all the major groups of organisms with the exception of those in domain Archaea. You will investigate plant evolution and animal evolution in subsequent lab topics. In this lab topic, you will survey the diversity of protists in several phyla, with particular attention to nutrition, locomotion, and cellular complexity. (The designations *phylum* and *division* are equivalent taxonomic groupings and we will use phylum when referring to protists and fungi. Zoologists traditionally used *phylum,* while botanists used *division.* However, both terms now are accepted by the Botanical Code for Nomenclature.) You will continue your investigation of diversity with the Fungi, a kingdom composed of multicellular, heterotrophic eukaryotes that absorb their food.

At the end of this lab topic you will be asked to design a simple experiment to further your investigation of the behavior, ecology, or physiology of one of the organisms studied. As you proceed through the exercises, ask questions about your observations and consider an experiment that you might design to answer one question.

EXERCISE 1
The Protists

In this exercise you will investigate the diversity of organisms traditionally considered protists. To organize your study, protists can be divided into three categories (not taxonomic groups) according to their mode of nutrition. The *protozoa* are **heterotrophic** protists that ingest their food by **phagocytosis** (the uptake of large particles or whole organisms by the pinching inward of the plasma membrane). Some protozoa, euglenoids for example, are **mixotrophic,** capable of photosynthesis and ingestion. The *algae* include all photosynthetic (**autotrophic**) unicellular organisms and their multicellular relatives. Traditionally, dinoflagellates have been considered algae, but recent evidence suggests that they are closely related to the protozoa, specifically ciliates. The green algae are included in the protists, although, as you will see, evidence indicates that land plants originated from ancestral green algae, and some classifications place green algae (or at least those known as charophytes) in the kingdom Plantae. The third category includes the *funguslike slime molds* that are heterotrophic, obtaining their nutrition by absorbing nutrients from decomposing organic material. Some scientists propose placing the slime molds in a separate kingdom, Mycetozoa, a name that reflects their close relationship with fungi (*myco*) and animals (*zoa*).

These three general categories—protozoa, algae, and slime molds—provide a framework for the study of the diverse organisms referred to as protists. For each organism that you investigate, you will find a brief statement about protistan classification that incorporates molecular and cytological evidence. (For further discussion of protistan classification, see Campbell and Reece, 2002.)

Lab Study A. Heterotrophic Protists—Protozoa

Materials

compound microscope
slides and coverslips
prepared slides of foraminiferans
prepared slides of radiolarians skeletons (demonstration only)
prepared slides of *Trypanosoma levisi*
cultures of living *Paramecium caudata*
Protoslo® or other quieting agent
solution of yeast stained with Congo red
cultures of *Paramecium caudata* that have been fed yeast stained with Congo red (optional)
dropper bottle of 1% acetic acid
transfer pipettes
freshwater and marine plankton tows

Introduction

Traditionally, single-celled heterotrophic protists are called *protozoa.* There are three categories of protozoa based on their mode of locomotion. In one group, organisms move and feed using cellular extensions called **pseudopodia.** Included in this group are amoebas, foraminiferans, and actinopods. Other protozoa move using **flagella,** motile structures supported by microtubules. The third means of locomotion in protozoa is by **cilia,** short cellular extensions supported by microtubules.

Protozoa That Move Using Pseudopodia

Although some taxonomists group all protists that move using pseudopodia into one phylum, others divide the group into several phyla. Given the present uncertainty of the protistan classification, we have selected three protozoans with pseudopodia that were traditionally in different phyla.

Rhizopods (Amoebas)

The rhizopod *Amoeba proteus* is a protozoan species of organisms that move using **pseudopodia**. Rhizopod is derived from *rhizo* or root and *pod* or foot; thus, rootlike foot. In this group, organisms have no fixed body shape, and they are naked; that is, they do not have a shell. Different species may be found in a variety of habitats, including freshwater and marine habitats. Recall that pseudopodia are cellular extensions. As the pseudopod extends, endoplasm flows into the extension. By extending several pseudopods in sequence and flowing into first one and then the next, the amoeba proceeds along in an irregular, slow fashion. Pseudopods are also used to capture and ingest food. When a suitable food particle such as a bacterium, another protist, or a piece of detritus (fragmented remains of dead organisms) contacts an amoeba, a pseudopod will flow completely around the particle and take it into the cell by phagocytosis.

Foraminiferans (Forams)

Foraminiferans, commonly called **forams,** are another example of organisms that move and feed using pseudopodia. Forams are marine planktonic (freely floating) or benthic (bottom-dwelling) organisms that secrete a shell-like *test* (a hard outer covering) made up of chambers. In many species, the test consists of chambers secreted in a spiral pattern, and the organism resembles a microscopic snail. Although most forams are microscopic, some species, called *living sands,* may grow to the size of several centimeters, an astounding size for a single-celled protist. Pseudopodia extend through special pores in the calcium carbonate test. The test can persist after the organism dies, becoming part of marine sand. Remains of tests can form vast limestone deposits.

Procedure

1. Obtain a prepared slide of representative forams (Figure 1a).
2. Observe the organisms first on the lowest power of the compound microscope and then on intermediate and high powers.
3. Note the arrangement and attempt to count the number of chambers in the test. In most species, the number of chambers indicates the relative ages of the organisms, with older organisms having more chambers. Which are more abundant on your slide, older or younger organisms?

   Chambers can be arranged in a single row, in multiple rows, or wound into a spiral. Protozoologists determine the foram species based on the appearance of the test. Are different species present?

Results

Sketch several different forams in the margin of your lab manual. Note differences in the organisms on your slide and those depicted in Figure 1a.

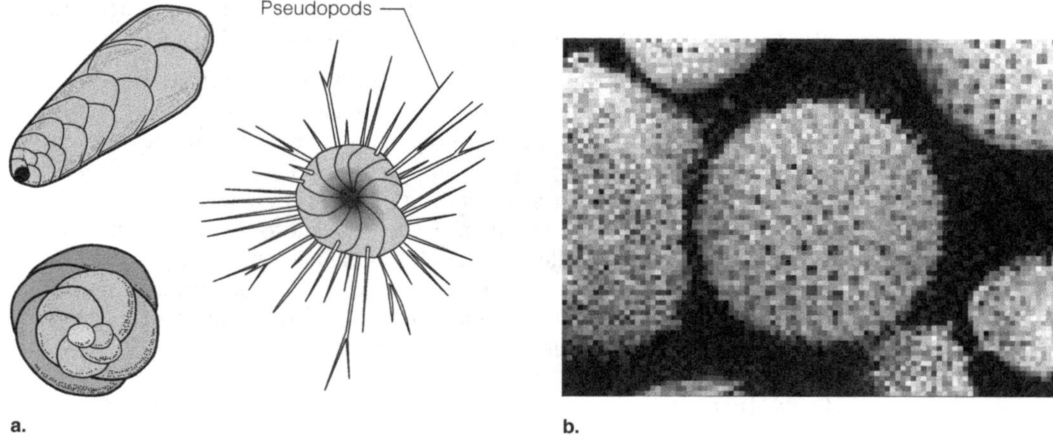

Figure 1.
Heterotrophic organisms (protozoa) that move using pseudopodia. (a) Forams have a shell-like test made of calcium carbonate. Slender pseudopods extend through pores in the test. (b) Radiolarians are supported by a skeleton of silicon dioxide.

Actinopods (Radiolarians)

Actinopods have pseudopodia that are supported by a bundle of microtubules forming very slender **axopodia.** The **radiolarians** studied here are common in marine plankton. They secrete skeletons of silicon dioxide that can, as with the forams, collect in vast deposits on the ocean floor. The axopodia extend outward through pores in the skeleton in all directions from the central spherical cell body.

Procedure

1. Observe slides of radiolarians on demonstration.
2. Observe the size and shape of the skeletons and compare your observations with Figure 1b.

Results

Sketch several different radiolarians skeletons in the margin of your lab manual, noting any differences between the organisms on demonstration and those in the figure.

Protozoa That Move Using Flagella

Flagellates are generally single-celled, heterotrophic protists. They may be free-living and parasitic, or they may live in symbiotic relationships with other organisms. The many diverse single-celled and colonial flagellates have been a particular challenge to taxonomists. Under the old two-kingdom system of classification, the heterotrophic flagellates were classified as animals, and the autotrophic flagellates (with chloroplasts) were classified as plants. However, the well-defined taxonomic group of flagellates, the euglenoids, has members of each type, and some members are mixotrophic, depending on their environment. Recent classification changes proposed for flagellates would place euglenoids together with symbiotic flagellates, like *Trypanosoma,* in a new category, the **Euglenozoa.**

The heterotrophic organisms that you investigate in this exercise move using one or more flagella, long cytoplasmic extensions supported by a nine-doublet of microtubules surrounding a single central doublet of microtubules. In this exercise, you will observe a flagellate, *Trypanosoma levisi.* Organisms in the genus *Trypanosoma* are parasites that alternate between a vertebrate and an invertebrate host. *Trypanosoma levisi* lives in the blood of rats and is transmitted by fleas. Its flagellum originates near the posterior end but passes to the front end as a marginal thread of a long undulating membrane. Another organism in this same genus, *T. gambiense,* causes African sleeping sickness in humans. Its invertebrate host is the tsetse fly.

Procedure

1. Obtain a prepared slide of *T. levisi* (Figure 2) and observe it, using low, intermediate, and high powers in the compound microscope.
2. Locate the organisms among the blood cells of the parasite's host.
3. Identify the **flagellum,** the **undulating membrane,** and the **nucleus** in several organisms.

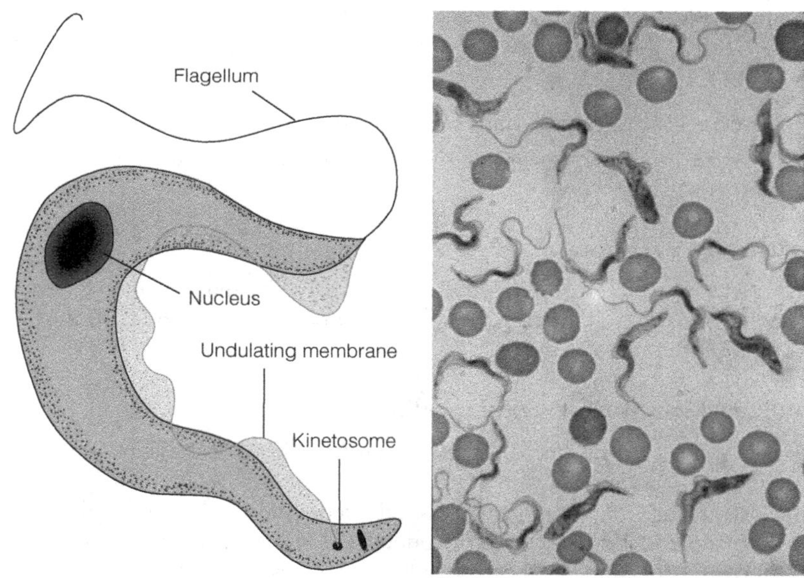

Figure 2.
Protozoa that move using flagella. *Trypanosoma* is a parasite that lives in the blood of its mammalian host. The flagellum originates near the posterior end but passes along an undulating membrane to the anterior end.

Results

In the margin of your lab manual, draw several representative examples of *T. levisi* and several blood cells to show relative cell sizes.

Protozoa That Move Using Cilia

Protozoans in this category move using cilia, short projections from the cell surface. Cilia are generally shorter and more numerous than flagella. Internally, both structures are similar in their core of a nine-doublet of microtubules surrounding a single central doublet of microtubules. Proposed groupings of protistans place ciliates and dinoflagellates (Lab Study B) into a new taxonomic category, the **Alveolata.** Members of the Alveolata have small subsurface membrane-bound cavities called **alveoli.** Until there is a consensus, we have included ciliates with the protozoans and the dinoflagellates with the algae. In this activity, you will observe the ciliate *Paramecium caudatum.*

Procedure

1. Using the compound microscope, examine a living *Paramecium.* Place a drop of water from the bottom of the culture on a clean microscope slide. Add a *small* drop of Protoslo or some other quieting solution to the water drop; then add the coverslip.
2. Observe paramecia on the compound microscope using low and then intermediate powers.
3. Describe the movement of a single paramecium. Does movement appear to be directional or is it random? Does the organism reverse direction only when it encounters an object, or does it appear to reverse direction even with no obstruction?
4. Locate a large, slowly moving organism, switch to high power, and identify the following organelles:

   Oral groove: depression in the side of the cell that runs obliquely back to the mouth that opens into a **gullet.**

   Food vacuole: forms at the end of the gullet. Food vacuoles may appear as dark vesicles throughout the cell.

   Macronucleus: large, grayish body in the center of the cell. The macronucleus has many copies of the genome and controls most cellular activities, including asexual reproduction.

   Micronucleus: often difficult to see in living organisms, this small round body may be lying close to the macronucleus. Micronuclei are involved in sexual reproduction. Many species of paramecia have more than one micronucleus.

   Contractile vacuole: used for water balance, two of these form, one at each end of the cell. Each contractile vacuole is made up of a ring of radiating tubules and a central spherical vacuole. Your organism may be under osmotic stress because of the Protoslo, and the contractile vacuoles may be filling and collapsing as they expel water from the cell.
5. Observe feeding in a paramecium. Add a drop of yeast stained with Congo red to the edge of the coverslip and watch as it diffuses around the paramecium.

   Study the movement of food particles from the oral groove to the gullet to the formation of a food vacuole that will subsequently move through the cell as the food is digested in the vacuole. You may be able to observe the discharge of undigested food from the food vacuole at a specific site on the cell surface.

6. Observe the discharge of **trichocysts,** structures that lie just under the outer surface of the paramecium. When irritated by a chemical or attacked by a predator, the paramecium discharges these long thin threads that may serve as a defense mechanism, as an anchoring device, or to capture prey. Make a new slide of paramecia. Add a drop of 1% acetic acid to the edge of the coverslip and carefully watch a paramecium. Describe the appearance of trichocysts in this species.

Results

Complete the drawing of a paramecium below, labeling all the organelles and structures shown in bold in the text.

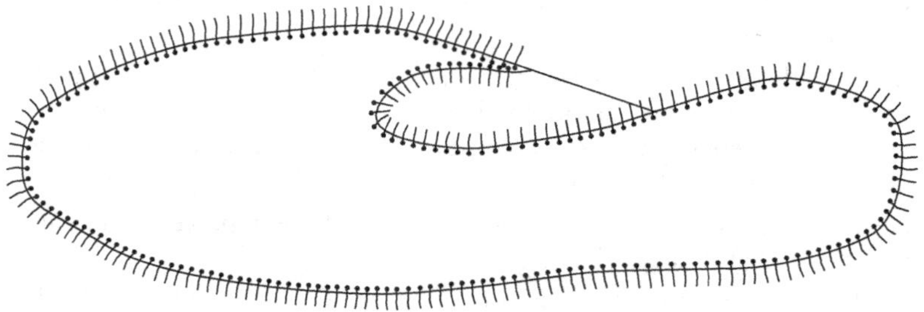

Discussion

1. Describe the mechanism for feeding in amoeboid, flagellated, and ciliated protozoans.

2. How do you think amoeboid organisms with skeletons, such as the radiolarians, move food to their cell bodies?

3. Compare the appearance and rate of locomotion in amoeboid, flagellated, and ciliated organisms observed in this exercise.

4. Describe mechanisms for defense in the organisms studied.

5. Give examples of modifications in cell shape or distribution of cilia or flagella allowing the organism to adapt to its environment.

6. Complete Table 1, summarizing characteristics of organisms in the heterotrophic protistan phyla.

Table 1
Characteristics of Heterotrophic Protists—Protozoa

Group	Nutritional Mode	Means of Locomotion	Protective Adaptations	Habitat or Lifestyle	Other Unusual Characteristics
Rhizopods					
Foraminiferans					
Actinopods					
Flagellates					
Ciliates					

Lab Study B. Autotrophic Protists—Algae

Materials

compound microscope
slides and coverslips
living cultures or prepared slides of dinoflagellates
living cultures of diatoms
prepared slides of diatomaceous earth, demonstration only
marine plankton samples
transfer pipettes for all cultures
demonstration materials of brown algae and red algae

Introduction

In this lab study you will investigate representatives of four phyla of algae. Body form, flagella, and photosynthetic pigments can distinguish the algae. In **unicellular** organisms, the body is only one cell, and daughter cells separate from each other after division. In **filamentous** organisms, cell division takes place in the same plane, and the daughter cells remain attached, resulting in a long line of cells—a filament. Whereas **aggregates** are random, temporary clusters of cells, **simple** and **complex colonies** are predictable organizations of cells either without physiological connections (a simple colony) or with them (a complex colony). In aggregates, simple colonies, and complex colonies, cell divisions take place in many planes. The complex bodies of **multicellular** algae are differentiated into specialized structures for photosynthesis, flotation, and anchorage.

The phyla of algae are characterized by differences in cellular structure and pigmentation. The exclusively microscopic algae demonstrate differences in cell walls (diatoms) and flagella (dinoflagellates). All the algae have chlorophyll *a* as their primary photosynthetic pigment, but brown and red algae have additional accessory pigments. Green algae, like land plants, have chlorophyll *b* as an accessory pigment. Accessory pigments increase the spectrum of light available for photosynthesis. This is particularly important for aquatic organisms because many wavelengths of light, including those absorbed by chlorophyll *a*, are absorbed as they pass through ocean waters. Finally, the red algae lack flagella at any stage in their life cycle. In this lab study, you will examine some of the most common and ecologically important protistan algae, learning the characteristics, ecological roles, and economic importance of each.

Dinoflagellates (Dinoflagellata)

Swirl your hand through tropical ocean waters at night, and you may notice a burst of tiny lights. Visit a warm, stagnant inlet and you might notice that the water appears reddish and dead fish are floating on the surface. Both of these phenomena may be due to activities of dinoflagellates, single-celled organisms that are generally photosynthetic. Some are able to bioluminesce, or produce light. They sometimes can *bloom* (reproduce very rapidly) and cause the water to appear red from pigments in their bodies. If the organisms in this "red tide" are a species of dinoflagellate that releases toxins, fish and other marine animals can be poisoned. Red tides in the Chesapeake Bay are thought to be caused by *Pfiesteria,* a dinoflagellate that produces deadly toxins resulting in invertebrate and fish kills, and that also may be implicated in human illness and death. Dinoflagellates have a cellulose cell wall that is often in the form of an armor of numerous plates with two perpendicular

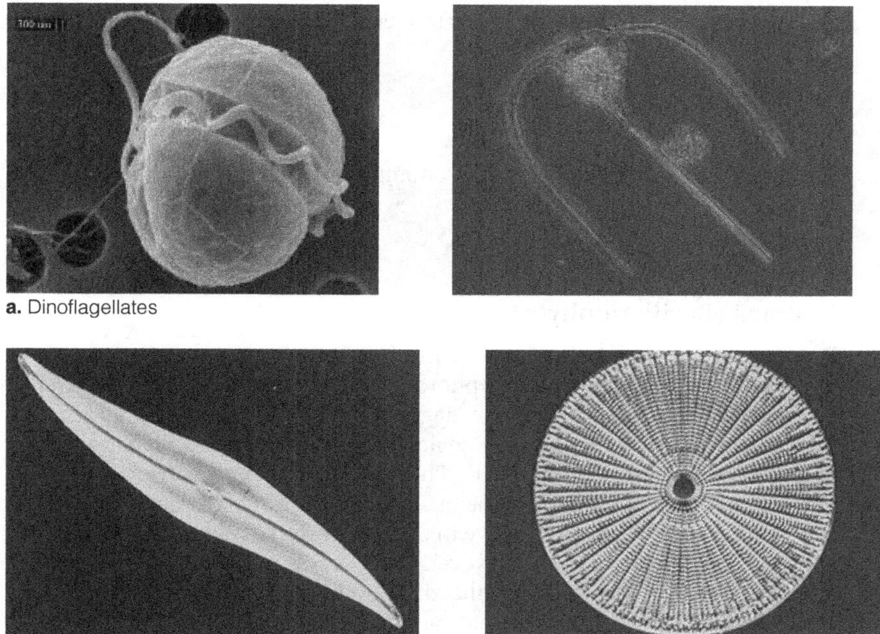

a. Dinoflagellates

b. Diatoms

Figure 3.
Autotrophic protists (algae). (a) Dinoflagellates have a cellulose cell wall in the form of plates with two grooves that house flagella. (b) Diatoms have a cell wall made of silica consisting of two valves. Species can be pennate forms or centric forms.

grooves, each containing a flagellum. These organisms play an important role in **primary productivity** in oceans, photosynthesis that ultimately provides food for all marine organisms.

Dinoflagellates have traditionally been considered algae, but as previously mentioned, they are now thought to share a common ancestor with ciliates, as evidenced by the presence of subsurface cavities called alveoli. In the future, dinoflagellates and ciliates may be placed in a single group, the Alveolata.

Procedure

1. Obtain a prepared slide or make a wet mount of dinoflagellates (Figure 3a).
2. Focus the slide on low power and attempt to locate the cells. You may have to switch to intermediate power to see them.
3. Switch to high power.
4. Identify the perpendicular **grooves** and the **cellulose plates** making up the cell wall. Are the plates in your species elongated into spines? **Flagella** may be visible in living specimens.

Results

1. Draw several examples of cell shapes in the margin of your lab manual. Note differences between the species on your slide and those in Figure 3a.

2. Summarize distinguishing characteristics of dinoflagellates.

3. Describe the ecological role and economic importance of these organisms.

Diatoms (Bacillariophyta)

Diatoms also play an important role in primary productivity in oceans. In fact, they are the most important photosynthesizers in cold marine waters. They can be unicellular, or they can aggregate into chains or starlike groups. Protoplasts of these organisms are enclosed by a cell wall made of silica that persists after the death of the cell. These cell wall deposits are mined as **diatomaceous earth** and have numerous economic uses, for example, in swimming pool filters and as an abrasive in toothpaste and silver polish. Perhaps the greatest value of diatoms, however, is the excess carbohydrate and oxygen they produce that can be utilized by other organisms. Ecologists are concerned about the effects of acid rain and changing climatic conditions on populations of diatoms and their rate of primary productivity.

Diatom cells are either elongated, boat-shaped, bilaterally symmetrical **pennate** forms or radially symmetrical **centric** forms. The cell wall consists of two valves, one fitting inside the other, in the manner of the lid and bottom of a petri dish. As scientists continue to utilize new information in classifying the protists, the diatoms, brown algae (in the next section), and golden algae (not included in this lab topic) are placed in a single group, **Stramenopila,** based on unique flagella structure usually observed in sex cells.

Procedure

1. Prepare a wet mount of diatoms (Figure 3b) from marine plankton samples or other living cultures.
2. Observe the organisms on low, intermediate, and high powers.
3. Describe the form of the diatoms in your sample. Are they centric, pennate, or both?

4. If you are studying living cells, you may be able to detect locomotion. The method of movement is uncertain, but it is thought that contractile fibers just inside the cell membrane produce waves of motion on the cytoplasmic surface that extends through a groove in the cell wall. What is the body form of motile diatoms?

5. Observe a single centric form on high power and note the intricate geometric pattern of the cell wall. Can you detect the two valves?
6. Look for chloroplasts in living forms.

7. Observe diatomaceous earth on demonstration and identify pennate and centric forms.

Results

1. Sketch several different shapes of diatoms in the margin of your lab manual.
2. Summarize distinguishing characteristics of diatoms.
3. Describe the ecological role and economic importance of these organisms.

Discussion

1. Compare dinoflagellates and diatoms. What important ecological role is shared by these two groups?
2. What is one characteristic that you could observe under the microscope to distinguish diatoms and dinoflagellates?

Brown Algae (Phaeophyta)

Some of the largest algae, the **kelps,** are brown algae. The Sargasso Sea is named after the large, free-floating brown algae *Sargassum.* These algae appear brown because of the presence of the brown pigment **fucoxanthin** in addition to chlorophyll *a*. Brown algae are perhaps best known for their commercial value. Have you ever wondered why commercial ice cream is smoother in texture than homemade ice cream? Extracts of **algin,** a polysaccharide in the cell wall of some brown algae, are used commercially as thickening or emulsifying agents in paint, toothpaste, ice cream, pudding, and in many other commercial food products. *Laminaria,* known as *kombu* in Japan, is added to soups, used to brew a beverage, and covered with icing as a dessert. As previously noted, the brown algae and diatoms may share a common ancestor and therefore be placed together in the Stramenopila.

Procedure

Observe the examples of brown algae that are on demonstration.

Results

In Table 2 on the next page, list the names and distinguishing characteristics of each brown algal species on demonstration. Compare the examples with those illustrated in Figure 4.

Table 2
Representative Brown Algae

Name	**Body Form** (single-celled, filamentous, colonial, leaflike; broad or linear blades)	**Characteristics** (pigments, reproductive structures, structures for attachment and flotation)

Red Algae (Rhodophyta)

The simplest red algae are single-celled, but most species have a macroscopic, multicellular body form. The red algae, unlike all the other algae, do not have flagella at any stage in their life cycle. Some scientists suggest that the red algae represent a monophyletic (having a single origin) group and should be placed in their own kingdom. Red algae contain chlorophyll *a* and the accessory pigments **phycocyanin** and **phycoerythrin** that often mask the chlorophyll, making the algae appear red. These pigments absorb

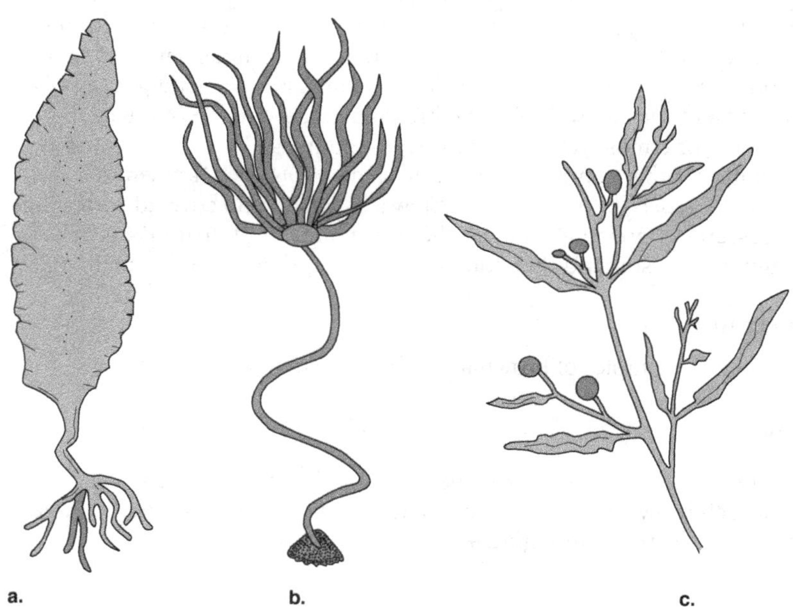

Figure 4.
Examples of multicellular brown algae (phylum Phaeophyta). The body of a brown alga consists of a broad **blade,** a stemlike **stipe,** and a **holdfast** for attachment. These body parts are found in the kelps (a) *Laminaria* and (b) *Nereocystis.* Rounded air bladders for flotation are seen in (c) *Sargassum* and other species of brown algae.

green and blue wavelengths of light that penetrate deep into ocean waters. Many red algae also appear green or black or even blue, depending on the depth at which they are growing. Because of this, color is not always a good characteristic to use when determining the classification of algae. **Agar** is a polysaccharide extracted from the cell wall of red algae. Another extract of red algae cell walls, **carrageenan,** is used to give the texture of thickness and richness to foods such as dairy drinks and soups. In Asia and elsewhere, the red algae *Porphyra* (known as *nori*) are used as seaweed wrappers for sushi. The cultivation and production of *Porphyra* constitute a billion-dollar industry.

Procedure

Observe the examples of red algae that are on demonstration.

Results

In Table 3, list the names and characteristics of the red algae on demonstration. Compare the demonstration examples with those illustrated in Figure 5.

Table 3
Representative Red Algae

Name	Body Form (single-celled, filamentous, colonial, leaflike)	Characteristics (reproductive structures, structures for attachment or flotation, pigments)

Discussion

1. What important ecological role is shared by the macroscopic algae (green, red, and brown)?

2. Based on your observations in the laboratory, what two characteristics might you use to distinguish brown and red algae?

Figure 5.
Examples of multicellular red algae (phylum Rhodophyta). (a) Some red algae have deposits of carbonates of calcium and magnesium in their cell walls and are important components of coral reefs. (b) Most red algae have delicate, finely dissected blades. (c) *Porphyra* (or *nori*) is used to make sushi.

Lab Study C. The Green Algae (Chlorophyta)—The Protist-Plant Connection

Materials

cultures or prepared slides of *Spirogyra* sp.
preserved *Ulva lactuca*
preserved *Chara* sp.

Introduction

The green algae include unicellular motile and nonmotile, colonial, filamentous, and multicellular species that inhabit primarily freshwater environments. Because green algae share many characteristics with land plants, including storage of starch and the presence of chlorophylls *a* and *b*, photosynthetic pathways, and organic compounds called flavonoids, most botanists support the hypothesis that plants evolved from green algae. Results of recent work in sequencing ribosomal and transfer RNA genes confirm the close relationship between green algae and land plants, and have led some scientists to propose that green algae, or at least those known as charophytes, be included in the Plant kingdom. In this exercise you will view several body forms of green algae on demonstration: single-celled, filamentous, colonial, and multicellular. Finally, you will observe the multicellular, branched green algae *Chara* (the stonewort), believed to be most similar to the green algae that gave rise to land plants over 460 million years ago.

If you completed the Microscopes and Cells lab, you may remember observing aggregates of single-celled algae, *Protococcus,* and the colonial green algae *Volvox.* In this lab study you will observe the filamentous alga *Spirogyra* sp. and the multicellular algae *Ulva* sp. and *Chara* sp.

Procedure

1. Using your compound microscope, observe living materials or prepared slides of the filamentous alga *Spirogyra* sp. (Figure 6a). This organism is common in small, freshwater ponds. The most obvious structure in the cells of the filament is a long chloroplast. Can you determine how the alga got its name? Describe the appearance of the chloroplast.

   Can you see a nucleus in each cell of the filament?
2. Observe the preserved specimen of *Ulva* sp., commonly called sea lettuce. This multicellular alga is commonly found on rocks or docks in marine and brackish water.
   a. Describe the body form of Ulva.

   b. Are structures present that would serve to attach *Ulva* to its substrate (dock or rock)? If so, describe them.

   c. Compare your specimen of *Ulva* with that shown in Figure 6b.
3. Examine the preserved specimen of the multicellular green alga *Chara*. This alga grows in muddy or sandy bottoms of clear lakes or ponds. Its body form is so complex that it is often mistaken for a plant, but careful study of its structure and reproduction confirms its classification as a green alga.

   Note the cylindrical branches attached to nodes. Compare your specimen to Figure 6c. Sketch the appearance of your specimen in the margin of your lab manual.

a.

b.

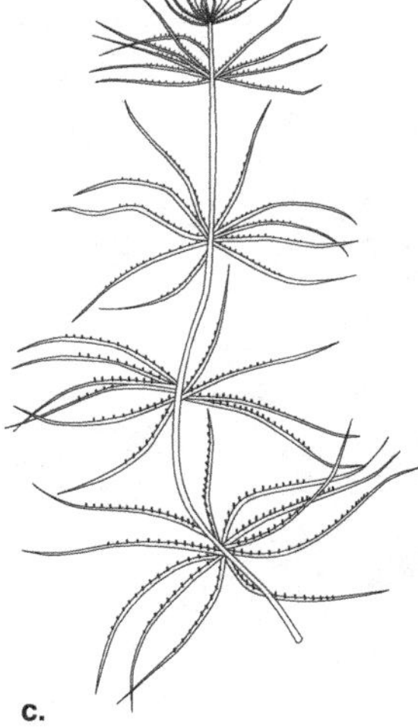

c.

Figure 6.
Examples of multicellular green algae (phylum Chlorophyta). (a) A filamentous green alga, *Spirogyra*. (b) Some green algae are multicellular as in *Ulva*, sea lettuce. (c) A multicellular, branched green alga, *Chara*.

Results

In Table 4, list the names and characteristics of each green algal species studied. Compare these examples with those illustrated in Figure 6.

Table 4
Representative Green Algae

Name	**Body Form** (single-celled, filamentous, colonial, leaflike)	**Characteristics** (pigments, specialized structures, flagella, structures for attachment)
Spirogyra		
Ulva		
Chara		

Lab Study D. Funguslike Protists—Slime Molds (Mycetozoa)

Materials

stereoscopic microscopes
Physarum growing on agar plates

Introduction

The organisms you will investigate in this lab study have been called plants, fungi, animals, fungus animals, protozoa, Protoctista, Protista, Mycetozoa, and probably many more names. William Crowder, in a classic *National Geographic* article (April 1926), describes his search for these creatures in a swamp on the north shore of Long Island. This is what he says: "Behold! Seldom ever before had such a gorgeous sight startled my unexpectant gaze. Spreading out over the bark [of a dead tree] was a rich red coverlet . . . consisting of thousands of small, closely crowded, funguslike growths. . . . A colony of these tiny organisms extended in an irregular patch . . . covering an area nearly a yard in length and slightly less in breadth. . . . Each unit, although actually less than a quarter of an inch in height, resembled . . . a small mushroom, though more marvelous than any I have ever seen."

The creatures Crowder was describing are commonly called **slime molds.** Many place them in the kingdom Fungi, but this classification causes difficulties because, whereas slime molds are phagocytic like protozoa, fungi are never phagocytic but obtain their nutrition by absorption. Characteristics other than feeding mode, including cellular ultrastructure, cell wall chemistry, and molecular studies, indicate that slime molds fit better with amoeboid protists than with fungi. However, the general consensus among taxonomists is that slime molds represent a separate kingdom, the **Mycetozoa** or "fungus-animals."

There are two types of slime molds, plasmodial slime molds and cellular slime molds. In this lab study, you will observe the plasmodial slime mold *Physarum*. The vegetative stage is called a **plasmodium,** and it consists of a multinucleate mass of protoplasm totally devoid of cell walls. This mass feeds on bacteria as it creeps along the surface of moist logs or dead leaves. When conditions are right, it is converted into one or more reproductive structures, called **fruiting bodies,** that produce spores. You may choose to investigate slime molds further in Exercise 3.

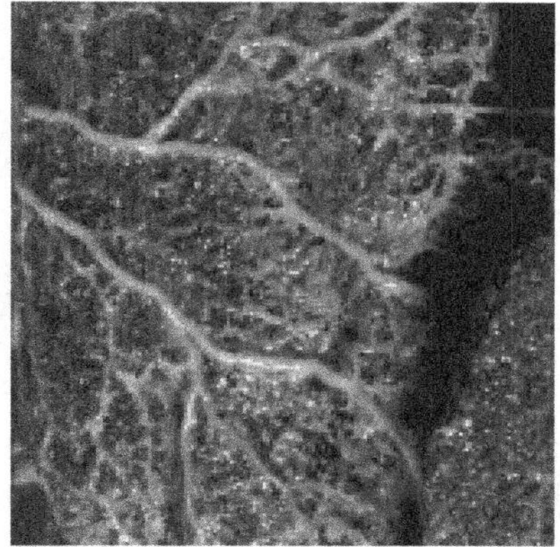

Figure 7.
Slime mold. Slime molds are protists that share some characteristics with both protozoa and fungi. The vegetative stage of a plasmodial slime mold includes an amoeboid phase consisting of a multinucleate mass known as a plasmodium.

Procedure

1. Obtain a petri dish containing *Physarum* and return to your lab bench to study the organism. Keep the dish closed.
2. With the aid of your stereoscopic microscope, examine the plasmodium (Figure 7). Describe characteristics such as color, size, and shape. Look for a system of branching veins. Do you see any movement? Speculate about the source of the movement. Is the movement unidirectional or bidirectional—that is, flows first in one direction and then in the other? Your instructor may have placed oat flakes or another food source on the agar. How does the appearance of the plasmodium change as it contacts a food source?
3. Examine the entire culture for evidence of forming or mature fruiting bodies. Are the fruiting bodies stalked or are they sessile, that is, without a stalk? If a stalk is present, describe it.

Results

Sketch the plasmodium and fruiting bodies in the margin of your lab manual. Label structures where appropriate.

Discussion

Slime molds were once placed in the kingdom Fungi. What characteristics suggest that these organisms are protistan?

EXERCISE 2
The Kingdom Fungi

Introduction

The kingdom Fungi includes a diverse group of organisms that play important economic and ecological roles. These organisms are unicellular (yeasts) or multicellular, heterotrophic organisms that obtain their nutrients by absorption, digesting their food outside their bodies and absorbing the digestion products into their cells. They often have complex life cycles with alternating sexual and asexual (vegetative) reproduction. They may produce spores either asexually by mitosis or sexually by meiosis.

Fungi are beneficial to humans in many ways. We have long used fungi to make wine and bake leavened bread. Yeast, a single-celled fungus, is used in the production of wine, beer, and bread; and other fungi are used to produce other foods. *Penicillium* is a fungus that is used to produce antibiotics. In ecosystems, fungi share with bacteria the essential role of decomposition, returning to the ecosystem the matter trapped in dead organisms.

Although many fungi are beneficial, others play destructive roles in nature. Some species parasitize animals and plants. Athlete's foot and ringworm are diseases commonly known to humans, and potato late blight and wheat rust are common plant diseases caused by fungi. The ergot fungus that parasitizes rye causes convulsive ergotism in humans who eat bread made with infested grains. The bizarre behavior of young women who were later convicted of witchcraft in Salem Village, Massachusetts, in 1692 has been attributed to convulsive ergotism. Fungi are also a source of food in many cultures, with truffles being the most expensive. Truffles are dark, edible subterranean fungi that sell for $200 per pound, with an annual harvest of 30 tons. Truffles cannot be grown in a lab or greenhouse, and are located by specially trained truffle-sniffing pigs or dogs.

In this exercise, you will learn about the structure of typical fungi and the characteristics of four important phyla of fungi: Zygomycota, Ascomycota, Basidiomycota, and Deuteromycota. You will see examples of lichens that are associations between fungi and algae. As you observe these examples, consider interesting questions that might be asked about fungi diversity or ecology. You can choose one of these questions to design a simple experiment in Exercise 3.

Lab Study A. Zygote Fungi—Zygomycota

Materials

compound microscope
stereoscopic microscope
cultures of *Rhizopus stolonifer* with sporangia
cultures of *Pilobolus crystallinus* on demonstration
forceps, ethyl alcohol, alcohol lamp
slides and coverslips
dropper bottles of water

Introduction

One common organism in the phylum Zygomycota is probably growing in your refrigerator right now. The common bread mold, *Rhizopus stolonifer,* grows on many foods as well as bread. In this lab study, you will observe the structure of this species to see many general fungi characteristics. Fungi are made up of threadlike individual filaments, called **hyphae,** which are organized into the body of the fungus, called the **mycelium.** This filamentous mass secretes enzymes into the substrate and digests food that will then be absorbed into its cells. Cells of fungi have cell walls made of **chitin** combined with other complex carbohydrates, including cellulose. You may recall that chitin is the main component of insect exoskeletons.

Rhizopus stolonifer

Rhizopus reproduces both sexually and asexually. In the Zygomycota, cells of the hyphae are haploid. Hyphae grow over a substrate, for example, a slice of bread, giving the bread a fuzzy appearance. In asexual reproduction, certain hyphae grow upright and develop **sporangia,** round structures, on their tips. Haploid spores develop in the sporangia following mitosis, and when they are mature, they are dispersed through the air. If they fall on a suitable medium, they will absorb water and germinate, growing a new mycelium.

Rhizopus also reproduces sexually when compatible mating types designated as (+) and (–) grow side by side. In this case, (+) and (–) hyphae fuse, and, ultimately, nuclei from opposite strains fuse to form 2*n* zygote nuclei that develop in a thick-walled **zygospore.** Following meiosis, haploid spores are produced in sporangia borne on filaments that emerge from the zygospore.

Pilobolus crystallinus

Pilobolus crystallinus (also called the *fungus gun,* or *shotgun fungus*) is another member of the phylum Zygomycota. This fungus is called a **coprophilous** fungus because it grows on dung. It displays many unusual behaviors, one of which is that it is positively phototropic. Perhaps you can investigate this behavior in Exercise 3. Bold et al. (1980) describe asexual reproduction in *Pilobolus.* This species has sporangia as does *Rhizopus,* but rather than similarly dispersing single spores, in *Pilobolus* the sporangium is forcibly discharged as a unit; the dispersion is tied to moisture and diurnal cycles. In nature, in the early evening the sporangia form; shortly after midnight, a swelling appears below the sporangium. Late the following morning, turgor pressure causes the swelling to explode, propelling the sporangium as far as 2 meters. The sticky sporangium will adhere to grass leaves and subsequently may be eaten by an animal—horse, cow, or rabbit. The intact sporangia pass through the animal's digestive tract and are excreted, and the spores germinate in the fresh dung.

In this lab study you will investigate *Rhizopus* and observe *Pilobolus* on demonstration.

Procedure

1. Obtain a culture of *Rhizopus* and carry it to your lab station.
2. Examine it using the stereoscopic microscope.
3. Identify the **mycelia, hyphae,** and **sporangia.**

4. Review the life cycle of *Rhizopus* (Figure 8). Locate the structures in this figure that are visible in your culture. Circle the structures involved in asexual reproduction.
5. Using forceps and aseptic technique, remove a small portion of the mycelium with several sporangia and make a wet mount.
6. Examine the hyphae and sporangia using the compound microscope. Are spores visible? How have the spores been produced?

   How do the spores compare with the hyphal cells genetically?

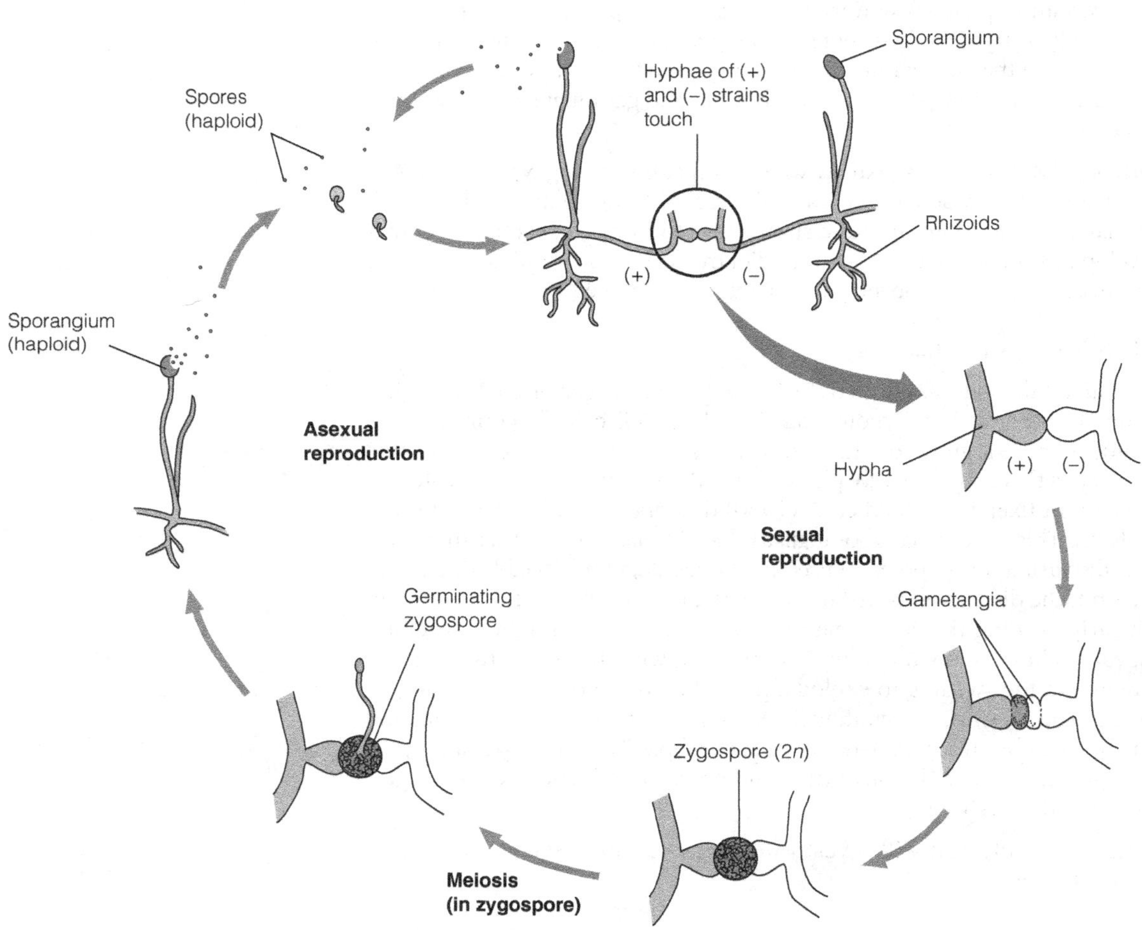

Figure 8.
Rhizopus stolonifer. *Rhizopus* reproduces both sexually by zygospores and asexually by sporangia producing asexual spores. In sexual reproduction, (+) and (–) mating types fuse and a $2n$ zygospore results.

How would spores produced by sexual reproduction differ from spores produced asexually?

7. Observe the cultures of *Pilobolus* (Figure 9) growing on rabbit dung agar that are on demonstration.
8. Identify the **sporangia, mycelia,** and **hyphae.** What color are the sporangia and spores?

Results

1. Review the life cycle of *Rhizopus* and the structures observed in the living culture and compare with Figure 8.
2. Review the structures observed in *Pilobolus* and compare with Figure 9.

Discussion

1. The body form of most fungi, including *Rhizopus,* is a mycelium composed of filamentous hyphae. Using your observations as a basis for your thinking, state why this body form is well adapted to the fungus mode of nutrition.

2. Refer back to the description of *Pilobolus*. Speculate about the adaptive advantage of having a system to propel sporangia, as seen in *Pilobolus.*

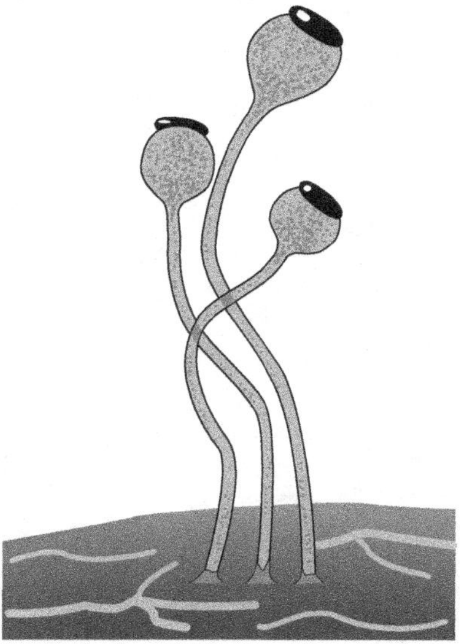

Figure 9.
Pilobolus crystallinus.

Lab Study B. Sac Fungi—Ascomycota

Materials

compound microscope
stereoscopic microscope
dried or preserved *Peziza* specimen
prepared slide of *Peziza* ascocarp
preserved or fresh morels
plastic mounts of ergot in rye or wheat

Introduction

Fungi in the phylum Ascomycota are called *sac fungi,* or ascopore-producing fungi. This division includes edible fungi, morels, and truffles, but it also includes several deadly plant and animal parasites. For example, chestnut blight and the Dutch elm disease have devastated native populations of chestnut and

American elm trees. The fungi causing these diseases were introduced into the United States from Asia and Europe.

Sexual reproduction in the ascomycota fungi produces either four or eight haploid **ascospores** after meiosis in an **ascus.** Spores in *Sordaria* form after meiosis within asci (Figure 7). Asci form within a structure called an **ascocarp.** In *Sordaria* the ascocarp, called a *perithecium,* is a closed, spherical structure that develops a pore at the top for spore dispersal. In some species of sac fungi, the asci are borne on open cup-shaped ascocarps called *apothecia* (sing., *apothecium*). In asexual reproduction, spores are produced, but rather than being enclosed within a sporangium as in zygote fungi, the spores, called **conidia,** are produced on the surface of special reproductive hyphae.

Other features of sac fungi also vary. For example, yeasts are ascomycetes, yet they are single-celled organisms. Yeasts most frequently reproduce asexually by **budding,** a process in which small cells form by pinching off the parent cell. When they reproduce sexually, however, they produce asci, each of which produces four or eight spores.

In this lab study, you will examine a slide of the sac fungi *Peziza* and will observe demonstrations of additional examples of Ascomycota.

Procedure

1. Obtain a dried or preserved specimen of *Peziza* (Figure 10a). Notice the open, cup-shaped apothecium, the **ascocarp,** that bears asci within the cup (not visible with the naked eye). Fungi with ascocarps shaped in this fashion are called **cup fungi.** The cup may be supported by a stalk.
2. Examine a prepared slide of *Peziza* using low and intermediate magnifications on the compound microscope. This slide is a section through the ascocarp. Identify **asci.** How many spores are present per ascus? Are they diploid or haploid?

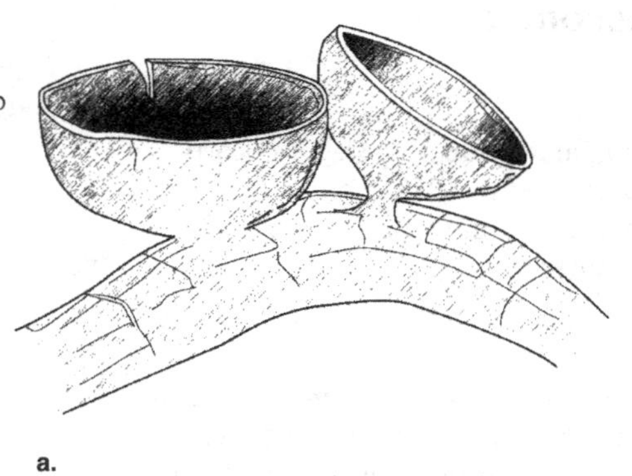

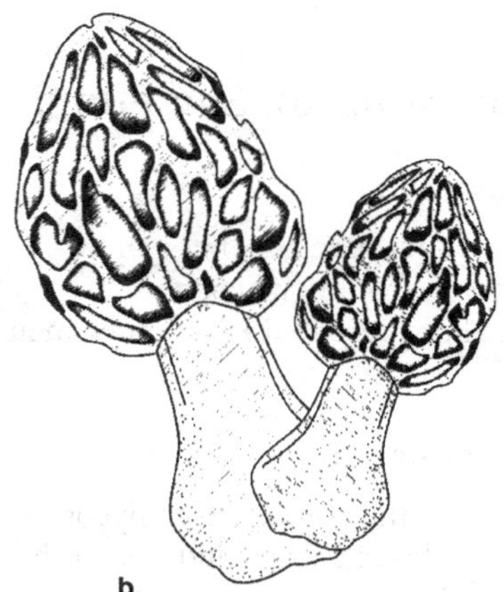

Figure 10.
Examples of sac fungi, phylum Ascomycota. (a) *Peziza* has a cup-shaped ascocarp with asci within the cup. (b) Morels are cup fungi that resemble mushrooms.

3. Complete the sketch of the ascocarp section below, labeling **asci, spores, hyphae,** and **mycelium.**

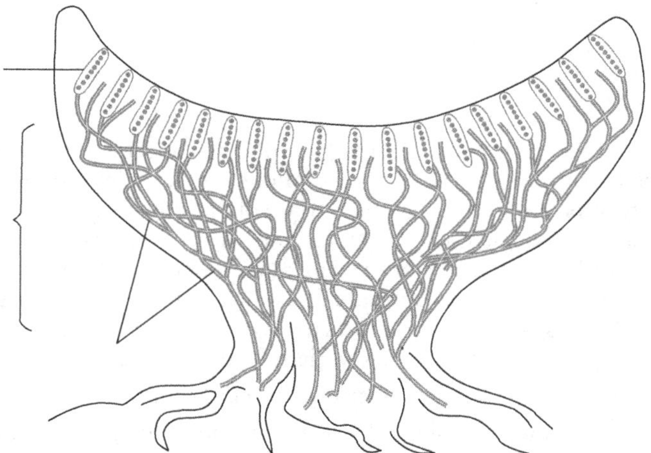

4. Observe the preserved **morels** that are on demonstration (Figure 14.10b). These fungi resemble mushrooms, but the "cap" is convoluted. Asci are located inside the ridges.
5. Observe demonstrations of the mature inflorescence of wheat or rye grass infected with the ascomycete *Claviceps purpurea,* the **ergot** fungus. The large black structures seen among the grains are the ergot.

Results

Review the structures observed in *Peziza,* morels, and ergot. Modify Figures 10a and 10b to reflect features of your examples not included in these figures. Sketch ergot examples in the margin of your lab manual.

Discussion

What characteristics are common to all sac fungi?

Lab Study C. Club Fungi—Basidiomycota

Materials

compound microscope
stereoscopic microscope
fresh, ripe mushroom basidiocarps
prepared slides of *Coprinus* pileus sections

Introduction

The Basidiomycota phylum (club fungi, or basidiospore-producing fungi) includes the fungi that cause the plant diseases wheat rust and corn smut as well as the more familiar puffballs, shelf fungi, and edible and nonedible mushrooms (the latter often called *toadstools*). A mushroom is actually a reproductive structure that grows upward from an underground mycelial mass and produces spores by meiosis. In asexual reproduction, conidia form by mitosis. In this lab study, you will study mushrooms and learn some features of their life cycle.

Procedure

1. Obtain a fresh mushroom, a **basidiocarp,** and identify its parts: The stalk is the **stipe;** the cap is the **pileus.** Look under the cap and identify **gills.** Spores form on the surface of the gills. Examine the gills with the stereoscopic microscope. Do you see spores? Children often make spore prints in scouts or in elementary school by placing a ripe mushroom pileus with the gill side down on a piece of white paper for several hours, allowing the spores to drop to the paper. Scientists use similar spore prints to accurately identify mushrooms.
2. Label the parts of the mushrooms in Figure 11a.
3. Obtain a prepared slide of a section through the pileus of *Coprinus* or another mushroom. Observe it on the compound microscope using low

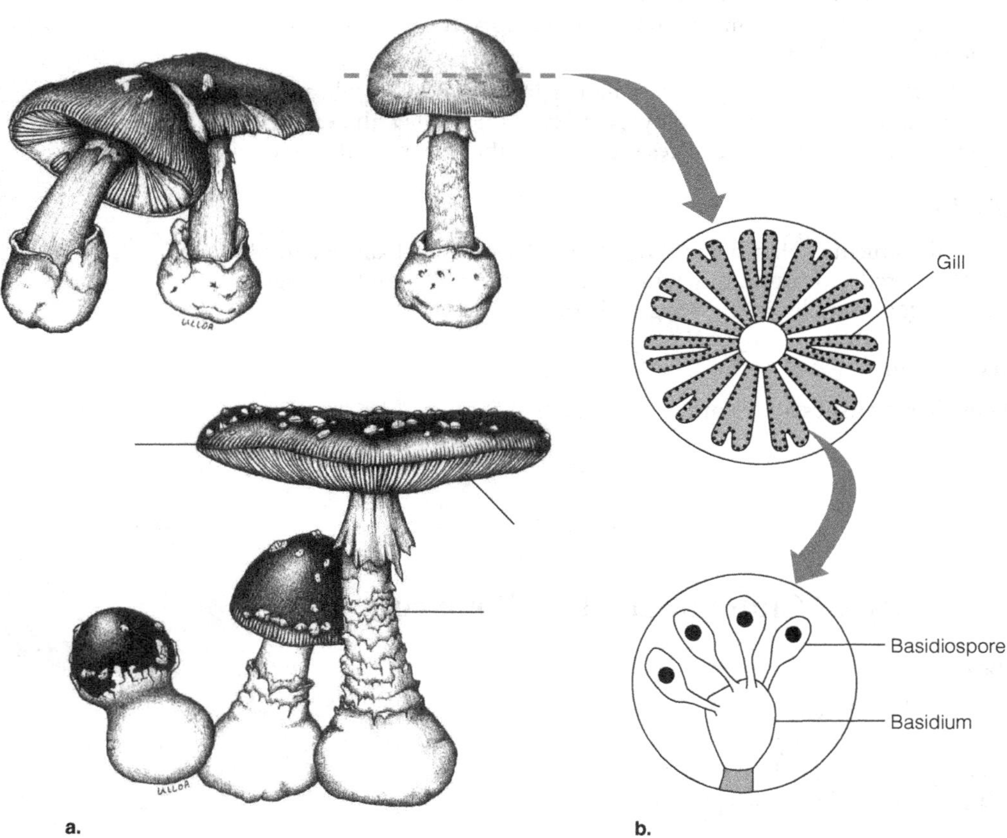

Figure 11.
Club fungi, phylum Basidiomycota. (a) Mushrooms, or basidiocarps, each consisting of a cap, the pileus; and a stalk, the stipe. (b) A section through the gills on a whole basidiocarp reveals basidia and basidiospores.

and then intermediate powers. Is your slide a cross section or a longitudinal section through the pileus? Make a sketch in the lab manual margin indicating the plane of your section through the basidiocarp. Compare your section with the fresh mushroom you have just studied and with Figure 11b.

4. Using the prepared slide, observe the surface of several gills using high power. Spores are produced at the tips of small club-shaped structures called **basidia.** Locate a basidium and focus carefully on its end. Here you may see four knoblike protuberances. Each protuberance has a haploid nucleus that formed following meiosis, and each becomes a **basidiospore.** When the spores are mature, they are discharged from the basidium and are dispersed by the wind.

Results

Review the structures observed and label Figure 11a. Modify the figure to include features observed in your materials that differ from the figure.

Discussion

State the characteristics shared by all Basidiomycota.

Lab Study D. Imperfect Fungi—Deuteromycota

Materials

cultures of *Penicillium* on demonstration
Roquefort cheese on demonstration

Introduction

Most fungi are classified based on their sexual reproductive structures; however, many fungi (as far as is known) reproduce only vegetatively. Because the sexual reproductive stages of these fungi do not exist or have not been found, they are called **asexual,** or **imperfect fungi** (following the botanical use of "imperfect" to indicate a flower lacking one reproductive part). This group is of interest because several human diseases—athlete's foot, ringworm, and candida "yeast" infections—are caused by species of imperfect fungi. Also in this group are several beneficial species—for example, one species of *Penicillium* that produces the antibiotic penicillin and another that is used to make Roquefort and blue cheeses.

Procedure

1. Observe the *Penicillium* on demonstration. You may have observed something similar growing on oranges or other foods in your refrigerator.
2. Describe the texture and the color of the mycelium.

Results

Sketch your observations of *Penicillium* in the margin of your lab manual. Note any features that may be important in distinguishing this organism.

Discussion

Compare the appearance of *Penicillium* with that of *Rhizopus.*

Lab Study E. Lichens

Materials

examples of foliose, crustose, and fruticose lichens on demonstration

Introduction

Lichens are symbiotic associations between fungi and usually algae or cyanobacteria forming a body that can be consistently recognized. The fungal component is usually a sac fungus or a club fungus. The lichen body, called a **thallus,** varies in shape and colors, depending on the species of the components. Reproductive structures can be bright red or pink or green. Photosynthesis in the algae provides nutrients for the fungus, and the fungus provides a moist environment for the algae or cyanobacterium. Because lichens can survive extremely harsh environments, they are often the first organisms to colonize a newly exposed environment such as volcanic flow or rock outcrops, and they play a role in soil formation.

Procedure

Observe the demonstrations of different lichen types: those with a leafy thallus (**foliose**), a crustlike thallus (**crustose**), or a branching, cylindrical thallus (**fruticose**) (Figure 12). Look for cup-shaped or clublike reproductive structures.

Results

1. Sketch the lichens on demonstration in the margins of your lab manual.
2. Identify and label each according to lichen type.

Discussion

Imagine that you are the first scientist to observe a lichen microscopically. What observations would lead you to conclude that the lichen is composed of a fungus and an alga?

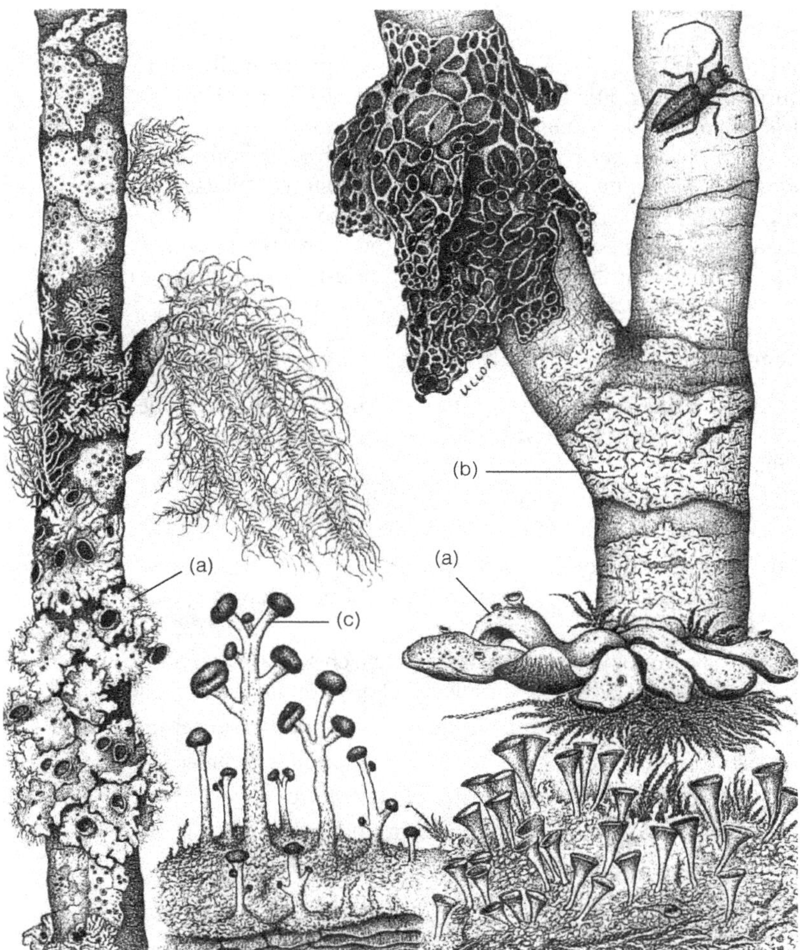

Figure 12.
Lichen types. Lichens may have (a) a leafy thallus (foliose), (b) a crust-like thallus (crustose), or (c) a cylindrical thallus (fruticose).

EXERCISE 3

Designing Your Independent Investigation

Introduction

In this exercise, you will choose one of the organisms observed in this lab topic and design a simple experiment answering a question about its behavior, growth patterns, or interactions with other species.

Be ready to assign tasks to members of your lab team. Be sure that everyone understands the techniques that will be used. Your experiment will be successful only if you plan carefully, cooperate with your team members, perform lab techniques accurately and systematically, and record and report data accurately.

Materials

protozoa and algae cultures
cultures of slime molds *Physarum, Didymium, Dictyostelium*
cultures of *Pilobolus crystallinus, Rhizopus, Penicillium*
sterile agar plates to grow each species
sterile agar with oat flakes
sterile agar with sugar
sterile agar with albumin
sterile agar with pH 6, 7, or 8
aluminum foil
various breads from the health food store—wheat, rye, corn, potato, rice
bread with preservatives
sterilized dung from various animals

Procedure

1. Choose a question from this list to investigate or choose a question from your own observations. *Write your question in the margin of your lab manual.*
   a. Will varying the molarity of the culture medium change the rate of contractile vacuole formation in paramecia?
   b. Do plasmodia of the same species of slime mold unite when growing on the same agar plate? How about different species of slime mold?
   c. Do slime mold plasmodia demonstrate chemotaxis (response to chemical stimuli such as food molecules) or phototaxis (response to light)?
   d. What happens to slime molds if grown in different temperatures?
   e. Do the same fungi grow on different varieties of bread?
   f. How effective are preservatives in preventing fungal growth on foods?
   g. Is *Pilobolus* phototaxic? What about other fungi?
   h. Does succession take place in dung cultures of fungi?
2. Formulate a testable hypothesis.
   Hypothesis:
3. Summarize the experiment. (Use separate paper.)
4. Predict the results of your experiment based on your hypothesis.
   Prediction: (If/then)
5. Outline the procedures used in the experiment.

   a. On a separate sheet of paper, list in numerical order each exact step of your procedure.
   b. Remember to include the number of replicates (usually a minimum of five), levels of treatment, appropriate time intervals, and controls for each procedure.
   c. If you have an idea for an experiment that requires materials other than those provided, ask your laboratory instructor about availability. If possible, additional supplies will be provided.
   d. When carrying out an experiment, remember to quantify your measurements when possible.
6. Perform the experiment, making observations and collecting data for analysis.
7. **Record observations and data** on a separate sheet of paper. Design tables and graphs, at least one of each. Be thorough when collecting data. Do not just write down numbers, but record what they mean as well. Do not rely on your memory for information that you will need when reporting your results.
8. **Prepare your discussion.** Discuss your results in light of your hypothesis.
   a. Review your hypothesis. Review your results (tables and graphs). Do your results support of falsify your hypothesis? Explain your answer, using data for support.
   b. Review your prediction. Did your results correspond to the prediction you made? If not, explain how your results are different from your predictions, and why this might have occurred.
   c. If you had problems with the procedure or questionable results, explain how they might have influenced your conclusion.
   d. If you had an opportunity to repeat and expand this experiment to make your results more convincing, what would you do?
   e. Summarize the conclusion you have drawn from your results.
9. **Be prepared to report your results to the class.** Prepare to persuade your fellow scientists that your experimental design is sound and that your results support your conclusions.
10. If your instructor requires it, **submit a written laboratory report** in the form of a scientific paper. Keep in mind that although you have performed the experiments as a team, you must turn in a lab report of *your original writing*. Your tables and figures may be similar to those of your team members, but your paper must be the product of your own literature search and creative thinking.

Questions for Review

1. Complete Table 5 comparing charactistics of algae.
2. Complete Table 6 comparing characteristics of fungi.

Table 5
Comparison of Algae by Major Features

Phylum	Example(s)	Characteristics	Ecological Role	Economic Importance
Dinoflagellata				
Bacillariophyta				
Phaeophyta (Brown Algae)				
Rhodophyta (Red Algae)				
Chlorophyta (Green Algae)				

3. Compare spore formation in sac fungi and club fungi.

Table 6
Comparison of Fungi by Major Features

Phylum	Example(s)	Sexual Reproductive Structures	Asexual Reproductive Structures
Zygomycota (Zygote Fungi)			
Ascomycota (Sac Fungi)			
Basidiomycota (Club Fungi)			
Deuteromycota (Imperfect Fungi)			

4. Using observations of pigments present, body form, and distinguishing characteristics of the three groups of macroscopic green, brown, and red algae, speculate about where they might be most commonly found in ocean waters.

Applying Your Knowledge

1. Scientists are concerned that the depletion of the ozone layer will result in a reduction of populations of marine algae such as diatoms and

dinoflagellates. Recall the ecological role of these organisms and comment on the validity of this concern.

2. Imagine an ecosystem with no fungi. How would it be modified?

3. In 1950 the living world was classified simply into two kingdoms: plants and animals. More recently, scientists developed the five-kingdom system of classification: plants, animals, monerans, protists, and fungi. In 2000 there was a general consensus among scientists that three domains with more than five kingdoms was a better system for classifying the diversity of life on Earth. However, there is still no consensus on the number of kingdoms or the clustering of organisms that best represents their evolutionary relationships. Using the protists studied in this lab topic, explain why the classification of this diverse group in particular is problematic. How is solving the problem of organizing protistan diversity a model for understanding the process of science?

References

Ahmadjian, V. "Lichens Are More Important Than You Think," *BioScience,* 1995, vol. 45, p. 124.

Alexopoulos, C., C. Mims, and M. Blackwell. *Introductory Mycology,* 4th ed. New York, NY: John Wiley and Sons, Inc., 1996.

Anderson, R. "What to Do with Protists?" *Australian Systematic Botany,* 1998, vol. 11, p. 185.

Bold, H., C. J. Alexopoulos, and T. Delevoryas. *Morphology of Plants and Fungi.* New York: Harper & Row, 1980, p. 654.

Campbell, N., and J. Reece. *Biology,* 6th ed. Menlo Park, CA: Benjamin/Cummings, 2002.

Crowder, W. "Marvels of Mycetozoa." *National Geographic Magazine,* 1926, vol. 49, pp. 421–443.

Doolittle, W. F. "Uprooting the Tree of Life," *Scientific American,* 2000, vol. 282, pp. 90–95.

Hickman, C. P., L. S. Roberts, and A. Larson. *Integrated Principles of Zoology,* 11th ed. Boston: McGraw-Hill, 2001.

Litten, W. "The Most Poisonous Mushrooms," *Scientific American,* 1975, vol. 232.

Websites

Excellent site discussing Protistan systematics:
http://www.ucmp.berkeley.edu/alllife/eukaryotasy.html

Protist Image Data. Excellent page links:
http://megasun.bch.umontreal.ca/protists/protists.html

Links to pictures of red, brown, and green algae:
http://www.sonoma.edu/biology/algae/algae.html

Seaweeds:
http://www.botany.uwc.ac.za/Envfacts/seaweeds/

Information about specific algae and other interesting links:
http://www.botany.uwc.ac.za/mirrors/UCG_Seawwwd/Algae/

Mycological Resources on the Internet:
http://muse/bio.cornell.edu/~fungi/

See an amoeba video and find interesting information on amoebas:
http://www.bms.ed.ac.uk/research/smaciver/amoeba.htm

Photo Credits

1b: ©Biophoto Associates/Science Source/Photo Researchers, Inc. 2b: Courtesy of John Mansfield, University of Wisconsin, Madison. 3a: Courtesy of the Virginia Institute of Marine Science/William and Mary. 3b: Courtesy of Jean-Marie CAVANIHAC/Jean-Marie CAVANIHAC. 3c: Courtesy of JoAnn Burkholder, North Carolina State University. 3d: ©Eric Grave/Photo Researchers, Inc. 3c: ©Michael Abbey/Photo Researchers, Inc. 3d: ©Cabisco/Visuals Unlimited. 5a: ©Gary Robinson/Visuals Unlimited. 5b: ©D. P. Wilson/Eric and David Hosking/Photo Researchers, Inc. 5c: Courtesy of Wayne Armstrong/Wayne's World. 6a: ©Kim Taylor/Bruce Coleman, Inc. 6c: ©Kerry A. Dressler/Biological Photo Service. 7: ©R. R. Degginger/Earth Scenes/Animals Animals.

Art Credits

6c: From Bold et al., *Morphology of Plants and Fungi,* 5th ed. (New York: Harper and Row, 1987), ©1987 by Harper and Row Publishers, Inc. Reprinted by permission of Addison Wesley Longman, Inc. 9, 10: Adapted from illustrations by Miguel Ulloa, Departamento de Botanica, Instituto de Biologia, Universidad Nacional Autonoma de Mexico. 11, 12: ©Miguel Ulloa.

Text Credits

Excerpt from William Crowder, "Marvels of Mycetozoa," *National Geographic Magazine*, April 1926. Copyright ©1926 National Geographic Society. Reprinted by permission.

The Peroxidase Enzyme

Introduction

Peroxidases have been found in animals, plants, fungi, and bacteria. Peroxidases, like the horseradish peroxidase (HRP) that is used in this lab, catalyze the oxidation of organic compounds by hydrogen peroxide:

$$\underset{\text{Reduced form}}{\text{H-R-O-H}} + H_2O_2 \longrightarrow \underset{\text{Oxidized form}}{\text{R=O}} + 2H_2O$$

The functions of these enzymes are not known in most cases, although a wide variety of functions have been suggested, and it is believed that they do have many different functions.

Microbodies present in plants, animal, and fungal cells function to detoxify cellular waste products, one of which is hydrogen peroxide. Any cell using aerobic respiration produces small amounts of hydrogen peroxide (H_2O_2) as a highly toxic by-product. Peroxide has a high reactive -O-O- structure, so it is important that enzymes remove it before it can damage the cell. Some microbodies contains peroxidases for this purpose.

In plants, peroxidases are mainly in the cell walls and in vacuoles. A well-documented major role of the cell wall enzyme is in the polymerization of lignin, the substance that makes wood hard, strong, and difficult for most organisms to metabolize.

In vacuoles in roots, peroxidases may play a role in protection against infection by pathogens. Perhaps that explains why horseradish root and turnip root are rich sources of peroxidase.

You will observe the oxidation of the organic compound, **guaiacol**, by hydrogen peroxide, a reaction that is catalyzed by peroxidase. The reaction can be summarized as follows:

$$\underset{\text{Reduced}}{\textbf{Guaiacol}} + \mathbf{H_2O_2} \longrightarrow \underset{\text{Oxidized}}{\textbf{brown products}} + \mathbf{H_2O}$$

Guaiacol is another name for the organic molecule o-methyl-phenol. It is a yellowish, oily liquid usually extracted from guaiacum resin. ***Guaiacum*** is a genus of the tropical shrubs and trees that includes the guaiac tree of Central

America. The resin was used in the treatment of syphilis and other diseases. Guaiacol is used as an expectorant and local anesthetic. Used as a substrate for HRP, it is a convenient and reliable indicator of enzyme activity. The product is a dark brown mixture of unknown composition, but probably includes dimers and multimers of guaiacol.

The dilute solution of guaiacol you will use appears colorless. The intensity of the color of the reaction mixture as it accumulates the brown products will be used to monitor the progress of the reaction.

The intensity of the brown color could be estimated visually but, to be more precise, it will be measured by a spectrophotometer.

OBJECTIVES

1. Prepare an enzyme extract from living tissue
2. Determine the effect of various enzyme concentrations on enzyme activity
3. Graph enzyme activity as a function of enzyme concentration

Materials

Horseradish root, fresh
10 mM $_2O_2$ solution
Buffer, Citrate PO_4/pH 7.0
25 mM Guaiacol solution
Buffer, Citrate PO_4/pH 5.0
Test tubes, 15 mL
5 mL pipettes
1 mL pipettes
100 mL beakers
100 mL graduated cylinders
blenders

Spectronic 20
cuvettes
cuvette racks
rulers
kimwipes
cheesecloth
paring knife
digital balance
scrub brush
marking pencils
pi-pumps

Procedures

A. Enzyme Extract Preparation

1. Scrub the horseradish root with a brush over the lab sink to remove any dirt present.
2. Peel off the outer covering with a knife.
3. Cut and weigh roughly 1.0 gram of the horseradish tissue on a digital balance.
4. Cut the sample into small pieces and place them into a blender jar.
5. Using a graduated cylinder, add 100 mL of **Cold 0.1M citrate-phosphate buffer, pH 7.0** to the blender jar
6. Homogenize for about 15 seconds in the blender jar
7. Place a double layer of cheesecloth over the mouth of a 100 mL beaker.
8. Pour the blender homogenate through the cheesecloth filter into the beaker. Squeeze the cheesecloth into a ball to increase the extract yield.
9. Label the extract preparation **"Enzyme Extract"** with a wax pencil. DO NOT WRITE ON THE FROSTED AREA OF THE BEAKER.

Hundreds of enzymes are present in the extract you have just prepared. Your study team, however, will be analyzing only the peroxidase.

B. Effect Of Enzyme Concentration On The Rate Of Reaction

1. Label a 100 mL beaker "**BUFFER.**" Using a graduated cylinder pour 25 mL of **0.1M Citrate Phosphate buffer ph 5.0** into it.

There will be two dispensers; one filled with 10 mM H_2O_2 and the other with 25 mM Guaiacol solutions. These dispensers will be equipped with precalibrated pumps.

2. Obtain two 5.0 mL pipettes and a green pi-pump and two 1.0 mL pipettes and a blue pi-pump, to be used to withdraw specific volumes from the beakers. Follow the instructor's directions for using the pipettes and the dispensers.
3. Label nine test tubes 1–9 with a wax pencil, taking care not to mark the frosted surface. Fill each of the nine test tubes with the specific volumes of the reagents according to Table 1. (For example: Test tube #1 is the "blank" which is used to calibrate the spectrophotometer. Fill it with 5.0 mL of buffer, 2.0 mL of H_2O_2, and 1.0 mL of guaiacol.)

Tube Number	Relative Enzyme Concetration (pH 5) in mL	0.1 Buffer in mL	10mM H_2O_2 in mL	ENZYME EXTRACT in mL	25 mM GUAIACOL
1	Blank	5.0	2.0	0	1.0
2	Dil 0.25	0	2.0	0	1.0
3	Dil 0.25	4.75	0	0.25	0
4	Dil 0.5	0	2.0	0	1.0
5	Dil 0.5	4.5	0	0.5	0
6	Dil 1.0	0	2.0	0	1.0
7	Dil 1.0	4.0	0	1.0	0
8	Dil 2.0	0	2.0	0	1.0
9	Dil 2.0	3.0	0	2.0	0

Table 1.

4. Use care in delivering the proper reagent and volume of reagent to the specific tube. **NOTE:** The total volume for each couplet (2-3, 4-5 etc.) as well as for the blank will be 8.0 mL. **ALSO:** Note that you are temporarily keeping the substrate and enzyme separate. **DO NOT MIX THE COUPLETS UNTIL YOU ARE READY TO READ THE MEASUREMENTS FROM THE SPECTRONIC – 20.**

C. Spectrophotometric Measurement

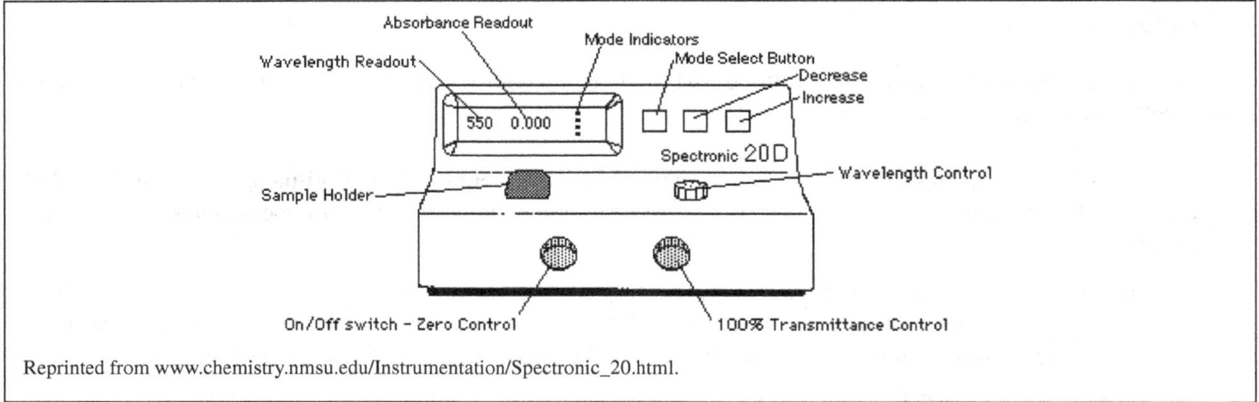

Reprinted from www.chemistry.nmsu.edu/Instrumentation/Spectronic_20.html.

Figure 1. The Spectrophotometer

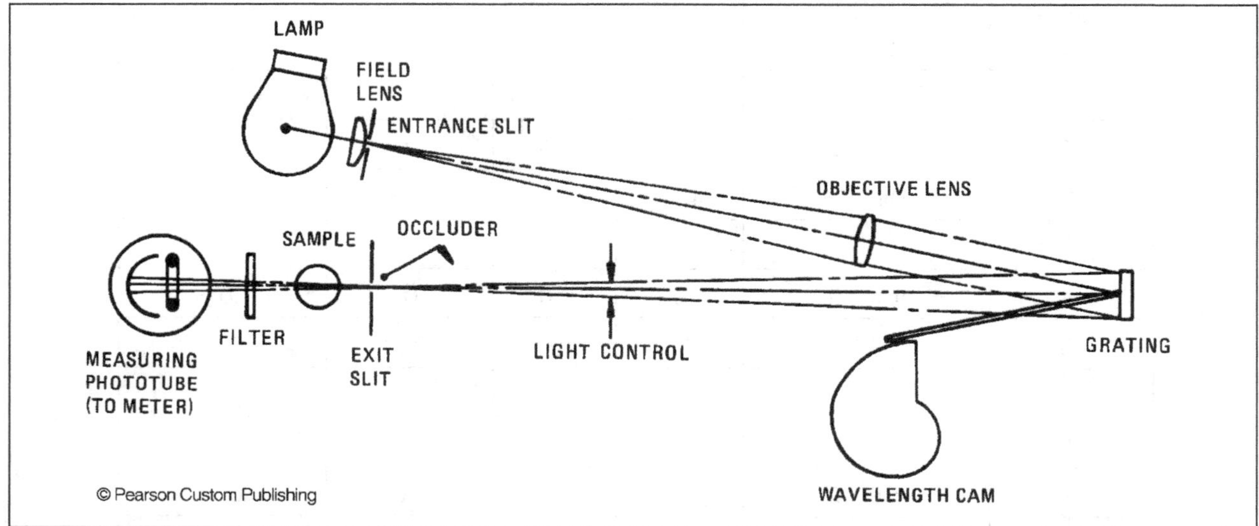

Figure 2. The Spectrophotometer—Internal Components

This instrument is a spectrophotometer. The particular model that we are using is called a Spectronic –20 (Spec–20)

1. Turn on the Spec–20. Let the instrument warm up for 5 minutes. You will see a digital readout in the window as shown in Figure 1.
2. Set the wavelength to 500 nm with the wavelength control knob.
3. With the Mode Select button set the Mode to Absorbance. A red dot will appear to the left of Absorbance.

4. With no tube in the sample holder turn the Zero Control knob clockwise until it stops. Then gradually turn it counterclockwise until the reading 1.999 appears in the readout. This is the infinity point just before flashing.
5. Transfer the contents of Tube #1 into a clean cuvette. Wipe the outside of the cuvette with a Kimwipe and insert the cuvette into the sample holder.
6. Turn the 100% transmittance control knob until the digital readout reads 0 absorbance. Why is this step necessary? This is your CONTROL TUBE.
7. The infinity point (1.999) should be checked before each experimental tube is run (if off reset the control tube). NOTE: this absorbance scale is based upon a logarithmic function relating the intensity of the incident of light to the intensity of transmitted light.

D. Testing Procedure

1. You should have one person from your group keeping time, another recording the data and another obtaining the readings from the Spec–20.
2. Obtain a reading from the 0.25 ml dilution in the following manner. Start timing as you mix the contents of tubes 2 and 3 back and forth two times to mix the contents of the tubes. Immediately pour into a clean cuvette tube. Insert the tube into the sample chamber. **Exactly 20 seconds after you started mixing the contents of tubes 2 and 3 read and record the absorbance in Table 2.**
3. The cuvette will remain in the chamber and at a time 40 seconds from mixing (time 0) again record the absorbance.
4. Continue to obtain readings every 20 seconds until a total of 120 seconds has passed.
5. Rezero the spectrophotometer (steps 4-6 under Spectrophotometric measurement). Repeat procedure as in 1-4 above using tubes 4 and 5. Enter your data in Table 2.
6. Rezero the spectrophotometer (steps 4-6 under Spectrophotometric measurement). Repeat procedure as in 1-4 above using tubes 6 and 7. Enter your data in Table 2.
7. Rezero the spectrophotometer (steps 4-6 under Spectrophotometric measurement). Repeat procedure as in 1-4 above using tubes 8 and 9. Enter your data in Table 2

Concentration	20 sec	40 sec	60 sec	80 sec	100 secs	120 secs
0.25 dil						
0.5 dil						
1.0 dil						
2.0 dil						

Table 2. Absorbance Readings

8. Plot the above data on graph paper for all concentrations. Use time on the x-axis and absorbance on the y-axis. Scale the graph correctly. If done on a computer calculate a trend line.

9. NOTE: Your instructor may ask you to prepare an additional graph showing the rate of reaction vs. enzyme concentration (measured in dil). The rate of reaction is obtained by calculating the **slopes** of the lines in the portion of the graph where enzyme activity is increasing. Slope = dy/dx.

Clean Up

1. **Save your enzyme extract for next week's lab according to your instructor's directions.**
2. Clean all glassware
3. Remove all markings from test tubes, beakers, etc
4. Wash all test tubes with soapy water, rinse and dry
5. Disinfect your table tops

Scientific Investigation

Before going to lab, read the Introduction and Exercises 1 and 2. Be prepared to answer all questions and contribute your ideas in a class discussion.

Laboratory Objectives

After completing this lab topic, you should be able to:

1. Identify and characterize questions that can be answered through scientific investigation.
2. Define *hypothesis* and explain what characterizes a good scientific hypothesis.
3. Identify and describe the components of a scientific experiment.
4. Summarize and present results in tables and graphs.
5. Discuss results and critique experiments.
6. Design a scientific experiment.
7. Interpret and communicate results.

Introduction

Biology is the study of the phenomena of life, and biological scientists—researchers, teachers, and students—observe living systems and organisms, ask questions, and propose explanations for those observations. Scientific investigation is a way of testing those explanations. Science assumes that biological systems are understandable and can be explained by fundamental rules or laws. Scientific investigations share some common elements and procedures, which are referred to as the *scientific method.* Not all scientists follow these procedures in a strict fashion, but each of the elements is usually present. Science is a creative human endeavor that involves asking questions, making observations, developing explanatory hypotheses, and testing those hypotheses. Scientists closely scrutinize investigations in their field, and each scientist must present his or her work at scientific meetings or in professional publications, providing evidence from observations and experiments that supports the scientist's explanations of biological phenomena.

In this lab topic, you will not only review the process that scientists use to ask and answer questions about the living world, but you will develop the skills to conduct and critique scientific investigations. Like scientists, you will work in research teams in this laboratory and others, collaborating as you ask questions and solve problems. Throughout this laboratory manual, you will be investigating biology using the methodology of scientists, asking questions, proposing explanations, designing experiments, predicting results, collecting and analyzing data, and interpreting your results in light of your hypotheses.

EXERCISE 1
Questions and Hypotheses

This exercise explores the nature of scientific questions and hypotheses. Before going to lab, read the explanatory paragraphs and then be prepared to present your ideas in the class discussion.

Lab Study A. Asking Questions

Scientists are characteristically curious and creative individuals whose curiosity is directed toward understanding the natural world. They use their study of previous research or personal observations of natural phenomena as a basis for asking questions about the underlying causes or reasons for these phenomena. For a question to be pursued by scientists, the phenomenon must be well defined and testable. The elements must be measurable and controllable.

There are limits to the ability of science to answer questions. Science is only one of many ways of knowing about the world in which we live. Consider, for example, this question: Do excessively high temperatures cause people to behave immorally? Can a scientist investigate this question? Temperature is certainly a well-defined, measurable, and controllable factor, but morality of behavior is not scientifically measurable. We probably could not even reach a consensus on the definition. Thus, there is no experiment that can be performed to test the question. Which of the following questions do you think can be answered scientifically?

1. Does binge drinking cause more brain damage in teenagers than in adults?
2. Is genetically modified corn safe to eat?
3. Do children who wash their hands often and bathe daily have a greater risk of asthma than those who wash their hands less often and bathe every other day?
4. Should endangered species be cloned to prevent extinction?
5. What is the function of spines on cacti?
6. Did the 19-year-old college student develop ulcers because of his stress and fast-food diet?

How did you decide which questions can be answered scientifically?

Lab Study B. Developing Hypotheses

As questions are asked, scientists attempt to answer them by proposing possible explanations. Those proposed explanations are called **hypotheses.** A hypothesis tentatively explains something observed. It proposes an answer to a question. Consider question 5, preceding. One hypothesis based on this question might be "Spines on cacti prevent animals from eating the cacti." The hypothesis has suggested a possible explanation for the observed spines.

A scientifically useful hypothesis must be testable and falsifiable (able to be proved false). To satisfy the requirement that a hypothesis be falsifiable, it must be possible that the test results do not support the explanation. In our example, if spines are removed from test cacti and the plants are not eaten by animals, then the hypothesis has been falsified. *Even though the hypothesis can be falsified, it can never be proved true.* The evidence from an investigation can only provide support for the hypothesis. In our example, if cacti without spines were eaten, the hypothesis has not been proved, but has been supported by the evidence. Other explanations still must be excluded, and new evidence from additional experiments and observations might falsify this hypothesis at a later date. In science seldom does a single test provide results that clearly support or falsify a hypothesis. In most cases, the evidence serves to modify the hypothesis or the conditions of the experiment.

Science is a way of knowing about the natural world (Moore, 1993) that involves testing hypotheses or explanations. The scientific method can be applied to the unusual and the commonplace. You use the scientific method when you investigate why your once-white socks are now blue. Your hypothesis might be that your blue jeans and socks were washed together, an assertion that can be tested through observations and experimentation.

Students often think that controlled experiments are the only way to test a hypothesis. The test of a hypothesis may include experimentation, additional observations, or the synthesis of information from a variety of sources. Many scientific advances have relied on other procedures and information to test hypotheses. For example, James Watson and Francis Crick developed a model that was their hypothesis for the structure of DNA. Their model could only be supported if the accumulated data from a number of other scientists were consistent with the model. Actually, their first model (hypothesis) was falsified by the work of Rosalind Franklin. Their final model was tested and supported not only by the ongoing work of Franklin and Maurice Wilkins but also by research previously published by Erwin Chargaff and others. Watson and Crick won the Nobel Prize for their scientific work. They did not perform a controlled experiment in the laboratory but tested their powerful hypothesis through the use of existing evidence from other research. Methods other than experimentation are acceptable in testing hypotheses. Think about other areas of science that require comparative observations and the accumulation of data from a variety of sources, all of which must be consistent with and support hypotheses or else be inconsistent and falsify hypotheses.

The information in your biology textbook is often thought of as a collection of facts, well understood and correct. It is true that much of the knowledge of biology has been derived through scientific investigations, has been thoroughly tested, and is supported by strong evidence. However, scientific knowledge is always subject to novel experiments and new technology, any aspect of which may result in modification of our ideas and a better understanding of biological phenomena. The structure of the cell membrane is an example of the self-correcting nature of science. Each model of the membrane has been modified as new results have negated one explanation and provided support for an alternative explanation.

Application

Before scientific questions can be answered, they must first be converted to hypotheses, which can be tested. For each of the following questions, write an explanatory hypothesis. Recall that the hypothesis is a statement that explains the phenomenon you are interested in investigating.

1. Does regular interaction with pets improve the health of the elderly?

2. What effect do high concentrations of the industrial pollutant PCB (polychlorinated biphenyl) have on killer whale reproduction?

Scientists often propose and reject a variety of hypotheses before they design a single test. Discuss with your class which of the following statements would be useful as scientific hypotheses and could be investigated using scientific procedures. Give the reason for each answer by stating whether it could possibly be falsified and what factors are measurable and controllable.

1. The number of fungiform papillae (bumps on the tongue) affects taste sensitivity.
2. Inflated self-esteem in young males increases the odds of aggression.
3. Anglers catch more bass during a full moon.
4. Exposure to environmental pollutants produces feminization in newly hatched male alligators.
5. Birds are the living descendants of dinosaurs.

EXERCISE 2
Designing Experiments to Test Hypotheses

The most creative aspect of science is designing a test of your hypothesis that will provide unambiguous evidence to falsify or support a particular explanation. Scientists often design, critique, and modify a variety of experiments and other tests before they commit the time and resources to perform a single experiment. In this exercise, you will follow the procedure for experimentally testing hypotheses, but it is important to remember that other methods, including observation and the synthesis of other sources of data, are acceptable in scientific investigations. An experiment involves defining variables, outlining a procedure, and determining controls to be used as the experiment is performed. Once the experiment is defined, the investigator predicts the outcome of the experiment based on the hypothesis.

Read the following description of a scientific investigation of the effects of sulfur dioxide on soybean reproduction. Then in Lab Study A you will determine the types of variables involved, and in Lab Study B, the experimental procedure for this experiment and for others.

Investigation of the Effect of Sulfur Dioxide on Soybean Reproduction

Agricultural scientists were concerned about the effect of air pollution, sulfur dioxide in particular, on soybean production in fields adjacent to coal-powered power plants. Based on initial investigations, they proposed that sulfur dioxide in high concentrations would reduce reproduction in soybeans. They designed an experiment to test this hypothesis (Figure 1). In this experiment, 48 soybean plants, just beginning to produce flowers, were divided into two groups, treatment and no treatment. The 24 treated plants were divided into four groups of 6. One group of 6 treated plants was placed in a fumigation chamber and exposed to 0.6 ppm (parts per million) of sulfur dioxide for 4 hours to simulate sulfur dioxide emissions from a power plant. The experiment was repeated on the remaining three treated groups. The no-treatment plants were placed similarly in groups of 6 in a second fumigation chamber and simultaneously exposed to filtered air for 4 hours. Following the experiment, all plants were returned to the greenhouse. When the beans matured, the number of bean pods, the number of seeds per pod, and the weight of the pods were determined for each plant.

Lab Study A. Determining the Variables

Read the description of each category of variable; then identify the variable described in the preceding investigation. The variables in an experiment must be clearly defined and measurable. The investigator will identify

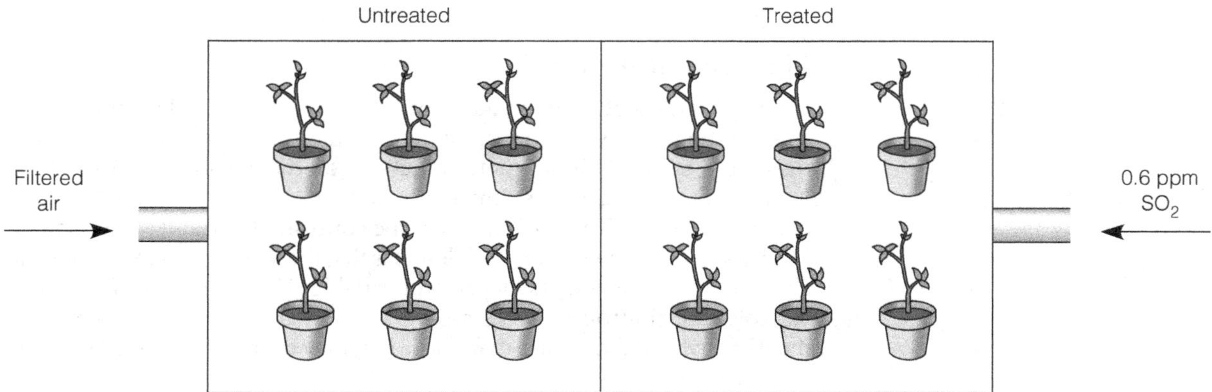

Figure 1.
Experimental design for soybean experiment. The experiment was repeated four times. Soybeans were fumigated for 4 hours.

and define *dependent, independent,* and *controlled variables* for a particular experiment.

The Dependent Variable

Within the experiment, one variable will be measured or counted or observed in response to the experimental conditions. This variable is the **dependent variable.** For the soybeans, several dependent variables are measured, all of which provide information about reproduction. What are they?

The Independent Variable

The scientist will choose one variable, or experimental condition, to manipulate. This variable is considered the most important variable by which to test the investigator's hypothesis and is called the **independent variable.** What was the independent variable in the investigation of the effect of sulfur dioxide on soybean reproduction?

Can you suggest other variables that the investigator might have changed that would have had an effect on the dependent variables?

Although other factors, such as light, temperature, time, and fertilizer, might affect the dependent variables, only one independent variable is usually chosen. Why is it important to have only one independent variable?

Why is it acceptable to have more than one dependent variable?

The Controlled Variable

Consider the variables that you identified as alternative independent variables. Although they are not part of the hypothesis being tested in this investigation, they would have significant effects on the outcome of this experiment. These variables must, therefore, be kept constant during the course of the experiment. They are known as the **controlled variables.** The underlying assumption in experimental design is that the selected independent variable is the one affecting the dependent variable. This is only true if all other variables are controlled. What are the controlled variables in this experiment? What variables other than those you may have already listed can you now suggest?

Lab Study B. Choosing or Designing the Procedure

The **procedure** is the stepwise method, or sequence of steps, to be performed for the experiment. It should be recorded in a laboratory notebook before initiating the experiment, and any exceptions or modifications should be noted during the experiment. The procedures may be designed from research published in scientific journals, through collaboration with colleagues in the lab or other institutions, or by means of one's own novel and creative ideas. The process of outlining the procedure includes determining control treatment(s), levels of treatments, and numbers of replications.

Level of Treatment

The value set for the independent variable is called the **level of treatment.** For this experiment, the value was determined based on previous research and preliminary measurements of sulfur dioxide emissions. The scientists may select a range of concentrations from no sulfur dioxide to an extremely high concentration. The levels should be based on knowledge of the system and the biological significance of the treatment level. What was the level of treatment in the soybean experiment?

Replication

Scientific investigations are not valid if the conclusions drawn from them are based on one experiment with one or two individuals. Generally, the same procedure will be repeated several times (**replication**), providing consistent results. Notice that scientists do not expect exactly the same results inasmuch as individuals and their responses will vary. Results from replicated experiments are usually averaged and may be further analyzed using statistical tests. Describe replication in the soybean experiment.

Control

The experimental design includes a **control** in which the independent variable is held at an established level or is omitted. The control or control treatment serves as a benchmark that allows the scientist to decide whether the predicted effect is really due to the independent variable. In the case of the soybean experiment, what was the control treatment?

What is the difference between the control and the controlled variables discussed previously?

Lab Study C. Making Predictions

The investigator never begins an experiment without a prediction of its outcome. The **prediction** is always based on the particular experiment designed to test a specific hypothesis. Predictions are written in the form of if/then statements: "If the hypothesis is true, then the results of the experiment will be . . ."; for example, "if cactus spines prevent herbivory, then removal of the spines will result in cacti being eaten by animals." Making a prediction provides a critical analysis of the experimental design. If the predictions are not clear, the procedure can be modified before beginning the experiment. For the soybean experiment, the hypothesis was: "Exposure to sulfur dioxide reduces reproduction." What should the prediction be? State your prediction.

To evaluate the results of the experiment, the investigator always returns to the prediction. If the results match the prediction, then the hypothesis is supported. If the results do not match the prediction, then the hypothesis is falsified. Either way, the scientist has increased knowledge of the process being studied. Many times the falsification of a hypothesis can provide more information than confirmation, since the ideas and data must be critically evaluated in light of new information. In the soybean experiment, the scientist may learn that the prediction is true (sulfur dioxide does reduce reproduction at the concentration tested). As a next step, the scientist may now wish to identify the particular level at which the effect is first demonstrated.

Return to the Application section of Exercise 1 and review your hypotheses for the numbered questions. Consider how you might design an experiment to test the first hypothesis. For example, you might measure "health" by determining blood pressure before and after interactions with a rabbit. The prediction might be:

> **If** regular interaction with pets improves the health of the elderly (*a restatement of the hypothesis*), **then** blood pressure will be lowered in elderly people who spend 15 minutes daily with a pet rabbit (*predicting the results from the experiment*).

Now consider an experiment you might design to test the second hypothesis. How will you measure killer whale "reproduction"?

State a prediction for this hypothesis and experiment. Use the if/then format:

The actual test of the prediction is one of the great moments in research: No matter the results, the scientist is not just following a procedure but truly testing a creative explanation derived from an interesting question.

Discussion

1. From this exercise, list the components of scientific investigations from asking a question to carrying out an experiment.

2. From this exercise, list the variables that must be identified in designing an experiment.

3. What are the components of an experimental procedure?

EXERCISE 3

Designing an Experiment

Materials

steps or platform, 8 in. high
clock with a second hand
metronome

Introduction

In this exercise, your entire class, working together, will practice investigating a question using what you have learned so far about the scientific process.

Question

Cardiovascular fitness can be determined by measuring a person's pulse rate and respiration rate before and after a given time of aerobic exercise. A person who is more fit may have a relatively slower pulse rate and a lower respiratory rate after exercise, and his or her pulse rate should return to normal more quickly than that of a person who is less fit. Your assignment is to investigate the effect of a well-defined, measurable, controllable independent variable on cardiovascular fitness.

In your research teams, take about 10 minutes to discuss several *specific* questions that you can ask about an independent variable related to the *broad* topic of cardiovascular fitness. List your questions in the space provided. For example, your question might be "Does cigarette smoking have an effect on cardiovascular fitness?" Choose your best question and propose a testable hypothesis. Contribute your question and hypothesis to a class list recorded by the instructor.

The entire class decides on the hypothesis, the experimental design, and the predicted results. The same experiment is performed by all teams.

Hypothesis

Record the hypothesis chosen by the class.

The Experiment

If you were performing an independent investigation, at this time you would go to the library and read relevant scientific articles or texts to determine an accepted procedure used by scientists to test cardiovascular fitness. You might discover that there is a test, called the ***step test***, that is used for this purpose (Kusinitz and Fine, 1987). Here are the basic elements of this test:

1. The subject steps up and down on a low platform, approximately 8 in. from the ground, for 3 minutes at a rate of 30 steps per minute. (Using a metronome to count steps ensures that all subjects maintain a constant step rate.) The subject should step up and then step down again, keeping the rate constant (Figure 2).
2. The subject's pulse rate is measured before the test and immediately after the test. The subject should be sitting quietly when the pulse is counted. Use three fingers to find the pulse in the radial artery (the artery in the wrist, above the thumb). Count the number of beats per minute. (Count the beats for 30 seconds and multiply by 2.)
3. Additionally, the pulse rate is measured at 1-minute intervals after the test until the pulse rate returns to normal (recovery time). Count the pulse for 30 seconds, rest 30 seconds, count 30 seconds, and rest 30 seconds. Repeat this procedure until the pulse returns to normal. Record the number of minutes to return to the normal pulse rate. (Do not record the pulse rate.)

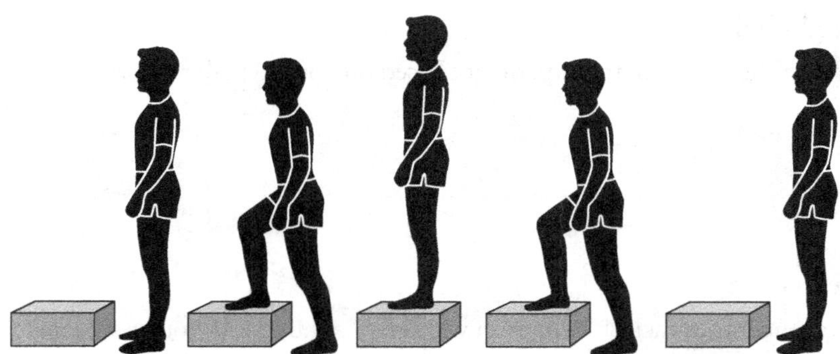

Figure 2.
The step test. Step up on the platform, and then step down again, keeping the rate constant.

As a class, design the experiment. Record the components of your experiment by completing the information below.

Dependent variable(s):

Independent variable:

Controlled variables:

Control:

Level of treatment:

Replication:

Summarize the experiment designed by your class:

Prediction

Predict the results of the experiment based on your hypothesis (if/then).

Procedure

Two students in each student team will serve as subjects. All other students in the team will be the investigators. The investigators will record the data for the two subjects.

Students with respiratory or circulatory disorders should not be the subjects in this experiment.

List in numerical order each exact step of your procedure. Begin with recruitment of the subjects in each treatment category. Refer to the description of the experimental test. Remember to designate persons to time the experiment and record the measurements.

Performing the Experiment

Following the procedures established by your investigative team, perform the experiment and record your results.

Results

Record the results for your team in Table 1. Record total class results in Table 2. Identify the treatment conditions at the top of the table.

Table 1
Results of Step Test for Your Team (Pulse rates are beats per minute.)

	Treatment 1: ______	Treatment 2: ______
Before step test Pulse rate		
After step test Pulse rate		
Recovery time (min)		

Table 2
Results of Step Test for All Teams (Pulse rates are beats per minute.)

Treatment 1: ______________________________

Subject	1	2	3	4	5	6	**Average**
Before step test Pulse rate							
After step test Pulse rate							
Recovery time (min)							

Treatment 2: ______________________________

Subject	1	2	3	4	5	6	**Average**
Before step test Pulse rate							
After step test Pulse rate							
Recovery time (min)							

EXERCISE 4
Presenting and Analyzing Results

Once the data are collected, they must be organized and summarized so that the scientists can determine if the hypothesis has been supported or falsified. In this exercise, you will design **tables** and graphs; the latter are also called **figures.** Tables and figures have two primary functions. They are used (1) to help you analyze and interpret your results and (2) to enhance the clarity with which you present the work to a reader or viewer.

Lab Study A. Tables

You have collected data from your experiment in the form of a list of numbers that may appear at first glance to have little meaning. Look at your data. How could you organize the data set to make it easier to interpret? You could *average* the data set for each treatment, but even averages can be rather uninformative. Could you use a summary table to convey the data (in this case, averages)?

Table 3 is an example of a table using data averages of the number of seeds per pod and number of pods per plant as the dependent variables and exposure to sulfur dioxide as the independent variable. Note that the number of replicates and the units of measurement are provided in the table and table legend.

Table 3
Effects of 4-Hour Exposure to 0.6 ppm Sulfur Dioxide on Average Seed and Pod Production in Soybeans

Treatment	Number	Seeds per Pod	Pods per Plant
Control	24	3.26	16
SO_2	24	1.96	13

Tables are used to present results that have a few to many data points. They are also useful for displaying several dependent variables. For example, average number of bean pods, average number of seeds per pod, and average weight of pods per plant for treated and untreated plants could all be presented in one table.

The following guidelines will help you construct a table:

- All values of the same kind should read down the column, not across a row. Include only data that are important in presenting the results and for further discussion.
- Information and results that are not essential (for example: test-tube number, simple calculations, or data with no differences) should be omitted.
- The headings of each column should include units of measurement, if appropriate.

- Tables are numbered consecutively throughout a lab report or scientific paper. For example: Table 4 would be the fourth table in your report.
- The **title,** which is located at the top of the table, should be clear and concise, with enough information to allow the table to be understandable apart from the text. Capitalize the first and important words in the title. Do not capitalize articles (a, an, the), short prepositions, and conjunctions.
- Refer to each table in the written text. Summarize the data and refer to the table; for example, "The plants treated with sulfur dioxide produced an average of 1.96 seeds per pod (Table 3)." Do not write, "See the results in Table 3."
- If you are using a database program, such as Excel, you should still sketch your table on paper before constructing it on the computer.

Application

1. Using the data from your experiment, design a summary table to present the results for *one* of your dependent variables, pulse rate. Your table need not be the same size or design as the sample. In your table, provide units of the dependent variable (pulse rate). Tell the reader how many replications (if any) were used to calculate the averages.
2. Compose a title for your table. Refer to the guidelines in the previous section.

Lab Study B. Graphs

The results of an experiment usually are presented graphically, showing the relationships among the independent and dependent variable(s). A graph or figure provides a visual summary of the results. Often, characteristics of the data are not apparent in a table but may become clear in a graph. By looking at a graph, then, you can visualize the effect that the independent variable has on the dependent variable and detect trends in your data. Making a graph may be one of the first steps in analyzing your results.

The presentation of your data in a graph will assist you in interpreting and communicating your results. In the final steps of a scientific investigation, you must be able to construct a logical argument based on your results that either supports or falsifies your starting hypothesis. Your graph should be accurately and clearly constructed, easily interpreted, and well annotated. The following guidelines will help you to construct such a graph.

- Use graph paper and a ruler to plot the values accurately. If using a database program, you should first sketch your axes and data points before constructing the figure on the computer.
- The independent variable is graphed on the *x* axis (horizontal axis, or abscissa), and the dependent variable, on the *y* axis (vertical axis, or ordinate).
- The numerical range for each axis should be appropriate for the data being plotted. Generally, begin both axes of the graph at zero (the extreme left corner). Then choose your intervals and range to maximize the use of the graph space. Choose intervals that are logically spaced and therefore will allow easy interpretation of the graph, for example, intervals of 5s or 10s. To avoid generating graphs with wasted space, you may signify unused graph space by two perpendicular tic marks between the zero and your lowest number on one or both axes.
- Label the axes to indicate the variable and the units of measurement. Include a legend if colors or shading is used to indicate different aspects of the experiment.
- Choose the type of graph that best presents your data. Line graphs and bar graphs are most frequently used. The choice of graph type depends on the nature of the variable being graphed.
- Compose a title for your figure, and write it below your graph. Graphs, diagrams, drawings, and photographs are all called ***figures*** and should be numbered consecutively throughout a lab report or scientific paper. Each figure is given a caption or title that describes its contents, giving enough information to allow the figure to be self-contained. Capitalize only the first word in a figure title and place a period at the end.

The Line Graph

Line graphs show changes in the quantity of the chosen variable and emphasize the rise and fall of the values over their range. Use a line graph to present continuous data. For example, changes in the dependent variable pulse rate, measured over time, would be depicted best in a line graph.

- Plot data as separate points.
- Whether to connect the dots on a line graph depends on the type of data and how they were collected. To show trends, draw smooth curves or straight lines to fit the values plotted for any one data set. Connect the points dot to dot when emphasizing meaningful changes in values on the *x* axis.
- If more than one set of data is presented on a graph, use different colors or symbols and provide a key or legend to indicate which set is which.
- A boxed graph, instead of one with only two sides, makes it easier to see the values on the right side of the graph.

Note the features of a line graph in Figure 3., which depicts the increase in gray whale populations along the California coast over 35 years.

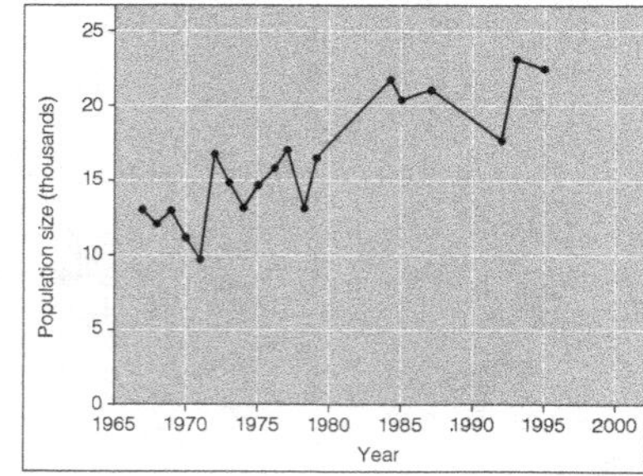

Figure 3.
Population size. Eastern North Pacific gray whales observed off the coast of California, 1965–2000. (After Gerber et al., 2000.)

The Bar Graph

Bar graphs are constructed following the same principles as for line graphs, except that vertical bars, in a series, are drawn down to the horizontal axis. Bar graphs are often used for data that represent separate or discontinuous groups or non-numerical categories, thus emphasizing the discrete differences between the groups. For example, a bar graph might be used to depict differences in number of seeds per pod for treated and untreated soybeans. Bar graphs are also used when the values on the *x* axis are numerical but grouped together. These graphs are called histograms.

Note the features of a bar graph in Figure 4., which indicates the area of cropland used for genetically modified crops.

You will be asked to design graphs throughout this laboratory manual. Remember, the primary function of the figure is to present your results in the clearest manner to enhance the interpretation of your data.

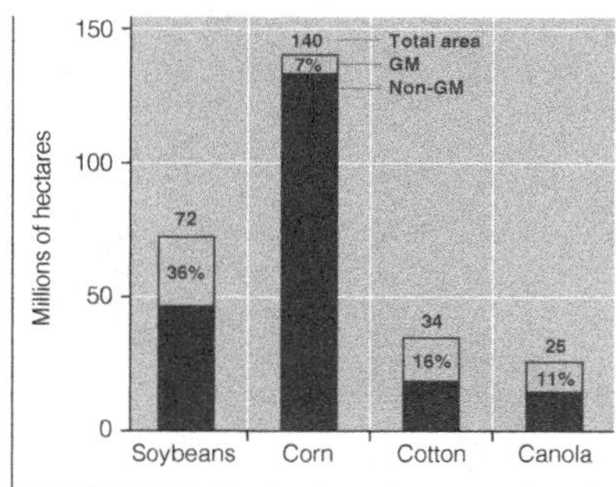

Figure 4.
Global area of genetically modified (GM) crops and non-GM crops grown in 2000. (After Brown, 2001.)

Application

1. Using data from your experiment and the grid provided below, design a bar graph that shows the relationship between the dependent and independent variables in this experiment. Discuss with your teammates how to design this figure so that it includes the data for pulse rate before and after exercise for the treatments selected for your experiment. Draw and label the figure, and compose a title for it.

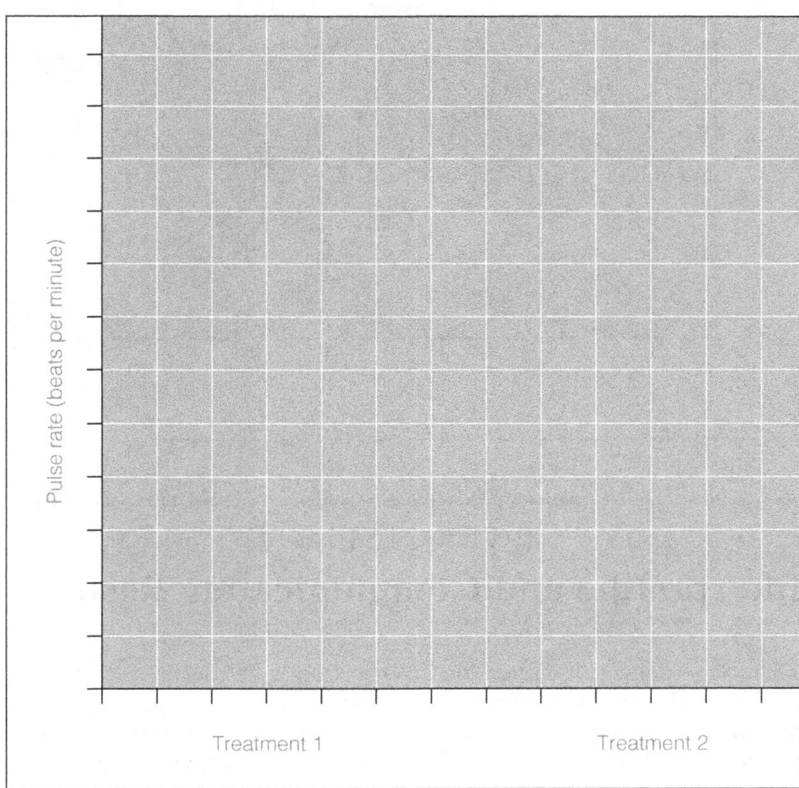

Figure 1.

a. What was your independent variable (treatment)?

b. Write the dependent variable on the appropriate axis. Write the independent variable on the appropriate axis.

2. Design an additional figure that will assist with interpreting the results of your experiment. You might use the data for recovery time or the difference in pulse rate before and after the step test for each treatment.
3. Draw, label, and compose a title for that figure using the grid provided below.

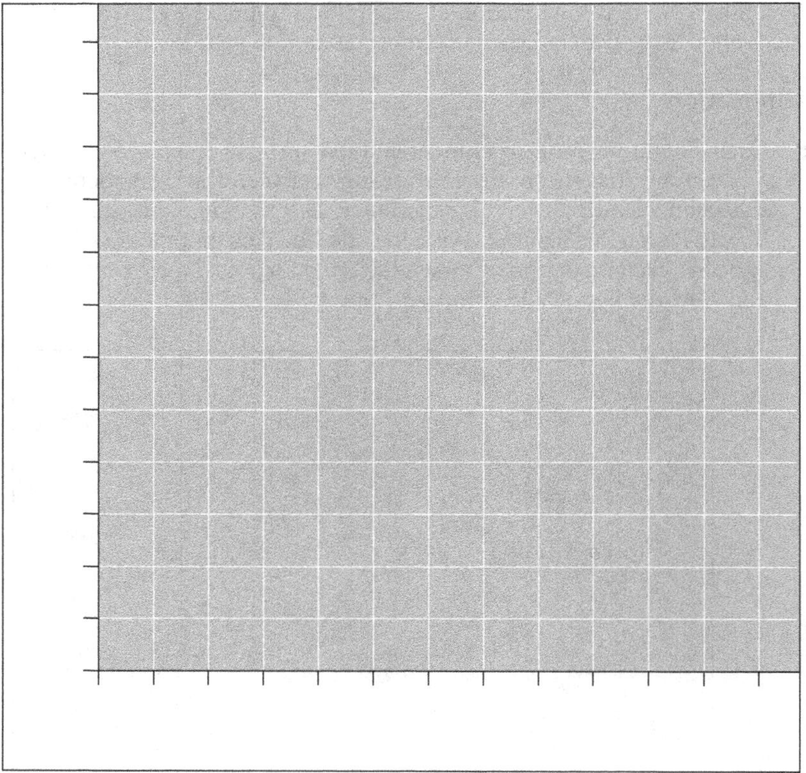

EXERCISE 5

Interpreting and Communicating Results

The last component of a scientific investigation is to interpret the results and discuss their implications in light of the hypothesis and its supporting literature. The investigator studies the tables and graphs and determines if the hypothesis has been supported or falsified. If the hypothesis has been falsified, the investigator must suggest alternate hypotheses for testing. If the hypothesis has been supported, the investigator suggests additional experiments to strengthen the hypothesis, using the same or alternate methods.

Scientists will thoroughly investigate a scientific question, testing hypotheses, collecting data, and analyzing results, until they are satisfied that they can explain the phenomenon of interest. The final phase of a scientific investigation is the communication of the results to other scientists. Preliminary results may be presented within a laboratory research group and at scientific meetings where the findings can be discussed. Ultimately, the completed project is presented in the form of a scientific paper that is reviewed by scientists within the field and published in a scientific journal. The ideas, procedures, results, analyses, and conclusions of all scientific investigations are critically scrutinized by other scientists. Because of this, science is sometimes described as *self-correcting,* meaning that errors that may occur are usually discovered within the scientific community.

Scientific communication, whether spoken or written, is essential to science. During this laboratory course, you often will be asked to present and interpret your results at the end of the laboratory period. Additionally, you will write components of a scientific paper for many lab topics.

Application

1. Using your tables and figures, analyze your results and discuss your conclusions with your group.
2. Write a summary statement for your experiment. Use your results to support or falsify your hypothesis. Be prepared to present your conclusions to the class.
3. Critique your experiment. What weaknesses do you see in the experiment? Suggest improvements.

Weaknesses in Experiment	Improvement
1.	
2.	
3.	
4.	
5.	

4. Suggest additional and modified hypotheses that might be tested. Briefly describe your next experiment.

5. Briefly describe the four major parts of a scientific paper. What is the abstract? What information is found in a References Cited section?

Questions for Review

1. Review the major components of an experiment by matching the following terms to the correct definition: *control, controlled variables, level of treatment, dependent variable, replication, procedure, prediction, hypothesis, independent variable.*
   a. Variables that are kept constant during the experiment (variables not being manipulated)

   b. Tentative explanation for an observation

   c. What the investigator varies in the experiment (for example, time, pH, temperature, concentration)

   d. Process used to measure the dependent variable

   e. Appropriate values to use for the independent variable

   f. Treatment that eliminates the independent variable or sets it at a standard value

g. What the investigator measures, counts, or records; what is being affected in the experiment

h. Number of times the experiment is repeated

i. Statement of the expected results of an experiment based on the hypothesis

2. Identify the dependent and independent variables in the following experiments. (***Circle*** the dependent variable and ***underline*** the independent variable.)
   a. The rate of oxygen production for yeast cells growing with and without cyanide, a respiratory inhibitor.

   b. Number of colorectal tumors for patients taking aspirin twice a day.

   c. Number of gray whales observed for 35 years.

3. Suggest a control treatment for each of the following experiments.
   a. Subjects ingest candied ginger (a spice) and then spin in chairs for 10 minutes. Bouts of nausea are recorded at the end of each treatment.

      Control treatment:

   b. Bean plants are sprayed with a water-based mist containing the growth hormone auxin. The length of the stem is measured after 2 weeks.

      Control treatment:

   c. Alligators are captured as they hatch from nests maintained at 22°C, 30°C, and 37°C. The number of males and females is recorded from each nest.

      Control treatment:

4. What is the essential feature of science that makes it different from other ways of understanding the natural world?

Applying Your Knowledge

Interpreting Graphed and Tabular Data

1. The winning times for men and women competing in the Boston Marathon from 1972 to 1990 are presented in Figure 5. Women were allowed to compete for the first time in 1972. Write a statement summarizing these results.

   a. For men:

   b. For women:

   c. Compare the slope of the two lines from 1972 to 1980. What possible explanation can you suggest for the rapid improvement in women's times compared to men's during this time period? During the 1980s, why did women's times level off?

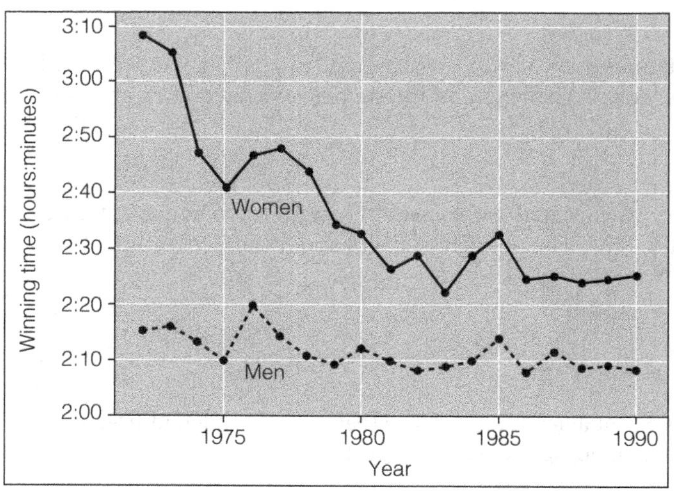

Figure 5.
Winning times for the Boston Marathon for men and women from 1972 to 1990. (After Gould, 1996.)

d. What is the independent variable?

What is the dependent variable?

2. Sherman and Billing (1999), investigating the uses of spices (plant products that flavor food), hypothesized that spices have been and are used to reduce foodborne illnesses and food poisoning. They predicted that if spices reduce these illnesses, then spices should have antibacterial activity. They reviewed the results of research by many scientists who documented bacterial inhibition for 30 spices commonly found in food. The spices were tested on foodborne bacteria, such as ***Salmonella, Escherichia,*** and ***Listeria.*** The number of bacterial species tested ranged from 4 to 31. The proportions of bacteria inhibited by each spice are presented in Figure 6.

   a. Which spices inhibited or killed all species of bacteria tested?

   b. How many spices inhibited at least 75% of the bacteria?

   c. Which spices inhibited 30–40% of the bacteria?

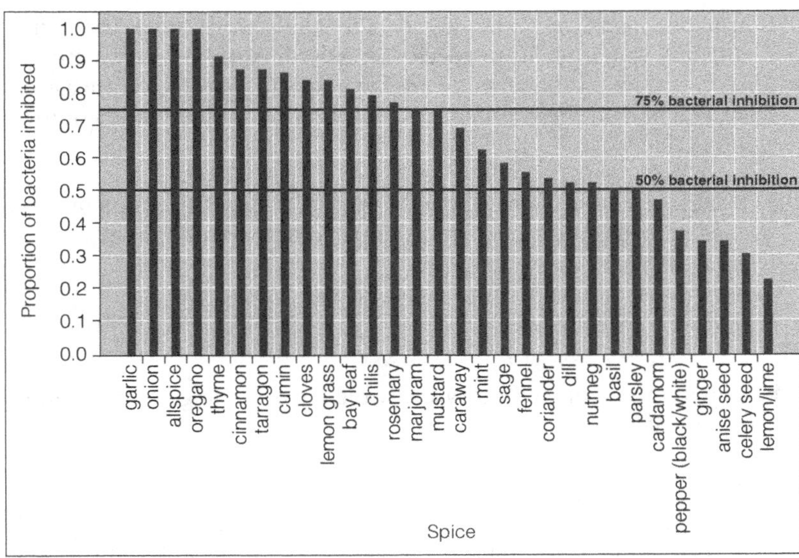

Figure 6.
Bacterial inhibition by 30 spices tested in the laboratory. The number of bacterial species tested ranged from 4 to 31. (After Sherman and Billing, 1999.)

3. Review the guidelines for graphs on pages 15–17 and critique Figure 7 below. This figure illustrates the changes in risk factors that are important in chronic diseases such as coronary heart disease, lung cancer, diabetes, and stroke.

Figure 7.
RISK-FACTOR PREVALENCE IN U.S.

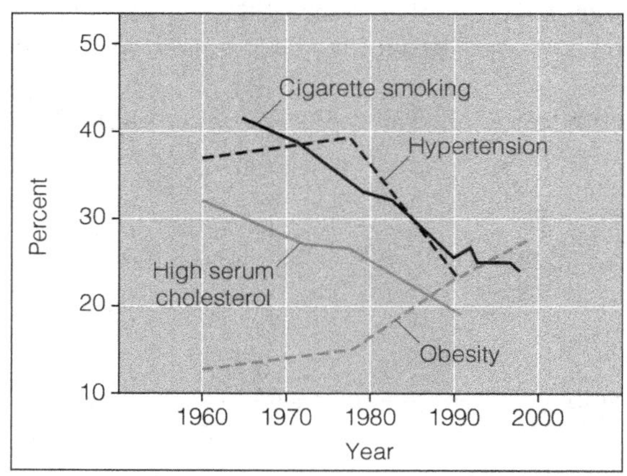

Source: Centers for Disease Control and Prevention. (After Doyle, 2001.)

4. Non-native invasive species are considered a serious threat to biodiversity and in particular to species already threatened by extinction. The percentage of threatened vertebrate species affected by invasive species differs on the continental mainlands versus the islands of the world (Table 4).

   a. Make a general statement about the effect of invasive species on threatened animals on the mainland compared to those on islands.

   b. Which taxonomic category has a higher percentage of mainland species affected than island species?

   c. Is there a greater number of threatened species among birds or mammals?

Table 4
Percentage of Threatened Terrestrial Vertebrate Species on Continental Mainlands and Islands Affected by Invasive Species (The number of threatened species is in parentheses.)

	Mainland Areas		Insular Areas	
Taxonomic Group	**%**	**(n)**	**%**	**(n)**
Mammals	19.4	(283)	11.5	(61)
Birds	5.2	(250)	38.2	(144)
Reptiles	15.5	(84)	32.9	(76)
Amphibians	3.3	(30)	30.8	(13)
Total for all groups considered	12.7	(647)	31.0	(294)

(After McNeely, 2000.)

Practicing Experimental Design

1. Students are interested in investigating the effect of temperature on the time needed for metamorphosis for caterpillars of the Eastern swallowtail butterfly. They design an experiment to test their hypothesis that increasing temperature will reduce the time needed for metamorphosis to take place. They predict that the time of metamorphosis will decrease as the temperature increases. The students collect eight caterpillars from the butterfly garden on campus over a 1-week period. They place pairs of caterpillars in four different temperature environments: the refrigerator, the laboratory, outdoors, and an incubator at 37°C. They record the time it takes for the caterpillars to become pupae (form a chrysalis) and then to emerge as butterflies. They are dismayed by their results. Three of the caterpillars died. The other data are inconclusive.

   Critique their experiment and suggest improvements. Your comments should address all aspects of the scientific method and reflect your understanding of experimental design.

2. Scientists have successfully moved genes from one species to another, resulting in genetically engineered organisms referred to as transgenic species. For example, plant breeders have transferred a gene from the bacterium ***Bacillus thuringiensis*** into corn and cotton, causing these plants to produce a compound called *Bt* toxin. These plants now have a built-in insecticide. As part of the environmental review of *Bt* cotton, researchers investigated the effect of the *Bt* toxin on soil invertebrates (Marvier, 2001).

   Can you state a hypothesis for this investigation?

They tested their hypothesis that there would be no significant effect on soil invertebrates by measuring the survival and weight of earthworms cultivated in soil containing ground leaves of *Bt* cotton. The experimental design called for batches of ten worms to be weighed and then placed in each of four cups containing the soil and leaf mixture. After 14 days the worms were removed from the cups, counted, and weighed again. The percent change in weight was calculated.

For this experiment, what is the independent variable?

What is the dependent variable?

Can you suggest a control treatment for this experiment?

What controlled variables might need to be considered in designing this experiment?

How many replicates were used?

Write a prediction for this experiment. (Remember that the prediction is written in the form of an if/then statement.)

The results from the experiment were the following:

> There was no difference in survival for the two treatments; only one worm died during the entire experiment. The average weight increase for the worms in each cup is shown in Figure 8. The worms in the treated soil increased in weight on average 49%, and the worms in the control soil increased in weight 78.5%. In other words, the worms in soil with transgenic cotton gained 29.5% less weight than those in soil with nontransgenic cotton. Because of the small sample size and variation from cup to cup, these results were not statistically significant and the researchers supported the hypothesis that *Bt* cotton had no significant negative effect on the soil invertebrates, specifically worms.

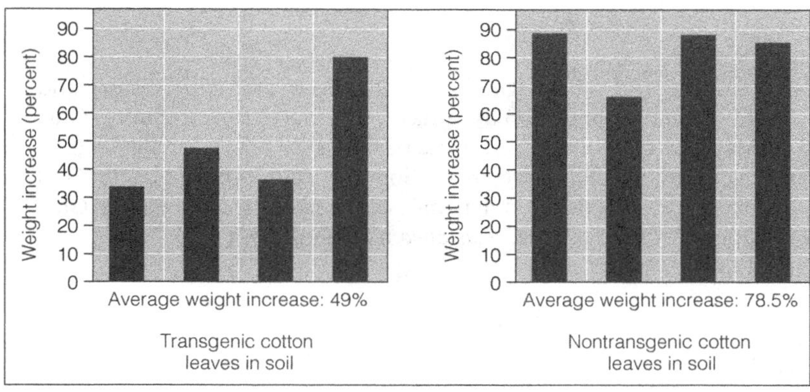

Figure 8.
The effect of soil mixed with crushed leaves of transgenic cotton or nontransgenic cotton on weight increase in earthworms. (From Marvier 2001—"Ecology of Transgenic Crops." *American Scientist,* vol. 89, pp. 160–167. Figure 6, p. 165.)

Given these results, what suggestions might you make for designing additional investigations?

References

Brown, K. "Seeds of Concern," 2001, *Scientific American,* vol. 284, pp. 52–57.

Campbell, N., and J. Reece. *Biology,* 6th ed. San Francisco, CA: Benjamin/Cummings, 2002.

Doyle, R. "Lifestyle Blues," *Scientific American,* vol. 284 (2001) p. 30.

Gerber, L., D. P. DeMaster, and S. P. Roberts. "Measuring Success in Conservation." *American Scientist,* 2000, vol. 88, pp. 316–324.

Gould, S. *Full House.* New York: Random House, 1996.

Kusinitz, I., and M. Fine. *Your Guide to Getting Fit,* 3rd ed. Palo Alto, CA: Mayfield, 1995.

Marvier, M. "Ecology of Transgenic Crops," *American Scientist,* 2001, vol. 89, pp. 160–167. (This article is an excellent model illustrating the scientific process.)

McNeely, J. A. "The Future of Alien Invasive Species: Changing Social Views." In *Invasive Species in a Changing World,* eds. H. A. Mooney and R. J. Hobbs. Washington, D.C.: Island Press, 2000.

Moore, J. *Science as a Way of Knowing.* Cambridge, MA: Harvard University Press, 1993.

Pechenik, J. *A Short Guide to Writing about Biology,* 4th ed. San Francisco, CA: Addison Wesley Longman, 2001.

Sherman, P. W., and J. Billing. "Darwinian Gastronomy: Why We Use Spices," *Bioscience,* 1999, vol. 49, pp. 453–463. (The second author contributed to this work through undergraduate research.)

The format and many ideas in this lab topic were based on an exercise written by Jean Dickey, published in J. Dickey, *Laboratory Investigations for Biology,* Menlo Park, CA: Addison Wesley Longman, 1995.

Websites

Good Science:

http://www.ucmp.berkeley.edu/diapsids/buzz/dinoscience.html

Information on Scientific Process:

http://koning.ecsu.ctstateu.edu/plants_human/scimeth.html

Art Credits

2: From *Your Guide to Getting Fit,* by Ivan Kusinitz and Morton Fine, by permission of Mayfield Publishing Company. Copyright ©1987, 1991, 1995 by Mayfield Publishing Company. 3: Adapted from *Full House*, by Stephen Jay Gould. Copyright ©1996 by Stephen Jay Gould. Reprinted by permission of Harmony Books, a division of Crown Publishers, Inc. 4: Adapted from J. E. Schwegman, "Some aspects of the life history and population dynamics of *Astralagus tennesseensis* A. Gray in Illinois," *Castanea* 63 (1998):64, fig. 1. 5: Adapted from J. E. Schwegman, "Some aspects of the life history and population dynamics of *Astralagus tennesseensis* A. Gray in Illinois," *Castanea* 63 (1998):65, fig 2.

Text Credits

Adapted from Neil A. Campbell, *Biology,* 4th ed. (Menlo Park, CA: Benjamin/Cummings, 1996), ©1996 The Benjamin/Cummings Publishing Company.

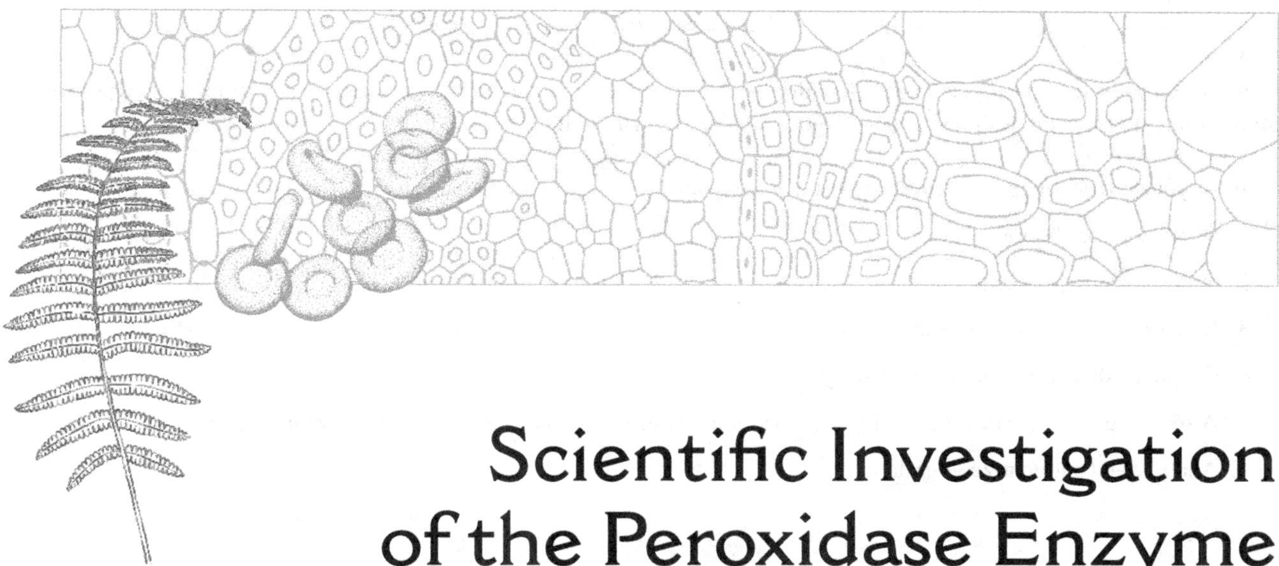

Scientific Investigation of the Peroxidase Enzyme

In your last lab, you investigated the question "What is the effect of enzyme concentration on the rate of enzyme activity?" This week your lab team will have the opportunity to investigate another question: "What is the effect of temperature on the rate of enzyme activity?" You will also have the opportunity to design your own experiment, using the scientific method, to explore this question.

Start by reading your textbook to gain an understanding of how temperature affects the rate of chemical reactions and the tertiary structure of proteins.

1. What is your hypothesis?
2. What information led you to make this hypothesis?

Scientists often read the literature, looking for protocols (procedures) that they can adapt to their specific experiment. Last week, you learned a method of assaying the activity of peroxidase using guaiacol and H_2O_2 as substrates and measuring the rate of formation of the brown products with a spectrophotometer. How can that procedure be adapted to answer this new question? Some factors that you need to consider when designing this experiment are:

1. What is the independent variable?
2. What is the dependent variable?
3. What variables must be controlled?
4. What will be the level of treatment (i.e. what temperatures will you test)?
5. What concentration of the enzyme will you use?

Start by brainstorming these questions with your lab group. Then design an experiment that will test the hypothesis. Show your experimental design to your instructor before performing it.

After your instructor approves your experimental design:

1. Write your prediction
2. Perform the experiment
3. Construct a table to display the data clearly
4. Graph the data as temperature vs. enzyme activity
5. A second graph may be required by your instructor to show the rate of the reaction vs. temperature
6. Analyze and summarize your data.

Diffusion and Osmosis

Laboratory Objectives

After completing this lab topic, you should be able to:

1. Describe the mechanism of diffusion at the molecular level.
2. List several factors that influence the rate of diffusion.
3. Describe a selectively permeable membrane, and explain its role in osmosis.
4. Define *hypotonic, hypertonic,* and *isotonic* in terms of relative concentrations of osmotically active substances.
5. Discuss the influence of the cell wall on osmotic behavior in cells.
6. Explain how incubating plant tissues in a series of dilutions of sucrose can give an approximate measurement of osmolarity of tissue cells.
7. Explain why diffusion and osmosis are important to cells.
8. Apply principles of osmotic activity to medical, domestic, and environmental activities.

Introduction

Maintaining the steady state of a cell is achieved only through regulated movement of materials through cytoplasm, across organelle membranes, and across the plasma membrane. This regulated movement facilitates communication within the cell and between cytoplasm and the external environment. The cytoplasm and extracellular environment of the cell are aqueous solutions. They are composed of water, which is the **solvent,** or dissolving agent, and numerous organic and inorganic molecules, which are the **solutes,** or dissolved substances. Organelle membranes and the plasma membrane are **selectively permeable,** allowing water to freely pass through but regulating the movement of solutes.

The cell actively moves some dissolved substances across membranes, expending adenosine triphosphate (ATP) (biological energy) to accomplish the movement. Other substances move passively, without expenditure of ATP from the cell, but only if the cell membrane is permeable to those substances. Water and selected solutes move passively through the cell and cell membranes by **diffusion,** a physical process in which molecules move from an area where they are in high concentration to one where their concentration is lower. The energy driving diffusion comes only from the intrinsic kinetic energy in all atoms and molecules. If nothing hinders the movement, a solute will diffuse until it reaches equilibrium.

Osmosis is a type of diffusion, the diffusion of water through a selectively permeable membrane from a region where it is highly concentrated to a region where its concentration is lower. The difference in concentration of water occurs if there is an unequal distribution of at least one dissolved substance on either side of a membrane and the membrane is impermeable to that substance. In this situation, the substance is called an **osmotically active substance (OAS).** For example, if a membrane that is impermeable to sucrose separates a solution of sucrose from distilled water, water will move from the distilled water, where it is in higher concentration, through the membrane into the sucrose solution, where it is in lower concentration. In this case, sucrose is the osmotically active substance.

Three terms, **hypertonic, hypotonic,** and **isotonic,** are used when referring to two solutions separated by a selectively permeable membrane (Figure 1). The hypertonic solution (Figure 1a) has a greater concentration of OAS than the solution on the other side of the membrane. It is described, therefore, as having a greater **osmolarity** (solute concentration expressed as molarity). The hypotonic solution (Figure 1b) has a lower concentration of OAS, or a lower osmolarity, than the solution on the other side of the membrane. When the two solutions are in equilibrium, the concentration of OAS being equal on both sides of the membrane, the osmolarities are equal and the substances are said to be isotonic (Figure 1c). The *net flow* of water is from the hypotonic to the hypertonic solution. When the solutions are isotonic, there is no net flow of water across the membrane.

The concept of osmotic pressure must be understood when studying osmosis. The movement of water from a hypotonic solution through the membrane into a hypertonic solution can be prevented by applying force or pressure on the hypertonic side (Figure 2). The force that must be applied to prevent osmotic movement of water from hypotonic to hypertonic, measured in atmospheres, is referred to as **osmotic pressure.** Solutions with greater concentrations of OAS have greater osmotic pressures because greater force is

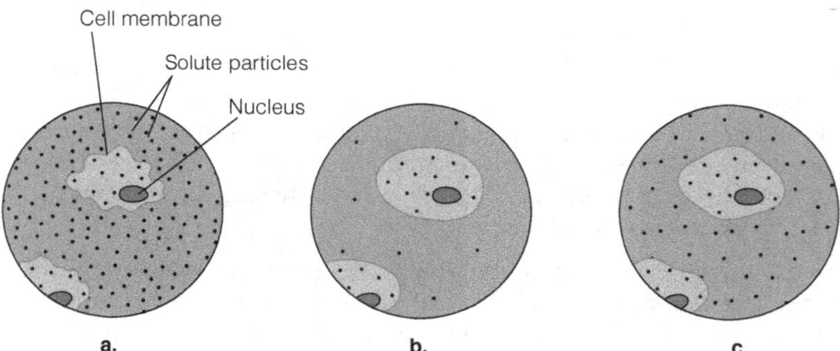

Figure 1.
Diagrammatic representation of cells in (a) hypertonic, (b) hypotonic, and (c) isotonic solutions. The hypertonic solution has a greater concentration of OAS than the solution on the other side of the membrane, the hypotonic solution has a lower concentration of OAS than the solution on the other side of the membrane, and the concentration of OAS is equal on both sides of the membrane in isotonic solutions.

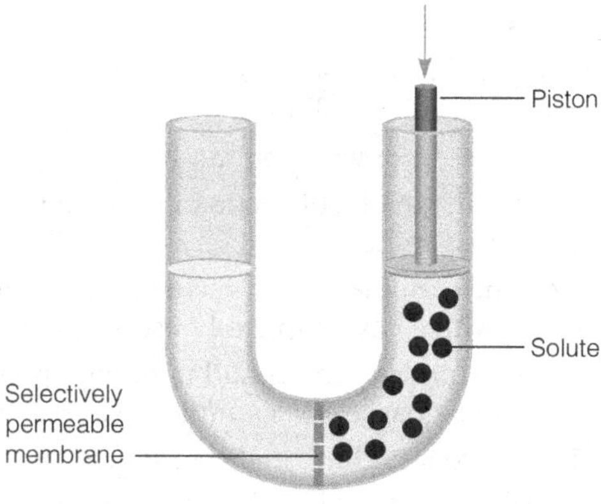

Figure 2.
Applying the correct pressure to the hypertonic side of two osmotically active solutions will prevent water movement into that solution.

required to prevent water movement into them. Distilled water has an osmotic pressure of zero.

EXERCISE 1

Diffusion of Molecules

In this exercise you will investigate characteristics of molecules that facilitate diffusion, factors that influence diffusion rates, and diffusion of solutes through a selectively permeable membrane.

Experiment A. Kinetic Energy of Molecules

Materials

dropper bottle of water
carmine powder
dissecting needle
slide and coverslip
compound microscope

Introduction

Molecules of a liquid or gas are constantly in motion because of the intrinsic kinetic energy in all atoms and molecules. In 1827, Robert Brown, a Scottish botanist, noticed that pollen grains suspended in water on a slide appeared to move by a force that he was unable to explain. In 1905, Albert Einstein, searching for evidence that would prove the existence of atoms and molecules, predicted that this type of motion must exist, although he did not realize that it had been studied for many years. Only after the kinetic energy of molecules was understood did scientists ask if the motion observed by Brown and predicted by Einstein could be the result of molecular kinetic energy being passed to larger particles. In this lab study, you will observe this movement, called **Brownian movement,** which we now know is the driving force of diffusion.

Procedure

Work in pairs. One person should set up the microscope while the other person makes a slide as follows:

1. Place a drop of water on the slide.
2. Touch the tip of a dissecting needle to the drop of water and then into the dry carmine.
3. Add the carmine on the needle to the drop of water on the slide, mix, cover with a coverslip, and observe under the compound microscope.
4. Observe on low power and then high power. Focus as much as possible on one particle of carmine.
5. Record your findings in the Results section, and draw conclusions based on your results in the Discussion section.

Results

Describe the movement of single carmine particles.

1. Is the movement random or directional?
2. Does the movement ever stop?
3. Do smaller particles move more rapidly than larger particles? Other observations?

Discussion

1. Are you actually observing molecular movement? Explain.

2. How can the movement being observed bring about diffusion?

3. Speculate about the importance of diffusion in cell metabolism.

Experiment B. Diffusion of Molecules Through a Selectively Permeable Membrane

Materials

string or rubber band
wax pencil
30% glucose solution
starch solution
I_2KI solution
Benedict's reagent
hot plate
500-mL beaker one-third filled with water
handheld test tube holder
3 standard test tubes
disposable transfer pipettes
2 400-mL beakers to hold dialysis bag
30-cm strip of moist dialysis tubing

Introduction

Dialysis tubing is a membrane made of regenerated cellulose fibers formed into a flat tube. If two solutions containing dissolved substances of different molecular weights are separated by this membrane, some substances may readily pass through the pores of the membrane, but others may be excluded.

Working in teams of four students, you will investigate the selective permeability of dialysis tubing. You will test the permeability of the tubing to glucose (molecular weight 180), starch (a variable-length polymer of glucose), and iodine potassium iodide (I_2KI). You will place a solution of glucose and starch into a dialysis tubing bag and then place this bag into a solution of I_2KI. Sketch and label the design of this experiment in the margin of your lab manual to help you develop your hypotheses.

You will use two tests in your experiment:

1. *I_2KI test for presence of starch.* When I_2KI is added to the unknown solution, the solution turns purple or black if starch is present. If no starch is present, the solution remains a pale yellow-amber color.
2. *Benedict's test for reducing sugar.* When Benedict's reagent is added to the unknown solution and the solution is heated, the solution turns green, orange, or orange-red if a reducing sugar is present (the color indicates the sugar concentration). If no reducing sugar is present, the solution remains the color of Benedict's reagent (blue).

Hypothesis

Hypothesize about the selective permeability of dialysis tubing to the substances being tested.

Prediction

Predict the results of the I_2KI and Benedict's tests based on your hypothesis (if/then).

Procedure

1. Prepare the dialysis bag with the initial solutions:
   a. Fold over 3 cm at the end of a 25- to 30-cm piece of dialysis tubing that has been soaking in water for a few minutes, pleat the folded end "accordion style," and close the end of the tube with the string or a rubber band, forming a bag. This procedure must secure the end of the bag so that no solution can seep through.
   b. Roll the opposite end of the bag between your fingers until it opens, and add 4 pipettesful of 30% glucose into the bag. Then add 4 pipettesful of starch solution to the glucose in the bag.
   c. Hold the bag closed and mix its contents. Record its color in Table 1 in the Results section. Carefully rinse the outside of the bag in tap water.
   d. Add 300 mL of water to a 400- to 500-mL beaker. Add several droppersful of I_2KI solution to the water until it is visibly yellow-amber. Record the color of the $H_2O + I_2KI$ solution in Table 1.
   e. Place the bag in the beaker so that the untied end of the bag hangs over the edge of the beaker (Figure 3). *Do not allow the liquid to spill out of the bag!* If the bag is too full, remove some of the liquid and rinse the outside of the bag again. If needed, place a rubber band around the beaker, holding the bag securely in place. If some of the liquid spills into the beaker, dispose of the beaker water, rinse, and fill again.
2. Leave the bag in the beaker for about 30 minutes. (You should go to another lab activity and then return to check your setup periodically.)
3. After 30 minutes, carefully remove the bag and stand it in a dry beaker.
4. Record in Table 1 the final color of the solution in the bag and the final color of the solution in the beaker.
5. Perform the Benedict's test for the presence of sugar in the solutions.
   a. Label three clean test tubes: control, bag, and beaker.
   b. Put 2 pipettesful of water in the control tube.
   c. Put 2 pipettesful of the bag solution in the bag tube.
   d. Put 2 pipettesful of the beaker solution in the beaker tube.
   e. Add 1 dropperful of Benedict's reagent to each tube.
   f. Heat the test tubes in a boiling water bath for about 3 minutes.
   g. Record your results in Table 1.

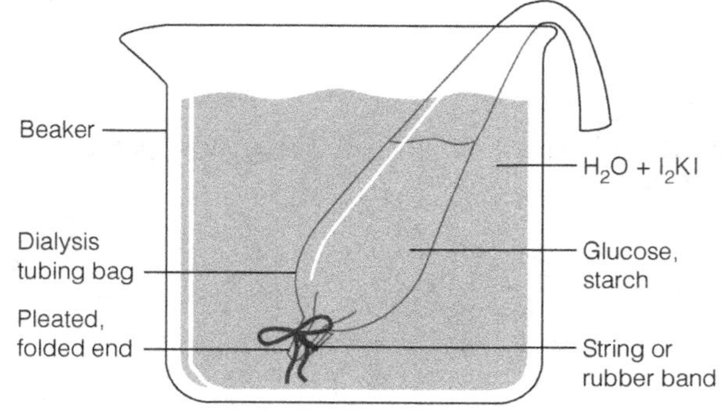

Figure 3.
Setup for Exercise 1, Experiment B.
The dialysis tubing bag, securely closed at one end, is placed in the beaker of water and I_2KI. The open end of the bag should drape over the edge of the beaker.

6. Review your results in Table 1 and draw your conclusions in the Discussion section.

Results

Complete Table 1 as you observe the results of Experiment B.

Table 1
Results of Experiment Investigating the Permeability of Dialysis Tubing to Glucose, I_2KI, and Starch

Solution Source	Original Contents	Original Color	Final Color	Color After Benedict's Test
Bag				
Beaker				
Control				

Discussion

1. What is the significance of the final colors and the colors after the Benedict's tests? Did the results support your hypothesis? Explain, giving evidence from the results of your tests.

2. How can you explain your results?

3. From your results, predict the size of I_2KI molecules relative to glucose and starch.

4. What colors would you expect if the experiment started with glucose and I_2KI inside the bag and starch in the beaker? Explain.

EXERCISE 2
Osmotic Activity in Cells

All organisms must maintain an optimum internal osmotic environment. Terrestrial vertebrates must take in and eliminate water using internal regulatory systems to ensure that the environment of tissues and organs remains in osmotic balance. Exchange of waste and nutrients between blood and tissues depends on the maintenance of this condition. Plants and animals living in fresh water must control the osmotic uptake of water into their hypertonic cells.

In this exercise, you will investigate the osmotic behavior of plant and animal cells placed in different molar solutions. What happens to these cells when they are placed in hypotonic or hypertonic solutions? This question will be investigated in the following experiments.

Experiment A. Osmotic Behavior of Animal Cells

Materials

4 clean microscope slides and coverslips
wax pencil
dropper bottle of ox blood
dropper bottles with three solutions of unknown osmolarity

Introduction

Mature red blood cells (erythrocytes) are little more than packages of hemoglobin bound by a plasma membrane permeable to small molecules, such as oxygen and carbon dioxide, but impermeable to larger molecules, such as proteins, sodium chloride, and sucrose. In mammals these cells even lack nuclei when mature, and as they float in isotonic blood plasma, their shape is flattened and pinched inward into a biconcave disk. Oxygen and carbon dioxide diffuse across the membrane, allowing the cell to carry out its primary function, gas transport, which is enhanced by the increased surface area created by the shape of the cell. When water moves into red blood cells placed in a hypotonic solution, the cells swell and the membranes burst, or undergo **lysis.** When water moves out of red blood cells placed in a hypertonic solution, the cells shrivel and appear bumpy, or **crenate.** In this experiment, you will investigate the behavior of red blood cells when the osmolarity of the environment changes from isotonic to hypertonic or hypotonic.

Hypothesis

Hypothesize about the behavior of red blood cells when they are placed in hypertonic or hypotonic environments.

Prediction

Predict the results of the experiment based on your hypothesis (if/then).

Procedure

Have your microscope ready, and observe slides immediately after you have prepared them. Do one slide at a time.

1. Label four clean microscope slides A, B, C, and D.
2. Place a drop of blood on slide D, cover with a coverslip, and observe the shape of red blood cells with no treatment. Record your observations in Table 2 in the Results section.
3. Put a drop of solution A on slide A and add a coverslip. Place the slide on the microscope stage and carefully add a small drop of blood to the edge of the coverslip. The blood cells will be drawn under the coverslip by capillary action.
4. As you view through the microscope, carefully watch the cells as they come into contact with solution A; record your observations in Table 2.
5. Repeat steps 3 and 4 with solutions B and C.
6. Record your observations in Table 2. Draw your conclusions in the Discussion section.

Results

Record your observations of red blood cell behavior in Table 2.

Table 2
Appearance of Red Blood Cells in Test Solutions

Solution	Appearance/Condition of Cells
D (blood only)	
A	
B	
C	

Discussion

Explain your results in terms of your hypothesis.

1. Based on your hypothesis and predictions, which of the three solutions is hypertonic to the red blood cells?

   Hypotonic?

   Isotonic?

   Verify your conclusions with the laboratory instructor.
2. What conditions might lead to results other than those expected?

Experiment B. Osmotic Behavior in Cells with a Cell Wall

Materials

On demonstration: 2 compound microscopes labeled A and B
1 slide of *Elodea* in a hypertonic salt solution
1 slide of *Elodea* in distilled water

Introduction

In their natural environment, cells of freshwater plants and algae are bathed in water with little OAS. The net flow of water is from the surrounding medium into the cells.

The presence of a cell wall and a large fluid-filled central vacuole in a plant or algal cell will affect the cell's response to solutions of differing molarities. When a plant cell is placed in a hypertonic solution, water moves out of the cell; the protoplast shrinks and may pull away from the cell wall. This process is called **plasmolysis,** and the cell is described as **plasmolyzed** (Figure 4). In a hypotonic solution, as water moves into the cell and ultimately into the cell's central vacuole, the cell's **protoplast** (the plant cell exclusive of the cell wall—the cytoplasm enclosed by plasma membrane) expands. The cell wall, however, restricts the expansion, resulting in **turgor pressure** (pressure of the protoplast on the cell wall owing to uptake of water). A high turgor pressure will prevent further movement of water into the cell. This process is a good example of the interaction between pressure and osmolarity in determining the direction of the net movement of water. The hypertonic condition in the cell draws water into the cell until the membrane-enclosed cytoplasm presses against the cell wall. Turgor pres-

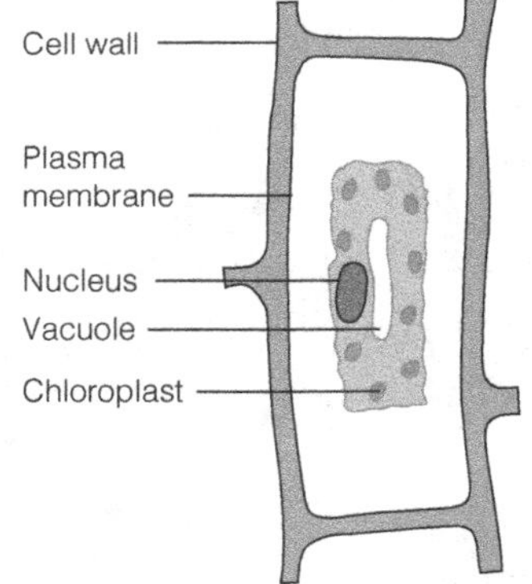

Figure 4.
Plant cell placed in a hypertonic solution. Water leaves the central vacuole and the cytoplasm shrinks, a process called plasmolysis.

sure begins to force water through the membrane and out of the cell, changing the direction of net flow of water (Figure 5).

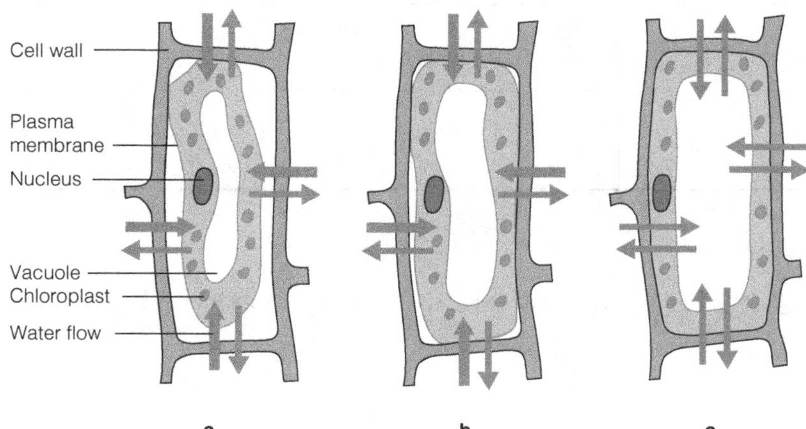

Figure 5.
The effect of turgor pressure on the cell wall and the direction of net flow of water in a plant cell. A plant cell undergoes changes in a hypotonic solution. (a) Low turgor pressure. The net flow of water comes into the cell from the surrounding hypotonic medium. (b) Turgor pressure increases. The protoplast begins to press on the cell wall. (c) Greatest turgor pressure. The tendency to take up water is ultimately restricted by the cell wall, creating a back pressure on the protoplast. Water enters and leaves the cell at the same rate.

For this experiment, two slides have been set up on demonstration microscopes. On each slide, *Elodea* has been placed in a different molar solution: One is hypotonic (distilled water) and one is hypertonic (concentrated salt solution).

Hypothesis

Hypothesize about the movement of water in cells with a cell wall when they are placed in hypertonic or hypotonic environments.

Prediction

Predict the appearance of *Elodea* cells placed in the two solutions (if/then).

Procedure

1. Observe the two demonstration microscopes with *Elodea* in solutions A and B.
2. Record your observations in Table 3 in the Results section, and draw your conclusions in the Discussion section.

Results

Describe the appearance of the *Elodea* cells in Table 3.

Table 3
Appearance of *Elodea* Cells in Unknown Solutions A and B

Solution	Appearance/Condition of Cells
A	
B	

Discussion

1. Based on your predictions and observations, which solution is hypertonic?

   Hypotonic?

2. Which solution has the greatest osmolarity?

3. Would you expect pond water to be isotonic, hypertonic, or hypotonic to *Elodea* cells? Explain.

4. Verify your conclusions with your laboratory instructor.

EXERCISE 3
Estimating the Osmolarity of Plant Cells

Frequently, plant scientists need to determine the optimum water content for normal physiological processes in plants. They know that for normal activities to take place, the amount of water relative to osmotically active substances in cells must be maintained within a reasonable range. If plant cells have a reduced water content, all vital functions slow down.

In the following experiments, you will estimate the osmolarity of potato tuber cells using two methods, change in weight and change in volume.

You will incubate pieces of potato tuber in sucrose solutions of known molarity. The object is to find the molarity at which weight or volume of the potato tuber tissue does not change, indicating that there has been no net loss or gain of water. This molarity is an indirect measure of the osmolarity of the potato tuber.

Work in teams of four. Each team will measure either weight change or volume change. Time will be available near the end of the laboratory period for each team to present its results to the class for discussion and conclusions.

Experiment A. Estimating Osmolarity by Change in Weight

Materials

1 large potato tuber
7 250-mL beakers (disposable cups may be substituted)
wax marking pencil
forceps
balance that weighs to the nearest 0.01 g
aluminum foil
petri dish
sucrose solutions: 0.1, 0.2, 0.3, 0.4, 0.5, 0.6 molar (*M*)
razor blade
cork borer
deionized (DI) water (0 molar)
paper towels
metric ruler
calculator

Introduction

In this experiment, you will determine the weight of several potato tuber cylinders and incubate them in a series of sucrose solutions. After the cylinders have incubated, you will weigh them and determine if they have gained or lost weight. This information will enable you to estimate the osmolarity of the potato tuber tissue.

Hypothesis

Hypothesize about the osmolarity of potato tuber tissue.

Prediction

Predict the results of the experiment based on your hypothesis (if/then).

Procedure

1. Obtain 100 mL of DI water and 100 mL of each of the sucrose solutions. Put each solution in a separate, appropriately labeled 250-mL beaker or paper cup.

Cork borers and razor blades can cut! Use them with extreme care! To use the cork borer, hold the potato in such a way that the borer will not push through the potato into your hand.

2. Use a sharp cork borer to obtain seven cylinders of potato. Push the borer through the length of the potato, twisting it back and forth. When the borer is filled, remove from the potato and push the potato cylinder out of the borer. You must have seven complete, undamaged cylinders at least 5 cm long.
3. Line up the potato cylinders and, using a sharp razor blade, cut all cylinders to a uniform length, about 5 cm, removing the peel from the ends.
4. Place all seven potato samples in a petri dish, and keep them covered to prevent their drying out.

In subsequent steps, treat each sample individually. Work quickly. To provide consistency, each person should do one task to all cylinders (one person wipe, another weigh, another slice, another record data).

5. Remove a cylinder from the petri dish, and place it between the folds of a paper towel to blot sides and ends.
6. Weigh it to the nearest 0.01 g on the aluminum sheet on the balance. Record the weight in Table 4 in the Results section.
7. Immediately cut the cylinder lengthwise into two long halves.
8. Transfer potato pieces to the water beaker.
9. Note what time the potato pieces are placed in the water beaker. Time: ____________.
10. Repeat steps 5 to 8 with each cylinder, placing potato pieces in the appropriate incubating solution from 0.1 to 0.6 *M*.

Be sure that the initial weight of the cylinder placed in each test solution is accurately recorded.

11. Incubate 1.5 to 2 hours. (As this takes place, you will be performing other lab activities.)
12. Swirl each beaker every 10 to 15 minutes as the potato pieces incubate.
13. At the end of the incubation period, record the time when the potato pieces are removed. Time: ____________.

    Calculate the approximate incubation time in Table 4.
14. Remove the potato pieces from the first sample. Blot the pieces on a paper towel, removing excess solution only.
15. Weigh the potato pieces and record the final weight in Table 4.
16. Repeat this procedure until all samples have been weighed in the chronological order in which they were initially placed in the test solutions.

17. Record your data in the Results section, and complete the questions in the Discussion section.

Results

1. Complete Table 4. To calculate percentage change in weight, use this formula:

$$\text{Percentage change in weight} = \frac{\text{weight change}}{\text{initial weight}} \times 100$$

If the sample gained in weight, the value should be positive. If it lost in weight, the value should be negative.

Table 4
Data for Experiment Estimating Osmolarity by Change in Weight

Approximate time in solutions: ____________							
	Sucrose Molarity						
	0.0	0.1	0.2	0.3	0.4	0.5	0.6
Final weight (g)							
Initial weight (g)							
Weight change (g)							
% change in weight							

2. Plot percentage change in weight as a function of the sucrose molarity in Figure 6.
   a. Place a 0 in the middle of the *y* axis. Choose appropriate scales.
   b. Label the axes of the graph: Determine dependent and independent variables, and place each on the appropriate axis.
   c. Graph your results. Weight increase (positive values) should be above the zero change line on the "percentage change in weight" axis. Weight decrease should be below the zero change line.
   d. Construct a curve that best fits the data points. Use this curve to estimate the osmolarity of the potato tuber.
   e. Compose an appropriate figure title.

Discussion

1. At what sucrose molarity does the curve cross the zero change line on the graph?

Figure 6.

2. Explain how this information can be used to determine the osmolarity of the potato tuber tissue.

3. Estimate the osmolarity of the potato tuber tissue.

Experiment B. Estimating Osmolarity by Change in Volume

Materials

1 large potato tuber
vernier caliper
7 250-mL beakers (disposable cups may be substituted)
wax marking pencil
forceps
petri dish
razor blade
cork borer (0.5-cm diameter)
sucrose solutions: 0.1, 0.2, 0.3, 0.4, 0.5, 0.6 *M*
DI water (0 *M*)
metric ruler
paper towels
calculator

Introduction

In this experiment, you will determine the volume of several potato tuber cylinders by measuring the length and diameter of each. You will then incubate them in a series of sucrose solutions. After the cylinders have incubated, you will again measure their length and diameter and determine if they have increased or decreased in size. This information will enable you to estimate the osmolarity of the potato tuber tissue.

Hypothesis

Hypothesize about the osmolarity of potato tuber tissue.

Prediction

Predict the results of the experiment based on your hypothesis (if/then).

Procedure

1. Practice measuring with the vernier caliper (Figure 7a, b).
   a. Identify the following parts of the caliper and add these labels on Figure 7a: *stationary arm, movable arm, ruler, vernier scale.* Notice that the numbers on the bottom ruler scale are centimeters; each graduated line is 1 mm.
   b. Choose a small object (a coin will work) and place it between the two arms, adjusting the movable arm until both arms just touch the object.
   c. Note the 0 mark on the vernier scale (Figure 7b). The graduated line on the ruler just to the left of the 0 mark is the distance between the caliper arms measured in whole millimeters. In Figure 7b, that number is 22 mm. Write that number for your object as the answer in blank (1), on the next page.
   d. Look at the graduated lines between 0 and 10 on the vernier scale. Note the line on the vernier scale that exactly matches with a line on the ruler. That line on the vernier scale is the measurement in tenths of a millimeter, which should be added to the whole-millimeter reading.

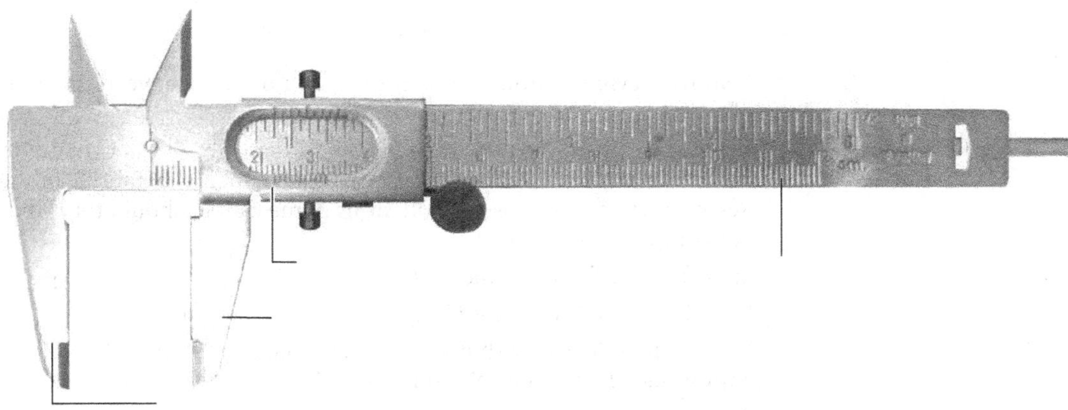

Figure 7a.
Vernier caliper. Identify the stationary arm, movable arm, ruler, and vernier scale.

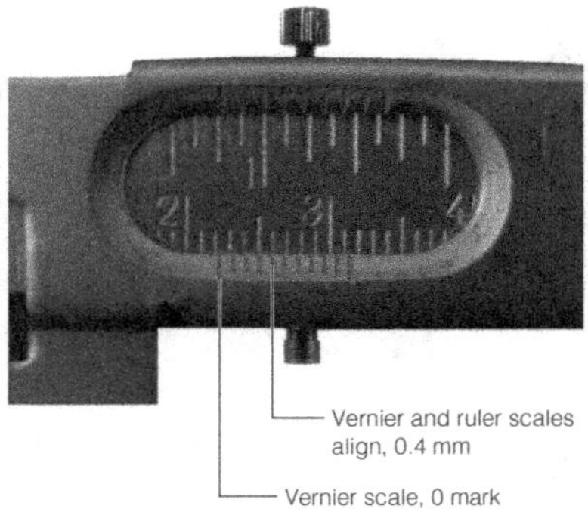

Figure 7b.
Enlarged vernier scale. The correct measurement is 22.4 mm.

In Figure 7b, that number is 4. Write the measurement in tenths of a millimeter for your object as the answer in blank (2) below.

What is the size of your object?

(1) ______________

(2) ______________

Total measurement: ______________

When you know how to measure using the caliper, proceed to the next step.

2. Obtain 100 mL of DI water and 100 mL of each of the sucrose solutions. Put each solution in a separate, appropriately labeled 250-mL beaker or paper cup.

Use cork borers and razor blades with extreme care! To use the cork borer, hold the potato in such a way that the borer will not push through the potato into your hand.

3. Use a sharp cork borer to obtain seven cylinders of potato. Push the borer through the length of the potato, twisting it back and forth. When the borer is filled, remove it from the potato and push the potato cylinder out of the borer. You must have seven complete, undamaged cylinders at least 5 cm long.
4. Line up the potato cylinders and, using a sharp razor blade, cut all cylinders to a uniform length, about 5 cm, removing the peel from the ends.
5. Place all seven potato samples in a petri dish, and keep them covered to prevent their drying out.

In subsequent steps, treat each sample individually. Work quickly. To provide consistency, each person should do one task to all cylinders (one person wipe, another measure, another record data).

6. Remove a cylinder from the petri dish, and place it between the folds of a paper towel to blot sides and ends.
7. Using the caliper, measure the length and diameter of the cylinder to the nearest 0.1 mm, and record these measurements in Table 5 in the Results section. To measure, both arms of the caliper should touch but not compress the cylinder.
8. Transfer the cylinder to the 0 *M* (water) beaker.
9. Note the time the cylinder is placed in the 0 *M* beaker. Time: __________.
10. Repeat steps 6 to 8 with each cylinder, placing the cylinders in the appropriate incubating solution from 0.1 to 0.6 *M*.

Be sure that the initial length and diameter of the cylinder placed in each test solution are accurately recorded.

11. Incubate from 1.5 to 2 hours. (During this time period, you will be performing other lab activities.)
12. Swirl each beaker every 10 to 15 minutes as the cylinders incubate.
13. At the end of the incubation period, record the time each cylinder is removed from a solution. Time: ____________.

    Calculate the approximate incubation time in Table 5.
14. Remove the cylinders in the chronological order in which they were initially placed in the test solutions.
15. Blot each cylinder as it is removed (sides and ends), and use the vernier caliper to measure the length and diameter to the nearest 0.1 mm.
16. Finish recording your data in the Results section, and answer the questions in the Discussion section.

Results

1. Complete Table 5. To calculate the volume of a cylinder, use this formula:

$$\text{Volume of a cylinder (mm}^3) = \pi(\text{diameter}/2)^2 \times \text{length}$$
$$(\pi = 3.14)$$

   To calculate percentage change in volume, use this formula:

$$\text{Percentage change in volume} = \frac{\text{change in volume}}{\text{initial volume}} \times 100$$

   If the sample increases in volume, the value will be positive. If it decreases in volume, the value will be negative.

Table 5
Data for Experiment Estimating Osmolarity by Change in Volume

Approximate time in solutions: ____________	Sucrose Molarity						
	0.0	0.1	0.2	0.3	0.4	0.5	0.6
Final diameter (mm)							
Final length (mm)							
Final volume (mm^3)							
Initial diameter (mm)							
Initial length (mm)							
Initial volume (mm^3)							
Change in volume (mm^3)							
% change in volume							

2. Plot percentage change in volume as a function of the sucrose molarity in Figure 8.
   a. Place a 0 in the middle of the y axis. Choose appropriate scales.
   b. Label the axes of the graph: Determine dependent and independent variables, and place each on the appropriate axis.
   c. Graph your results. Volume increase should be above the zero change line on the "percentage change in volume" axis. Volume decrease should be below the zero change line.

Figure 8.

____

____

____

   d. Construct a curve that best fits the data points. Use this curve to estimate the osmolarity of the potato tuber.
   e. Compose an appropriate figure title.

Discussion

1. At what sucrose molarity does the curve cross the zero change line on the graph?

2. Explain how this information can be used to determine the osmolarity of the potato tuber tissue.

3. Estimate the osmolarity of the potato tuber tissue.

Questions for Review

Once you complete this lab topic, you should be able to define and use the following terms. Provide examples if appropriate.

selectively permeable, solvent, solute, diffusion, osmosis, osmotically active substance, hypotonic, hypertonic, isotonic, turgor pressure, osmotic pressure, osmolarity, Brownian movement, lysis, crenate, plasmolysis, plasmolyzed, turgid

Applying Your Knowledge

1. Describe plant wilting in terms of turgor pressure.

2. One traditional method for preserving pork has been to cover the meat with salt and spices. The resulting "country ham" can be stored for months without refrigeration. How do you think this process works? Consider the organisms responsible for food spoilage and how curing ham with salt might prevent spoilage.

3. The emergency room intern treated a patient by administering fluids intravenously. The patient died as a result of her error. What kind of osmotic solution would have resulted in the patient's death? Why?

4. A student read that plants require several essential elements for healthy growth and decided to fertilize his yellowing begonia. When he mixed the plant food, he made the solution three times as concentrated as the directions suggested. The next day his plant was not only yellow but also badly wilted. Can you help the student understand his error and suggest a remedy?

5. Constipation in infants can be a problem to treat because the common adult remedies, such as additional fiber in the diet or mild laxatives, are not options for small babies. One home remedy sometimes suggested is increasing fluids and adding dark Karo syrup to the infant's milk. Can you explain why this remedy might work?

6. Shrimp fishing off the coast of Georgia was closed in 2001 due to a drastic reduction in the shrimp population. Captain Forsyth, a local shrimper, suspects that increased salinity has killed the shrimp larvae. Three years of drought and greatly reduced freshwater flow from underground aquifers resulted in increased salinity in the coastal estuaries. These habitats between open ocean and fresh water are the "nurseries" for many marine animals. Design an experiment to determine the range of salt concentration that can be tolerated by shrimp larvae.

7. Water pollution is one of the most serious environmental problems of our time. Using information learned in this lab, predict one impact of pollutants in lakes, ponds, rivers, and streams on the plant and animal inhabitants.

References

Lang, F., and S. Waldegger. "Regulating Cell Volume." *American Scientist,* 1997, vol 85, pp. 456–463.

Exercise 4.1, Experiment A, was adapted from D. R. Helms and S. B. Miller, *Principles of Biology: A Laboratory Manual for Biology 110.* Apex, NC: Contemporary Publishing, 1978. Used by permission.

Photo Credits

7a,b: Eloise Carter. Page 183: ©Carolina Biological Supply/Phototake NYC.

Art Credits

2: Adapted from Neil Campbell, Jane Reece, and Larry Mitchell, *Biology*, 5th ed. (Menlo Park, CA: Benjamin/Cummings, 1999), ©1999 The Benjamin/Cummings Publishing Company.

Text Credits

Experiment B adapted from D. R. Helms and S. B. Miller, *Principles of Biology: A Laboratory Manual for Biology 110* (Apex, NC: Contemporary Publishing, 1978), by permission.

Cellular Respiration and Fermentation

This lab topic gives you an opportunity to practice the scientific process. Before going to lab, carefully read through this lab exercise. Be prepared to use this information to design an experiment in fermentation or cellular respiration.

Laboratory Objectives

After completing this lab topic, you should be able to:

1. Describe alcoholic fermentation, naming reactants and products.
2. Describe cellular respiration, naming reactants and products.
3. Explain oxidation/reduction reactions in cellular respiration.
4. Name and describe environmental factors that influence enzymatic activity.
5. Explain spectrophotometry and describe how this process can be used to measure aerobic respiration.
6. Propose hypotheses and make predictions based on them.
7. Design and execute an experiment testing factors that influence fermentation or cellular respiration.
8. Practice scientific persuasion and communication by analyzing and interpreting experimental results.

Introduction

This lab topic investigates energy transformations in cells. Photosynthesis is the process of transferring the sun's radiant energy to organic molecules, namely, glucose (Figure 1). This lab topic investigates **fermentation** and **cellular respiration**, cellular processes that transfer the energy in glucose bonds to bonds in **adenosine triphosphate** (ATP). The energy in ATP can then be used to perform cellular work. Fermentation is an anaerobic (without oxygen) process; cellular respiration is aerobic (utilizing oxygen). *All living organisms, including bacteria, protists, plants, and animals, produce ATP in fermentation or cellular respiration and then use ATP in their metabolism.*

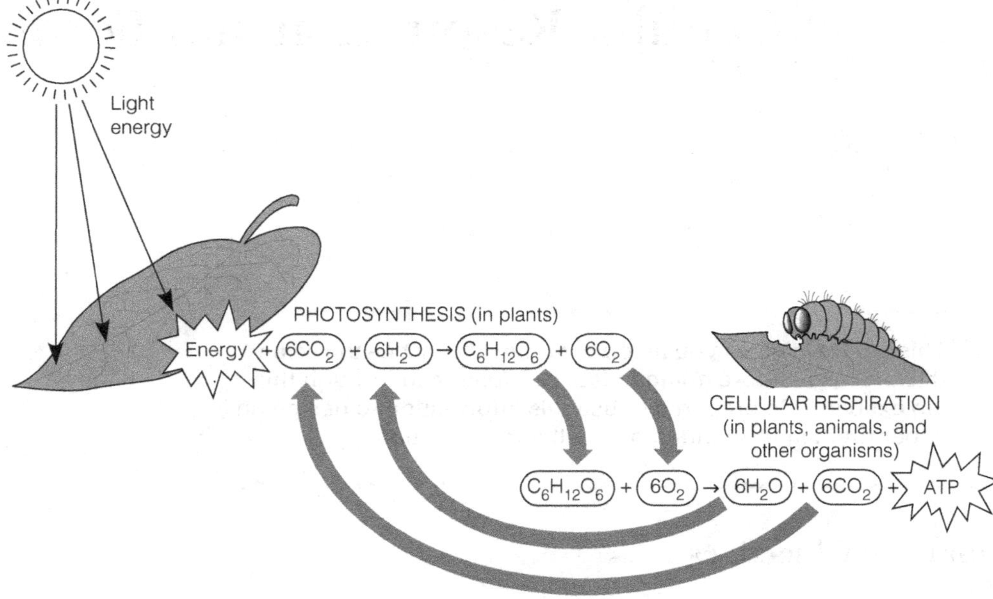

Figure 1.
Energy flow through photosynthesis and cellular respiration. Light energy from the sun is transformed to chemical energy in photosynthesis. Carbon dioxide and water are converted to glucose and oxygen. The energy stored in plant organic molecules—glucose, for example—can be utilized by plants or by consumers. The energy in organic molecules is released during cellular respiration in plants, animals, and other organisms.

Fermentation and cellular respiration involve oxidation-reduction reactions (redox reactions). Redox reactions are always defined in terms of electron transfers, oxidation being the *loss* of electrons and reduction the *gain* of electrons. In cellular respiration, two hydrogen atoms are removed from glucose (oxidation) and transferred to a coenzyme called nicotinamide adenine dinucleotide (**NAD^+**), reducing this compound to **NADH**. Think of these two hydrogen atoms as 2 electrons and 2 protons. NAD^+ is the oxidizing agent that is reduced to NADH by the addition of 2 electrons and one proton. The other proton (H^+) is released into the cell solution. NADH transfers electrons to the electron transport chain. The transfer of electrons from one molecule to another releases energy, and this energy can be used to synthesize ATP.

Cellular respiration is a sequence of three metabolic stages: **glycolysis** in the cytoplasm, and the **Krebs cycle** and the **electron transport chain** in mitochondria (Figure 2). Fermentation involves glycolysis but does not involve the Krebs cycle and the electron transport chain, which are inhibited at low oxygen levels. Two common types of fermentation are **alcoholic fermentation** and **lactic acid fermentation.** Animals, certain fungi, and some bacteria convert pyruvate produced in glycolysis to lactate. Plants and some fungi, yeast in particular, convert pyruvate to ethanol and carbon dioxide. Cellular respiration is much more efficient than fermentation in producing ATP. Cellular respiration can produce a maximum of 38 ATP molecules; fermentation produces only 2 ATP molecules.

Before you begin today's lab topic, refer to the preceding paragraph and Figure 2 as you review major pathways, reactants, and products of fermentation and cellular respiration by answering the following questions:

1. Which processes are anaerobic?

2. Which processes are aerobic?

3. Which processes take place in the cytoplasm of the cell?

4. Which processes take place in mitochondria?

5. What is the initial reactant in cellular respiration?

6. What is (are) the product(s) of the anaerobic processes?

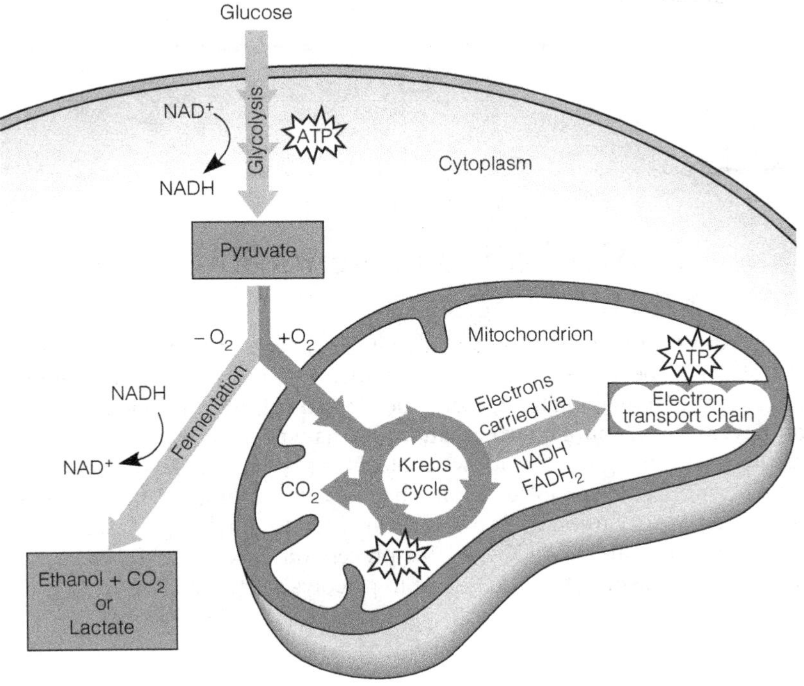

Figure 2.
Stages of cellular respiration and fermentation. Cellular respiration consists of glycolysis, the Krebs cycle, and the electron transport chain. Glycolysis is also a stage in fermentation.

7. What is (are) the product(s) of the aerobic processes?

8. Which gives the greater yield of ATP, alcoholic fermentation or cellular respiration?

In this lab topic you will investigate alcoholic fermentation first and then cellular respiration. Working in teams of two to four students, you will first perform two introductory lab studies (Lab Study A of each exercise). Lab Study B in each exercise provides questions and background to help you propose one or more testable hypotheses based on questions from the lab studies or your prior knowledge. Your team will then design and carry out an independent investigation based on your hypotheses, completing your observations and recording your results in this laboratory period. After discussing the results, your team will prepare an oral presentation in which you will persuade the class that your experimental design is sound and that your results support your conclusions. If required to do so by the lab instructor, *each of you* independently will submit Results and Discussion sections describing the results of your experiment.

First complete Lab Study A in each exercise. Then discuss possible questions for investigation with your research team. Be certain you can pose an interesting question from which to develop a testable hypothesis. Design and perform the experiment today. Prepare to report your results in oral and/or written form.

EXERCISE 1
Alcoholic Fermentation

For centuries, humans have taken advantage of yeast fermentation to produce alcoholic beverages and bread. Consider the products of fermentation and their roles in making these economically and culturally important foods and beverages. Alcoholic fermentation begins with glycolysis, a series of reactions breaking glucose into two molecules of **pyruvate** with a net yield of 2 ATP and 2 NADH molecules. In anaerobic environments, in two steps the pyruvate (a 3-carbon molecule) is converted to ethyl alcohol (ethanol, a 2-carbon molecule) and CO_2. In this process the 2 NADH molecules are oxidized, replenishing the NAD^+ used in glycolysis (Figure 2).

Lab Study A. Alcoholic Fermentation in Yeast

Materials

4 respirometers:
- test tubes, 1-mL graduated pipettes, aquarium tubing, flasks, binder clips

pipette pump
3 5-mL graduated pipettes, labeled "DI water," "yeast," and "glucose"
3-inch donut-shaped metal weights
yeast solution
glucose solution
DI water
water bath
wax pencil

Introduction

In this lab study, you will investigate alcoholic fermentation in a yeast (a single-celled fungus), *Saccharomyces cerevisiae*, or "baker's yeast." When oxygen is low, some fungi, including yeast and most plants, switch from cellular respiration to alcoholic fermentation. In bread making, starch in the flour is converted to glucose and fructose, which then serve as the starting compounds for fermentation. The resulting carbon dioxide is trapped in the dough, causing it to rise. Ethanol is also produced in bread making but evaporates during baking.

In this laboratory experiment, the carbon dioxide (CO_2) produced, being a gas, bubbles out of the solution and can be used as an indication of the relative rate of fermentation taking place. Figure 3 shows the respirometers you will use to collect CO_2. The rate of fermentation, a series of enzymatic reactions, can be affected by several factors, for example, concentration of yeast, concentration of glucose, or temperature. In this lab study you will

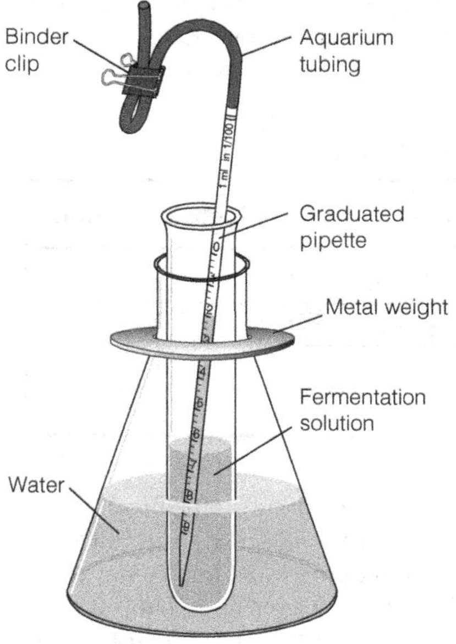

Figure 3.
Respirometer used for yeast fermentation.

investigate *the effects of yeast concentration.* In your independent study you may choose to investigate other independent variables.

Hypothesis

Hypothesize about the effect of different concentrations of yeast on the rate of fermentation.

Prediction

Predict the results of the experiment based on your hypothesis (if/then).

Procedure

1. Obtain four flasks and add enough tap water to keep them from floating in a water bath (fill to about 5 cm from the top of the flask). Label the flasks 1, 2, 3, and 4. To stabilize the flasks, place a 3-inch donut-shaped metal weight over the neck of the flasks.
2. Obtain four test tubes (fermentation tubes) and label them 1, 2, 3, and 4. Add solutions as in Table 1 to the appropriate tubes. Rotate each tube to distribute the yeast evenly in the tube. Place tubes in the corresponding numbered flasks.
3. To each tube, add a 1-mL graduated pipette to which a piece of plastic aquarium tubing has been attached.
4. Place the flasks with the test tubes and graduated pipettes in the water bath at 30°C. Allow them to equilibrate for about 5 minutes.

Table 1
Contents of Fermentation Solutions (volumes in mL)

Tube	DI Water	Yeast Suspension	Glucose Solution
1	4	0	3
2	6	1	0
3	3	1	3
4	1	3	3

5. Attach the pipette pump to the free end of the tubing on the first pipette. Use the pipette pump to draw the fermentation solution up into the pipette. Fill it past the calibrated portion of the tube, but do not draw the solution into the tubing. Fold the tubing over and clamp it shut with the binder clip so the solution does not run out. Open the clip slightly, and allow the solution to drain down to the 0-mL calibration line (or slightly below). Quickly do the same for the other three pipettes.

6. In Table 2, quickly record your initial readings for each pipette in the "Initial reading" row in each "Actual (A)" column. This will be the *initial* time (I).
7. Two minutes after the initial readings for each pipette, record the actual readings (A) in mL for each pipette in the "Actual (A)" column. Subtract I from A to determine the total amount of CO_2 evolved (A – I). Record this value in the "CO_2 Evolved (A – I)" column. *From now on, you will subtract the initial reading from each actual reading to determine the total amount of CO_2 evolved.*
8. Continue taking readings every 2 minutes for each of the solutions for 20 minutes. Remember, take the actual reading from the pipette and subtract the initial reading to get the total amount of CO_2 evolved in each test tube.
9. Record your results in Table 2.

Results

1. Complete Table 2.

Table 2
Total CO_2 Evolved by Different Concentrations of Yeast. Actual values are the graduated pipette readings. For CO_2 evolved values, subtract the initial reading from the actual reading. This is the amount of CO_2 accumulated over time.

Time (min)	**Tube 1**		**Tube 2**		**Tube 3**		**Tube 4**	
	Actual (A)	CO_2 Evolved (A – I)	Actual (A)	CO_2 Evolved (A – I)	Actual (A)	CO_2 Evolved (A – I)	Actual (A)	CO_2 Evolved (A – I)
Initial reading (I)		X		X		X		X
2								
4								
6								
8								
10								
12								
14								
16								
18								
20								

2. Using Figure 4, construct a graph to illustrate your results.
   a. What is (are) the independent variable(s)? Which is the appropriate axis for this variable?

   b. What is the dependent variable? Which is the appropriate axis for this variable?

   c. Choose an appropriate scale and label the x and y axes.
   d. Should you use a legend? If so, what would this include?

   e. Compose a figure title.

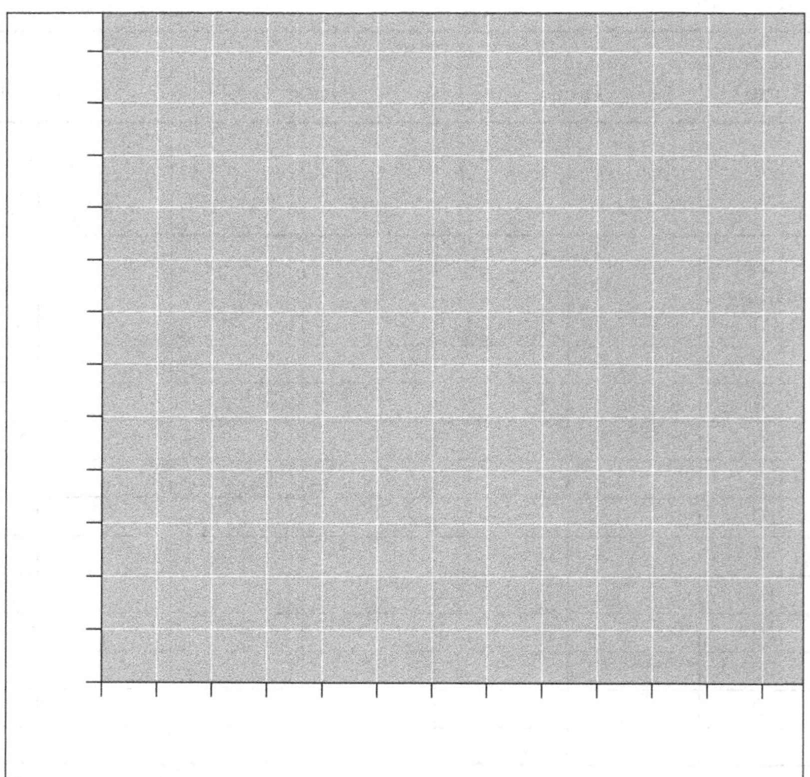

Figure 4.

Discussion

1. Explain the experimental design. What is the purpose of each test tube? Which is (are) the control tube(s)?

2. Which test tube had the highest rate of fermentation? Explain why.

3. Which test tube had the lowest rate of fermentation? Explain why.

4. Why were different amounts of water added to each fermentation solution?

Lab Study B. Additional Investigations of Alcoholic Fermentation

Materials

all materials from Lab Study A
beakers
graduated pipettes of various sizes
different substrates: sucrose, saccharin, Nutrasweet™, fructose, starch, glycogen, honey, corn syrup, pyruvate
different types of yeast: dry active, quick rise, Pasteur champagne (for wine making)
various fermentation inhibitors: sodium fluoride, ethyl alcohol
various salt solutions
various pH buffers
spices: ground cinnamon, cloves, caraway, ginger, cardamom, nutmeg, mace, thyme, dry mustard, chili powder
disposable gloves
additional glassware

Introduction

If your team chooses to study alcoholic fermentation for your independent investigation and report, design a simple experiment to investigate some factor that affects alcoholic fermentation. Use the available materials or ask your instructor about the availability of additional materials.

Procedure

1. Collaborating with your research team, read the following potential questions, and choose a question to investigate using this list or an idea from your prior knowledge. You may want to check your text and other sources for supporting information. You should be able to explain the rationale behind your choice of question. For example, if you choose to investigate *starch* as a substrate, you should be able to explain that the yeast must first digest starch before the glucose can be used in alcoholic fermentation and the impact this might have on the experiment.
   a. Would other substrates be as effective as glucose in alcoholic fermentation? Possible substrates:
      sucrose (table sugar—glucose and fructose disaccharide)
      honey (mainly glucose and fructose)
      corn syrup (fructose and sucrose)
      starch (glucose polymer in plants)
      saccharin
      fructose
      pyruvate
   b. Would fermentation rates change with different types of yeasts?
   c. What environmental conditions are optimum for alcoholic fermentation?
      What temperature ranges?
      What pH ranges?
   d. What is the maximum amount of ethyl alcohol that can be tolerated by yeast cells?

If you select toxins or fermentation inhibitors for your investigation, ask the instructor about safety procedures. Post safety precautions and follow safety protocol, including wearing gloves and protective eyewear. Notify the instructor of any spills.

   e. Sodium fluoride, commonly used to prevent tooth decay, inhibits an enzyme in glycolysis. At what concentration is it most effective?
   f. Would adding $MgSO_4$ enhance glycolysis? $MgSO_4$ provides Mg^{++}, a cofactor necessary to activate some enzymes in glycolysis.
   g. Does a high concentration of sucrose inhibit fermentation?
   h. An old German baker's wisdom says, "A pinch of ginger will make your yeast work better." Some spices enhance yeast activity while others inhibit it (Corriher, 1997). What effect do spices have on yeast activity? Try ginger, ground cardamom, caraway, cinnamon, mace, nutmeg, thyme, dry mustard, or others.
   i. Salt is often used as a food preservative to prevent bacterial and fungal growth (for example, in country ham). But salt is also important to enhance the flavor of bread when added in small amounts. At what concentration does salt begin to inhibit yeast fermentation?

2. Design your experiment, proposing hypotheses, making predictions, and determining procedures as instructed in Exercise 3.

EXERCISE 2
Cellular Respiration

Most organisms produce ATP using cellular respiration, a process that involves glycolysis, the Krebs cycle, and the electron transport chain. In cellular respiration, many more ATP molecules are produced than were produced in alcoholic fermentation (potentially 38 compared to 2), and water, unlike ethanol, is not toxic to the cells. After the series of reactions in the cytoplasm (glycolysis), pyruvate enters the mitochondria, where enzymes for the Krebs cycle and the electron transport chain are located. The Krebs cycle is a series of eight steps, each catalyzed by a specific enzyme. As one compound is converted to another, CO_2 is given off and hydrogen ions and electrons are removed. The electrons and hydrogen ions are passed to NAD^+ and another electron carrier, FAD (flavin adenine dinucleotide). NADH and $FADH_2$ carry the electrons to the electron transport chain, where the electrons pass along the chain to the final electron acceptor, oxygen. In the process, ATP molecules are produced (Figure 2).

Lab Study A. Oxidation-Reduction Reactions in a Mitochondrial Suspension

Materials

mitochondrial suspension
succinate
buffer
DPIP solution
1-mL graduated pipette
pipette pump
4 cuvettes or small test tubes
Parafilm® squares
Kimwipes®
spectrophotometer
wax pencil

Introduction

In this lab study, you will investigate cellular respiration in isolated mitochondria. Your instructor has prepared a mitochondrial suspension from pulverized lima beans. The suspension has been kept on ice to prevent enzyme degradation, and the Krebs cycle will continue in the mitochondria as in intact cells. Sucrose has been added to the mitochondrial suspension as a source of glucose for respiration.

One step in the Krebs cycle is the enzyme-catalyzed conversion of succinate to fumarate in a redox reaction. In intact cells, succinate loses hydrogen ions and electrons to FAD, and, in the process, fumarate is formed (Figure 5).

We will utilize this step in the Krebs cycle to study the rate of cellular respiration under different conditions. To perform this study, we will add a substance called DPIP (di-chlorophenol-indophenol), an electron acceptor that

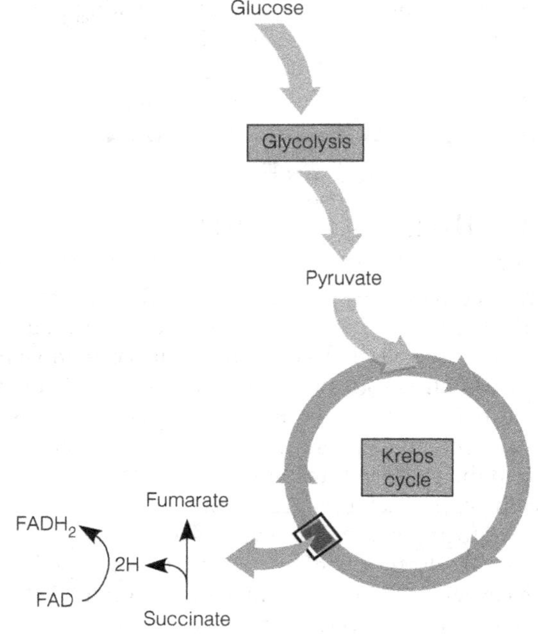

Figure 5.
At one point in the Krebs cycle, succinate is converted to fumarate. Hydrogens from succinate pass to FAD, reducing it to $FADH_2$.

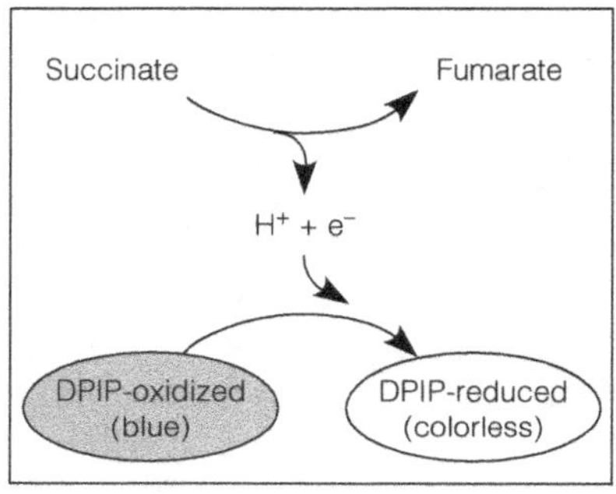

Figure 6.
DPIP intercepts the hydrogen ions and electrons as succinate is converted to fumarate. DPIP changes from blue to colorless.

intercepts the hydrogen ions and electrons released from succinate, changing the DPIP from an oxidized to a reduced state. DPIP is *blue* in its oxidized state but changes from blue to *colorless* as it is reduced (Figure 6).

We can use this color change to measure the respiration rate. To do this, however, we must have some quantitative means of measuring color change. An instrument called a **spectrophotometer** will allow us to do this. A spectrophotometer measures the amount of light absorbed by a pigment. In the spectrophotometer, a specific wavelength of light (chosen by the operator) passes through the pigment solution being tested—in this case, the blue DPIP. The spectrophotometer then measures the proportion of light *transmitted* or, conversely, *absorbed* by the DPIP and shows a reading on a calibrated scale. As the DPIP changes from blue to clear, it will absorb less light and more light will pass through (be transmitted through) the solution. The change in transmittance will be read by the spectrophotometer. As more light passes through the solution, the transmittance reading goes up. As aerobic respiration takes place, what should happen to the percent transmittance of light through the DPIP?

Our experiment will involve using succinate as the substrate and investigating the effect that *changing the amount of succinate will have on the cellular respiration rate.*

Hypothesis

Hypothesize about the effect of an increased amount of substrate on the rate of cellular respiration.

Prediction

Predict the results of the experiment based on your hypothesis (if/then).

Procedure

1. Prepare the spectrophotometer.

   The instructions that follow are for a Bausch & Lomb Spectronic 20 (Figure 7). Turn on the machine (power switch C) at least 5 minutes before beginning.

   a. Using the wavelength control knob (A), select the wavelength: 600 nm. Your instructor has previously determined that this wavelength is absorbed by DPIP.

   b. Zero the instrument by adjusting the control knob (the same as power switch C) so that the meter needle reads 0% transmittance. There should be no cuvette in the instrument, and the sample holder cover must be closed. Once it is set, do not change this setting.

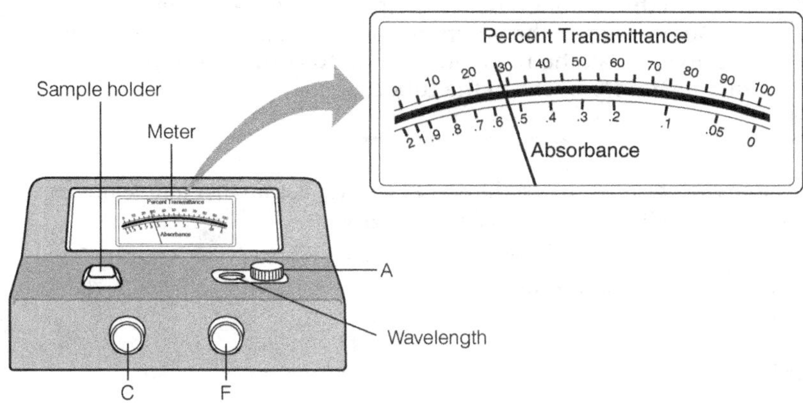

Figure 7.
The Bausch & Lomb Spectronic 20. A spectrophotometer measures the proportion of light of different wavelengths absorbed and transmitted by a pigment solution. Inside the spectrophotometer, light is separated into its component wavelengths and passed through a sample. Transmittance or absorbance can be read on a calibrated scale.

2. Obtain four cuvettes and label them B, 1, 2, and 3. The B will be the blank.
3. Prepare the blank first by measuring 4.6 mL buffer, 0.3 mL mitochondrial suspension, and 0.1 mL succinate into the B cuvette. Cover the cuvette tightly with Parafilm and invert it to mix the reactants thoroughly.
4. Calibrate the spectrophotometer as follows: Wipe cuvette B with a Kimwipe and insert it into the sample holder. Be sure you align the etched mark on the cuvette with the line on the sample holder. Close the cover. Adjust the light control (F) until the meter reads 100% transmittance, or 0 absorption. Remove cuvette B. You are now ready to prepare the experimental cuvettes. The blank corrects for differences in transmittance due to the mitochondrial solution.
5. Measure the buffer, DPIP, and mitochondrial suspension into cuvettes 1, 2, and 3 as specified in Table 3.

   Do not add the succinate yet!

Table 3
Contents of Experimental Tubes (volumes in mL)

Tube	Buffer	DPIP	Mitochondrial Suspension	Succinate (add last)
1	4.4	0.3	0.3	0
2	4.3	0.3	0.3	0.1
3	4.2	0.3	0.3	0.2

6. Perform the next two steps as *quickly* as possible. First, add the succinate to each cuvette.
7. Cover tube 1 with Parafilm, wipe it with a Kimwipe, insert it into the sample holder, and record the percent transmittance in Table 4 in the Results section. Repeat this step for tubes 2 and 3.

If the initial reading is higher than 30%, tell your instructor immediately. You may need to add another drop of DPIP to each tube and repeat step 7. The reading must be low enough (the solution dark enough) to give readings for 20–30 minutes. If the solution is too light (the transmittance is above 30%), the reactions will go to completion too quickly to detect differences in the tubes.

8. Before each reading, insert the blank, cuvette B, into the sample holder. Adjust to 100% transmittance if necessary.
9. Continue to take readings at 5-minute intervals for 20–30 minutes. *Each time, before you take a reading, cover the tube with Parafilm and invert it to mix the contents.* Record the results in Table 4.

Results

1. Complete Table 4. Compose a title for the table.

Table 4

Tube	Time (min)						
	0	5	10	15	20	25	30
1							
2							
3							

2. Using Figure 8, construct a graph to illustrate your results.
   a. What is (are) the independent variable(s)? Which is the appropriate axis for this variable?

   b. What is the dependent variable? Which is the appropriate axis for this variable?

   c. Choose an appropriate scale and label the x and y axes.
   d. Should you use a legend? If so, what would this include?

   e. Compose a figure title.

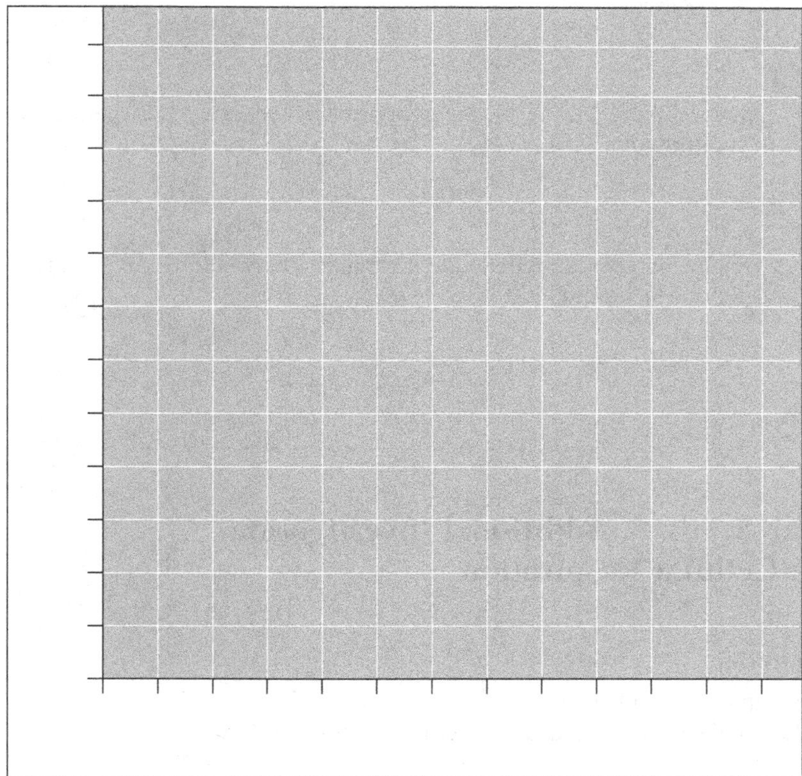

Figure 8.

Discussion

1. Explain the experimental design. What is the role of each of the components of the experimental mixtures?

2. Which experimental tube is the control?

3. In which experimental tube did transmittance increase more rapidly? Explain.

4. Why should the succinate be added to the reaction tubes last?

5. Was your hypothesis falsified or supported by the results? Use your data to support your answer.

6. What are some other independent variables that could be investigated using this technique?

Lab Study B. Additional Investigations in Cellular Respiration

Materials

all materials from Lab Study A
additional substrates: glucose, fructose, maltose, artificial sweeteners, starch, glycogen
inhibitors: rotenone, oligomycin, malonate, antimycin A
different pH buffers
ice bath
water bath
disposable gloves

Introduction

If your team chooses to study cellular respiration for your independent investigation and report, design a simple experiment to investigate some factor that affects cellular respiration. Use the available materials, or ask your instructor about the availability of additional materials.

If you select toxins or respiratory inhibitors for your investigation, ask the instructor about safety procedures. Post safety precautions and follow safety protocol, including wearing gloves and protective eyewear. Notify the instructor of any spills.

Procedure

1. Collaborating with your research team, read the following potential questions, and choose a question to investigate using this list or an idea from your prior knowledge. You may want to check your text and other sources for supporting information.
   a. Would other substrates be as effective as glucose in cellular respiration? Possible substrates:
      sucrose (table sugar—glucose and fructose disaccharide)
      starch (glucose polymer in plants)
      saccharin, Nutrasweet™, or other artificial sweeteners
      fructose
   b. What environmental conditions are optimum for cellular respiration?
      What temperature ranges?
      What pH ranges?
   c. What inhibitors of cellular respiration are most effective? Consider the following list:
      Rotenone, an insecticide, inhibits electron flow in the electron transport chain.
      Oligomycin, an antibiotic, inhibits ATP synthesis.
      Malonate blocks the conversion of succinate to malate. How would you determine if this is competitive or noncompetitive inhibition?
      Antimycin A is an antibiotic that inhibits the transfer of electrons to oxygen.
2. Design your experiment, proposing hypotheses, making predictions, and determining procedures as instructed in Exercise 3.

EXERCISE 3
Designing and Performing Your Independent Investigation

Materials

See each Lab Study B materials list in Exercises 1 and 2.

Introduction

Now that you have completed both introductory investigations, your research team should decide if you will investigate fermentation or cellular respiration. Use Lab Topic 1 as a reference for designing and performing a scientific investigation. Be ready to assign tasks to members of your lab team. Be sure that everyone understands the techniques that will be used. Your experiment will be successful only if you plan carefully, cooperate with your team members, perform lab techniques accurately and systematically, and record and report data accurately.

Procedure

1. **Decide on one or more questions to investigate.**
   Question:

2. **Formulate a testable hypothesis.**
   Hypothesis:

3. **Summarize the experiment.** (Use separate paper.)
4. **Predict the results of your experiment based on your hypothesis.**
   Prediction: (If/then)

5. **Outline the procedures used in the experiment.**
   a. On a separate sheet of paper, list each step in your procedure in numerical order.
   b. Remember to include the number of repetitions (usually a minimum of five), levels of treatment, appropriate time intervals, and controls for each procedure.

c. If you have an idea for an experiment that requires materials other than those provided, ask your laboratory instructor about their availability. If possible, additional supplies will be made available.

d. When carrying out an experiment, remember to quantify your measurements when possible.

6. **Perform the experiment**, making observations and collecting data for analysis.

If your experiment involves the use of toxins or respiration inhibitors, use them only in liquid form as provided by the instructor. Wear protective gloves and eyewear. Ask your instructor about proper disposal procedures. If a spill occurs, notify your instructor immediately for proper cleanup.

7. **Record observations and data** on a separate sheet of paper. Design tables and graphs, at least one of each. Be thorough when collecting data. Do not just write down numbers, but record what they mean as well. Do not rely on your memory for information that you will need when reporting your results.

8. **Prepare your discussion.** Discuss your results in light of your hypothesis.

   a. Review your hypothesis. Review your results (tables and graphs). Do your results support or falsify your hypothesis? Explain your answer, using your data for support.

   b. Review your prediction. Did your results correspond to the prediction you made? If not, explain how your results are different from your predictions, and why this might have occurred.

   c. If you had problems with the procedure or questionable results, explain how they might have influenced your conclusion.

   d. If you had an opportunity to repeat and expand this experiment to make your results more convincing, what would you do?

   e. Summarize the conclusion you have drawn from your results.

9. **Be prepared to report your results to the class.** Prepare to persuade your fellow scientists that your experimental design is sound and that your results support your conclusions.

10. If your instructor requires it, **submit Results and Discussion sections** of a scientific paper. Keep in mind that although you have performed the experiments as a team, you must turn in a lab report of *your original writing*. Your tables and figures may be similar to those of your team members, but your Results and Discussion sections must be the product of your own literature search and creative thinking.

Questions for Review

1. Having completed this lab topic, you should be able to define, describe, and use the following terms: *aerobic, anaerobic, substrate, reactants, products, spectrophotometer, respirometer,* NAD^+, *NADH, FAD,* $FADH_2$, *ATP.*

2. State the beginning reactants and the end products of glycolysis, alcoholic fermentation, the Krebs cycle, and the electron transport chain. Describe where these processes take place in the cell and the conditions under which they operate (aerobic or anaerobic).

   glycolysis:

   alcoholic fermentation:

   Krebs cycle:

   electron transport chain:

3. Suppose you do another experiment using DPIP to study cellular respiration in isolated mitochondria, and the results using the spectrophotometer show a final percent transmittance reading of 42% in tube 1 and 78% in tube 2. Both tubes had an initial reading of 30%. In which tube did the greater amount of cellular respiration occur? Explain your answer in terms of the changes that take place in DPIP.

4. How do you know that the electrons causing the change in color of DPIP are involved in the succinate–fumarate step?

Applying Your Knowledge

1. Your mother has been making yeast bread all afternoon, and she has just put two loaves in the oven. You open the oven door to see what is baking. Your mother yells, "Don't slam the door!" Why?

2. Two characteristics of natural wines are that they have a maximum alcohol content of 14% and are "sparkling" wines. Apply your understanding of alcoholic fermentation to explain these characteristics.

3. In the spring of 2001, more than 500 stillbirths and deaths of newborn foals were reported for Kentucky thoroughbred horses. Veterinarians and scientists investigating the cause of these deaths discovered that these foals tested positive for cyanide. Scientists uncovered an ecological web beginning with black cherry trees that concentrate cyanide in their leaves. These were eaten by abundant tent caterpillars, which in turn fell to the ground or defecated, thus contaminating the pastures and water sources. Pregnant mares ingested large quantities of cyanide in grass and water. News reports erroneously claimed that cyanide blocked oxygen delivery. However, cyanide is a respiratory inhibitor that combines with a cytochrome (not oxygen) in the electron transport chain. What would be the result of blocking the terminal cytochrome in the electron transport chain?

4. Skunk cabbage is a plant that is able to generate heat and regulate its body temperature, like a warm-blooded animal. Botanists have suggested that the ability to produce heat is important in these plants because it provides a warm environment for pollinators. The heat may also help to dissipate the carrion-like scent produced by some skunk cabbage flowers. Clearly, these plants must have a high respiratory rate to produce temperatures as high as 37°C. How could you determine if the temperature is the result of cellular respiration? What features of the plant surface and cell structure might be present if respiration is actively occurring in the flowers?

References

Campbell, N. and J. Reece. *Biology*, 6th ed. San Francisco, CA: Benjamin/Cummings, 2002.

Corriher, S. O. *Cookwise: The Hows and Whys of Successful Cooking*. New York: William Morrow, 1997.

Lehninger, A. L., D. L. Nelson, and M. M. Cox. *Principles of Biochemistry*, 3rd ed. New York: Worth Publishers, 2000.

Seymour, R. S. "Plants That Warm Themselves." *Scientific American,* 1997, vol. 276, pp. 104–107.

Some procedures and many ideas in this lab topic were based on an exercise written by Jean Dickey, published in J. Dickey, *Laboratory Investigations for Biology*. Menlo Park, CA: Addison Wesley Longman, 1995.

The procedure used to assay mitochondrial activity was based on a procedure from "Succinic Acid Dehydrogenase Activity of Plant Mitochondria," in F. Witham, D. Blaydes, and R. Devlin, *Exercises in Plant Physiology*. Boston, MA: Prindle, Weber & Schmidt, 1971.

Art Credits

2, 5: Adapted from Neil Campbell, Jane Reece, and Larry Mitchell, *Biology,* 5th ed. (Menlo Park, CA: Benjamin/Cummings, 1999), ©1999 The Benjamin/Cummings Publishing Company.

Photosynthesis

Laboratory Objectives

After completing this lab topic, you should be able to:

1. Describe the roles played by light and pigment in photosynthesis.
2. Name and describe pigments found in photosynthesizing tissues.
3. Explain the separation of pigments by paper chromatography, based on their molecular structure.
4. Demonstrate an understanding of the process of spectrophotometry and the procedure for using the spectrophotometer.

Introduction

Without photosynthesis, there could be no life on Earth as we know it. The Earth is an open system constantly requiring an input of energy to drive the processes of life. All energy entering the biosphere is channeled from the sun into organic molecules via the process of photosynthesis. As the sun's hydrogen is converted to helium, energy in the form of photons is produced. These photons pass to Earth's surface and are absorbed by pigments in the chloroplasts of plants, initiating the process of photosynthesis.

Photosynthesis ultimately produces glucose and oxygen from carbon dioxide and water. Glucose, a primary source of energy for all cells, may be converted to sucrose and transported or stored in the polymer starch. These organic molecules are building blocks for plant growth and development. Animals consume plants and convert the plant molecules into their own organic molecules and energy sources—the ultimate in recycling. Oxygen, also produced by photosynthesis, is necessary for aerobic respiration in the cells of plants, animals, and other organisms (Figure 1).

In this laboratory, you will investigate cellular and environmental components utilized in the process of photosynthesis. In several experiments, you will determine photosynthetic activity by testing for the production of starch, using iodine potassium iodide (I_2KI), which stains starch purple-black. A change from the yellow-amber color of the iodine solution to a purple-black solution is a positive test for the presence of starch.

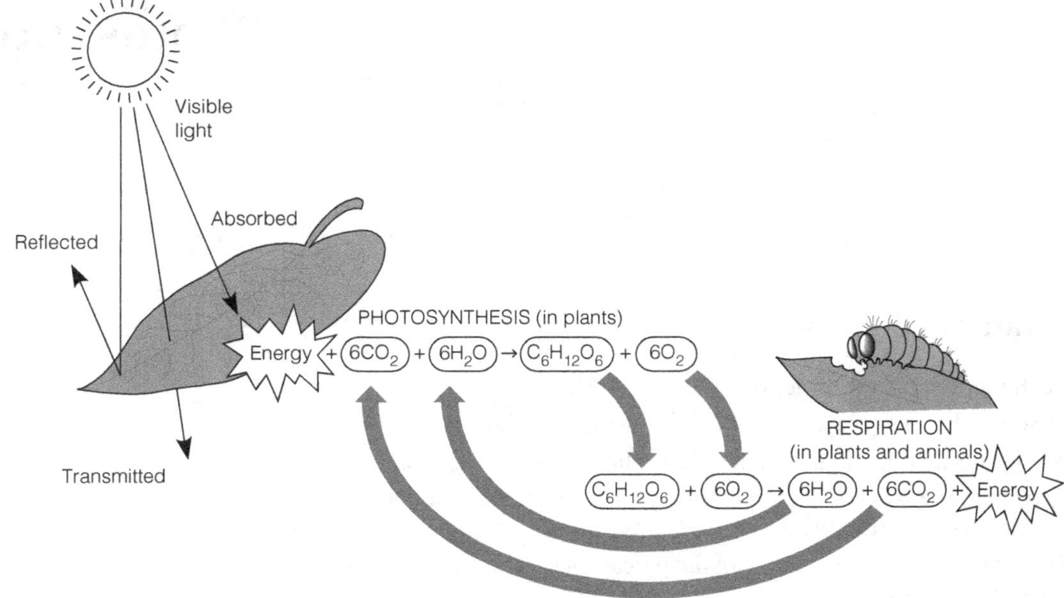

Figure 1.
Energy flow through plants and animals. Energy flows from the sun into the biological systems of Earth, and visible light is reflected, transmitted, or absorbed. Plants absorb light energy and convert it to chemical energy during photosynthesis. In this process, carbon dioxide and water are converted to oxygen and glucose and ultimately to other organic molecules. These organic molecules and the energy stored in them can be utilized by animals and other organisms that consume them. The energy in organic molecules is released during cellular respiration in plants and animals.

EXERCISE 1

The Wavelengths of Light for Photosynthesis

Materials

black construction paper
green, red, and blue plastic filters
paper clips
forceps
hot plate
petri dish
squirt bottle of water
scissors
1 geranium plant with at least 4 good leaves per 8 students
1 1,000-mL beaker filled with 300 mL of water
1 400-mL beaker filled with 200 mL of 80% ethyl alcohol
dropper bottle with concentrated I_2KI solution

Introduction

In this exercise, you will determine if products of photosynthesis are present in leaf tissue that has been exposed to different wavelengths of light for several days. Working with other students in groups of eight, you will cover small portions of different leaves of a geranium plant with pieces of black paper and green, red, and blue plastic filters. Each pair of students will be responsible for one of the four treatments. Later you will determine photosynthetic activity by testing for the presence of starch under the paper or filters.

What wavelength of light will be reflected and transmitted by the black paper and the colored filters? Note that the same wavelengths of light are reflected and transmitted by the filters.

Hypothesis

Hypothesize about photosynthetic activity in cells treated as described.

Prediction

Predict the results of the experiment based on your hypothesis (if/then).

Procedure

1. Four to five days before the experiment is to be carried out, cut a piece from each color of plastic filter and one from the black construction paper. Each piece should be a rectangle approximately 2.5 cm by 5 cm. Double over the strip and slide the edge of a healthy geranium leaf, still attached to the plant, between the folded edges. Carefully slip a slightly sprung paper clip over the paper, securing the paper to the leaf. The paper should be on both sides of the leaf. Follow this procedure with the other colors and the black construction paper, using a different leaf for each strip. Return the plant with treated leaves to bright light. Your instructor may have already carried out this step for you.
2. On the day of the lab, carry the plant with leaves covered to your desk. You will have to be able to recognize each leaf after the paper is removed and the leaf is boiled. To facilitate this, with your teammates devise a way to distinguish each leaf, and write the distinction in the space provided. Differences in size or shape may distinguish different leaves, but it may be necessary to introduce distinguishing features, such as by cutting the petioles to different lengths or cutting out small notches in a

portion of the leaf not covered by the paper. Record below the distinguishing differences for each treatment.

black paper:

green filter:

red filter:

blue filter:

3. After you have distinguished each leaf, sketch the leaf in the Results section, showing the position of the paper or filter on the leaf.
4. Set up the boiling alcohol bath. Place a 1,000-mL beaker containing 300 mL of water on the hot plate. Carefully place the 400-mL beaker containing 200 mL of 80% ethyl alcohol into the larger beaker of water. Turn on the hot plate and bring the nested beakers to a boil. Adjust the temperature to maintain slow boiling. Do not place the beaker of alcohol directly on the hot plate.

Ethyl alcohol is highly flammable! Do not place the beaker of alcohol directly on the hot plate. To bring it to a boil, raise the temperature of the hot plate until the alcohol just boils, and then reduce the temperature to maintain slow boiling. Do not leave boiling alcohol unattended.

5. Remove the paper and filters from each leaf; using forceps, carefully drop all the leaves into the boiling alcohol solution to extract the pigments. Save the plastic filters.
6. When the leaves are almost white, use forceps to remove them from the alcohol. Place them in separate petri dishes, rinse with distilled water, and add enough distilled water to each dish to just cover the leaf. Turn off the hot plate if all teams have completed boiling leaves for this exercise (and Exercise 2).
7. Add drops of I_2KI solution to the water until a pale amber color is obtained. I_2KI reacts with starch to produce a purple-black color.
8. Wait about 5 minutes and sketch each leaf in the Results section, showing which areas of the leaf tested positive for starch.

Results

1. Sketch and label each leaf before boiling, showing the location of the paper or filter.

2. Sketch and label each leaf after staining to show the location of the stain.

Discussion

1. Which treatment allowed the greatest photosynthetic activity? (Explain your results in terms of your hypothesis.)

2. When the red filter is placed on a leaf, what wavelengths of light pass through and reach the leaf cells below? (Check wavelengths in Color Plate 9, which shows the electromagnetic spectrum.)

   Green filter?

   Blue filter?

3. Was starch present under the black construction paper? Explain this in light of the fact that black absorbs all wavelengths of light.

EXERCISE 2

Pigments in Photosynthesis

Materials

Coleus plant with multicolored leaves
forceps
1 1,000-mL beaker filled with 300 mL of water
1 400-mL beaker filled with 200 mL of 80% ethyl alcohol
dropper bottle with concentrated I_2KI solution
hot plate
squirt bottle of water

Introduction

A variety of pigments are found in plants, as anyone who visits a botanical garden in spring or a deciduous forest in autumn well knows. A pigment is a substance that absorbs light. If a pigment absorbs all wavelengths of visible light, it appears black. The black construction paper used in Exercise 1 is colored with such a pigment. Other pigments absorb some wavelengths and reflect others. Yellow pigments, for example, reflect light wavelengths in the yellow portion of the visible light spectrum, green reflects in the green portion, and so on.

Some colors are produced by only one pigment, but an even greater diversity of colors can be produced by the cumulative effects of different pigments in cells. Green colors in plants are produced by the presence of chlorophylls *a* and *b* located in the chloroplasts. Yellow, orange, and bright red colors are produced by carotenoids, also in chloroplasts. Blues, violets, purples, pinks, and dark reds are usually produced by a group of water-soluble pigments, the anthocyanins, that are located in cell vacuoles and do not contribute to photosynthesis. Additional colors may be produced by mixtures of these pigments in cells.

Working with one other student, you will use the I_2KI test for starch as in Exercise 1 to determine which pigment(s) in a *Coleus* leaf support photosynthesis. Before beginning the experiment, examine your *Coleus* leaf and hypothesize about the location of photosynthesis based on the leaf colors.

Hypothesis

Hypothesize about the location of photosynthesis based on the leaf colors.

Prediction

Predict the results of the experiment based on your hypothesis (if/then).

Procedure

1. Remove a multicolored leaf from a *Coleus* plant that has been in strong light for several hours.
2. In Table 1, list the colors of your leaf, predict the pigments present to create that color, and predict the results of the I_2KI starch test in each area of the leaf.
3. Sketch the leaf outline in the Results section, mapping the color distribution before the I_2KI test.
4. Extract the pigments as previously described in Exercise 1, and test the leaf for photosynthetic activity using I_2KI.

Ethyl alcohol is highly flammable! Do not place the beaker of alcohol directly on the hot plate. To bring it to a boil, raise the temperature of the hot plate until the alcohol just boils, and then reduce the temperature to maintain slow boiling. Do not leave boiling alcohol unattended.

5. Sketch the leaf again in the Results section, outlining the areas showing a positive starch test.

Results

1. Record the results of the I_2KI test in Table 1.
2. Compare the sketches of the *Coleus* leaf before and after the I_2KI test.

   Before I_2KI Test: **After I_2KI Test:**

3. Which pigments supported photosynthesis? Record your results in Table 1.

Discussion

Describe and explain your results based on your hypothesis.

Table 1
Predicted and Observed Results for the Presence of Starch in Colored Regions of the *Coleus* Leaf

Color	Pigments	Starch Present (predicted) + or –	Starch Present (actual results) + or –
Green			
Purple			
Pink			
White			
Other			

EXERCISE 3

Separation and Identification of Plant Pigments by Paper Chromatography

Materials

capillary tube
beakers
extractions of leaf pigments in acetone
forceps
scissors
acetone
chromatography paper stapled into a cylinder marked with a pencil line about 1 cm from one end
quart jar with lid, containing solvent of petroleum ether and acetone

Introduction

Your instructor has prepared an extract of chloroplast pigments from fresh green grass or fresh spinach. A blender was used to rupture the cells, and the pigments were then extracted with acetone, an organic solvent. Working with one other student, begin this exercise by separating the pigments extracted using paper chromatography. To do this, you will apply the pigment extract to a cylinder of chromatographic paper. You will then place the cylinder in a jar with the organic solvents petroleum ether and acetone. The solvents will move up the paper and carry the pigments along; the pigments will move at different rates, depending on their different solubilities in the solvents used and the degree of attraction to the paper. The leading edge of the solvent is called the **front.** Discrete pigment bands will be formed from the front back to the point where pigments were added to the paper.

The following information will be helpful to you as you make predictions and interpret results:

1. **Polar molecules** or substances dissolve (or are attracted to) polar molecules.
2. **Nonpolar molecules** are attracted to nonpolar molecules to varying degrees.
3. Chromatography paper (cellulose) is a polar (charged) substance.
4. The solvent, made of petroleum ether and acetone, is relatively nonpolar.
5. The *most nonpolar* substance will dissolve in the nonpolar solvent *first*.
6. The *most polar* substance will be attracted to the polar chromatography paper; therefore, it will move *last*.

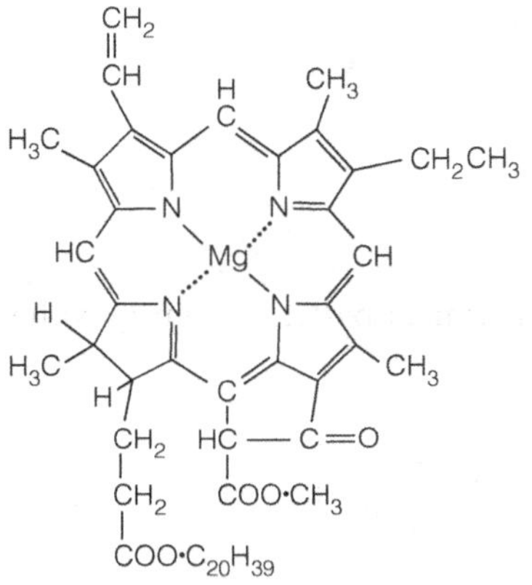

a. Chlorophyll *a*

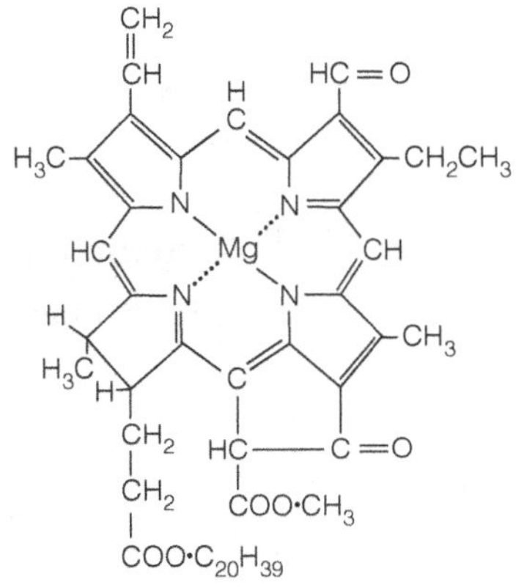

b. Chlorophyll *b*

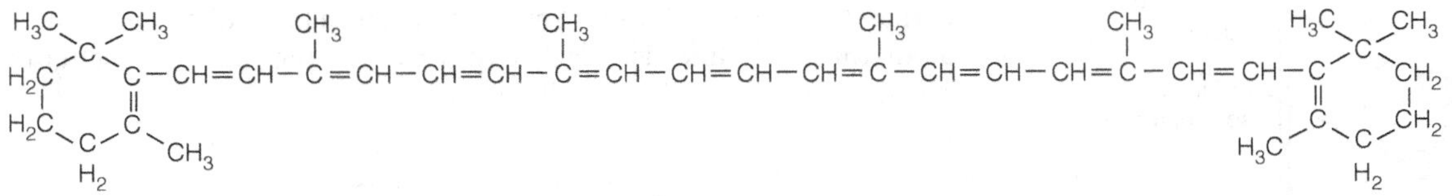

c. Beta carotene

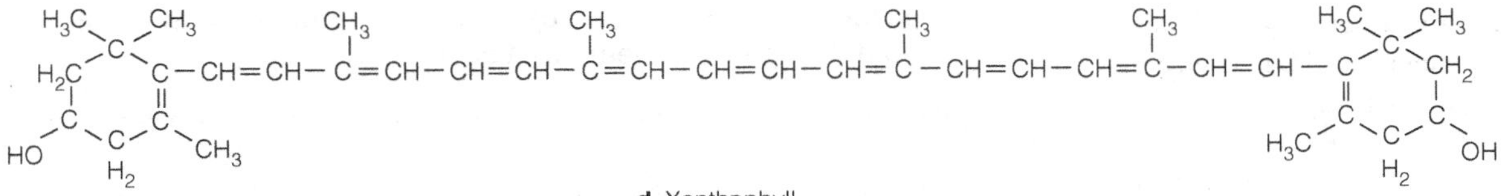

d. Xanthophyll

Figure 2.
Molecular structure of major leaf pigments. The molecular structure of chlorophyll *a*, chlorophyll *b*, carotene, and xanthophyll. To determine polarity, count the number of polar oxygens present in each molecule.

Use this information and the molecular structure of major leaf pigments to predict the relative solubilities and separation patterns for the pigments and to identify the pigment bands. Study the molecular structure of the four common plant pigments in Figure 2. As you study these diagrams, rank the pigments according to polarity in the space provided.

Most polar:

Least polar:

Hypothesis

State a hypothesis relating polarities and solubilities of pigments.

Prediction

Predict the results of the experiment based on your hypothesis (if/then).

Procedure

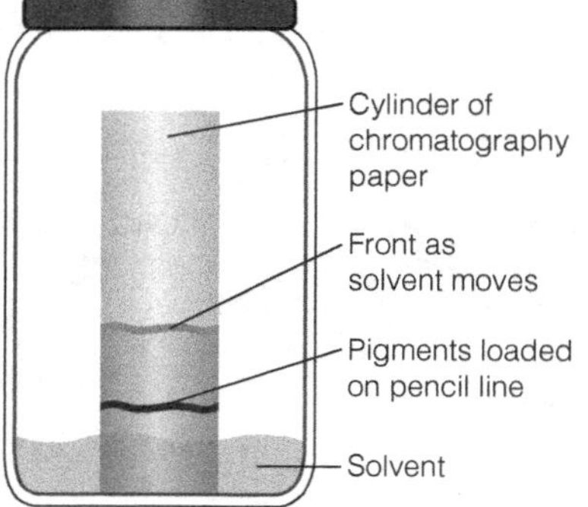

Figure 3.
Paper chromatography of photosynthetic pigments. Add the pigment solution to the paper cylinder along the pencil line. Then carefully place the cylinder into a jar containing a small amount of solvent. Close the lid and watch the pigments separate according to their molecular structures and solubilities.

1. Using a capillary tube, streak the leaf pigment extract on a pencil line previously drawn 1 cm from the edge of the paper cylinder. Allow the chlorophyll to dry. Repeat this step three or four times, allowing the extract to air-dry each time. You should have a band of green pigments along the pencil line. The darker your band of pigments, the better the results of your experiment will be.

Perform the next step in a hood or in a well-ventilated room. Do not inhale the fumes of the solvent. *NO SPARKS!* Acetone and petroleum ether are extremely flammable. Avoid contact with all solutions. Wash hands with soap and water. If a spill occurs, notify the instructor. If an instructor is not available, do not attempt to clean up. Leave the room.

2. Obtain the jar containing the petroleum ether and acetone solvent. Using forceps, carefully lower the loaded paper cylinder into the solvent, and quickly cover the jar tightly with the lid (Figure 3). *Avoid inhaling the solvent.* The jar should now contain a saturated atmosphere of the solvent. Allow the chromatography to proceed until the solvent front has reached to within 3 cm of the top of the cylinder.

3. Remove the cylinder from the jar, allow it to dry, and remove the staples.
4. Save your paper with the separated pigments for the next exercise.

Results

Sketch the chromatography paper. Label the color of the various bands. The front, or leading edge of the paper, should be at the top. The pencil line where pigment was added originally should be at the bottom.

Discussion

Based on your hypothesis and predictions, identify the various pigment bands. *The entire class should come to a consensus about the identifications.* Label your drawing in the Results section above, indicating the correct identification of the pigment bands.

EXERCISE 4

Determining the Absorption Spectrum for Leaf Pigments

Materials

spectrophotometer
Kimwipes®
2 cuvettes
20-mL beakers to elute pigments
1 150-mL beaker to hold cuvettes
acetone
cork stoppers for cuvettes

Introduction

In Exercise 1, you applied colored plastic filters and black paper to leaves to determine which wavelengths of light would support photosynthesis. Review your conclusions from that exercise and from Exercise 2 about pigments used in photosynthesis. Which pigments did you conclude support photosynthesis?

In Exercise 4, you will work in teams of four or five students, carrying your investigation a step further by plotting the absorption spectrum of leaf pigments separated by paper chromatography. The **absorption spectrum** is the absorption pattern for a particular pigment, showing relative absorbance at different wavelengths of light. For example, we know that chlorophyll *a* is a green pigment, and we know that it reflects or transmits green wavelengths of light. We do not know, however, the relative proportions of wavelengths of light absorbed by chlorophyll *a*. This information is of interest because it suggests that those wavelengths showing greatest absorbance are important in photosynthesis.

The absorption spectrum can be determined with an instrument called a **spectrophotometer,** or **colorimeter.** A spectrophotometer measures the proportions of light of different wavelengths (colors) absorbed and transmitted by a pigment solution. It does this by passing a beam of light of a particular wavelength (designated by the operator) through the pigment solution being tested. The spectrophotometer then measures the proportion of light transmitted or, conversely, absorbed by that particular pigment and shows the reading on the calibrated scale.

Before measuring the absorption spectrum of the four pigments separated by paper chromatography, consult the diagram of the electromagnetic spectrum, and predict the wavelengths of light at which absorption will be greatest for each pigment. Record your predictions in Table 2.

Table 2
Predicted Wavelengths of Greatest Absorption
for the Photosynthetic Pigments

Pigment	**Wavelengths of Greatest Absorption (predicted)**
1. Chlorophyll *a*	
2. Chlorophyll *b*	
3. Carotene	
4. Xanthophyll	

Hypothesis

State a hypothesis that describes the general relationship of each of the pigments to the color of light that it absorbs.

Prediction

Predict the results based on your hypothesis (if/then).

Procedure

1. Cut out the pigments you separated by paper chromatography, and distribute the paper strips as follows:

   Team 1: carotene

   Team 2: xanthophyll

   Team 3: chlorophyll *a*

   Team 4: chlorophyll *b*

   Teams 5 and 6: will determine the absorption spectrum of the total pigment solution

Perform the next three steps in a hood or in a well-ventilated room. Do not inhale the fumes of the solvent. *NO SPARKS!* Acetone is extremely flammable. Avoid contact with all solutions. If a spill occurs, notify the instructor. Wash hands with soap and water.

2. *Teams 1 to 4.* Dilute the pigments as follows: Cut up the chromatography paper with your assigned pigment into a small (20-mL) beaker. Add 10 mL of acetone to the beaker and swirl. This solution containing a single pigment will be your solution B, to be used to determine the absorption spectrum for that pigment. Your reference material will be acetone with no pigments, solution A.
3. *Teams 5 and 6.* Add drops of the original chlorophyll extract solution (acetone pigment mixture) to 10 mL of acetone until it looks pale green. This will be your pigment solution for cuvette B. Your reference material will be acetone with no pigment. This will be in cuvette A.
4. Each team should fill two cuvettes two-thirds full, one (B) with the pigment solution, the other (A) with the reference material (acetone only). Wipe both cuvettes with a Kimwipe to remove fingerprints, and handle cuvettes only with Kimwipes as you proceed.

   What is the purpose of the cuvette with reference material only?

5. Measure the absorption spectrum. Record your measurements in Table 6.3. The instructions that follow are for a Bausch & Lomb Spectronic 20 (Figure 4). Turn on the machine (power switch C) for at least 5 minutes before beginning.

   a. *Select the beginning wavelength* using the wavelength control knob (A). Begin measurements at 400 nanometers (nm).

   b. *Zero the instrument* by adjusting the 0 control knob (same as the power switch C) so that the meter needle reads 0% transmittance. There should be no cuvette in the instrument, and the sample holder cover must be closed.

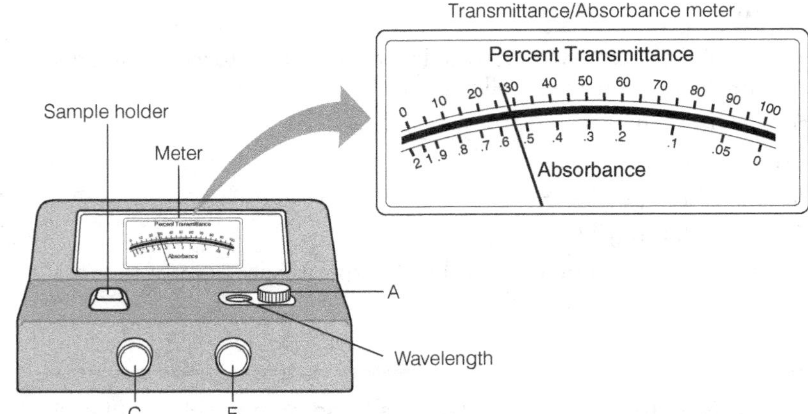

Figure 4.
The Bausch & Lomb Spectronic 20. A spectrophotometer measures the proportion of light of different wavelengths absorbed and transmitted by a pigment solution. Inside the spectrophotometer, light is separated into its component wavelengths and passed through a sample. The graph of absorption at different wavelengths for a solution is called an *absorption spectrum.*

c. *Calibrate the instrument.* Insert cuvette A into the sample holder and close the lid. (Be sure to align the etched mark on the cuvette with the line on the sample holder.) Adjust the light control (F) until the meter reads 100% transmittance, or 0 absorption. You are now ready to make your first reading.

d. *Begin your readings.* Remove cuvette A and insert cuvette B. (Align the etched mark.) Close the cover. Record the reading on the absorbance scale. Remove cuvette B.

e. *Recalibrate the instrument.* Insert cuvette A into the sample holder, and set the wavelength to 420 nm. Again, calibrate the instrument to 100% transmittance (0 absorption) with cuvette A in place, using the light control (F).

f. *Take the second reading.* Remove cuvette A and insert cuvette B. Record absorbance at 420 nm. Remove cuvette B.

g. *Continue your observations,* increasing the wavelength by 20-nm increments until you reach 720 nm. Be sure to recalibrate each time you change the wavelength.

6. Pool data from all teams to complete Table 3.

Results

1. Using the readings recorded in Table 3, plot in Figure 5 the absorption spectrum for each pigment.
2. Choose appropriate scales for the axes, determine dependent and independent variables, and plot data points. Draw smooth curves to fit the values plotted. Label the graph for easy identification of pigments plotted, or prepare a legend and use colored pencils.

Discussion

1. List in the margin or on another page the pigments extracted and the optimum wavelength(s) of light for absorption for each pigment.

Table 3
Absorbance of Photosynthetic Pigments Extracted from Fresh ______________________*

Wavelength	Chlorophyll *a*	Chlorophyll *b*	Xanthophyll	Carotene	Total Pigment
400					
420					
440					
460					
480					
500					
520					
540					
560					
580					
600					
620					
640					
660					
680					
700					
720					

*Complete title with name of plant used for extract, for example, beans.

2. Which pigment is most important in the process of photosynthesis? Support your choice with evidence from your results.

3. Chlorophyll *b* and carotenoids are called *accessory pigments*. Using data from your results, speculate about the roles of these pigments in photosynthesis.

Figure 5.
Absorption spectrum for chlorophyll *a*, chlorophyll *b*, carotene, and xanthophyll. Plot your results from Exercise 6.4. Label all axes, and draw smooth curves to fit the data. Label the graph for easy identification of pigments.

Questions for Review

1. Write a summary equation for photosynthesis.

2. Using your previous knowledge of photosynthesis and the results from today's exercises, explain the role, origin, or fate of each factor involved in the process of photosynthesis.

3. A pigment solution contains compound A with 4 polar groups and compound B with 2 polar groups. You plan to separate these compounds using

paper chromatography with a nonpolar solvent. Predict the location of the two bands relative to the solvent front. Explain your answer.

Applying Your Knowledge

1. In what form is carbohydrate transported out of the leaf to other parts of the plant, and when does this occur?

2. Dr. William C. Dooley's students did not get the expected results for their investigation of the effects of different wavelengths of light on photosynthesis in the geranium (Exercise 1). Regardless of the treatment, all their geranium leaves tested positive for the presence of starch. Confused by these results, Dr. Dooley began to look for problems in the preparation of the experiment that could be responsible for the presence of starch under even the black paper. Can you suggest one or more problems that might lead to these results?

3. In response to shortened day length and cool temperatures, many trees begin a period of senescence when the breakdown of chlorophyll exceeds chlorophyll production. The leaves of these trees appear to change to yellow and orange. Using your knowledge of photosynthetic pigments, explain the source of these yellow-orange hues.

4. Land plants and many algae appear green, due to the chlorophyll stored in their chloroplasts. However, the deep-ocean-dwelling red algae, as

their name suggests, range in color from pink to red to dark purple, almost black. These red colors are attributed to the photosynthetic pigment phycoerythrin. What color and wavelengths of light do you think phycoerythrin absorbs? Can you suggest how the environmental conditions of red algae might be related to this different pigment system?

References

Lehninger, A. L., D. L. Nelson, and M. M. Cox. *Principles of Biochemistry,* 2nd ed. New York: Worth Publishers, 1993.

Taiz, L., and E. Zeigler. *Plant Physiology,* 2nd ed. Sunderland, MA: Sinauer, 1998.

Uno, G., R. Storey, and R. Moore. *Principles of Botany.* Boston, MA: McGraw-Hill Co., 2001.

Website

The Photosynthesis Center:
http://photoscience.la.asu.edu/photosyn/default.html

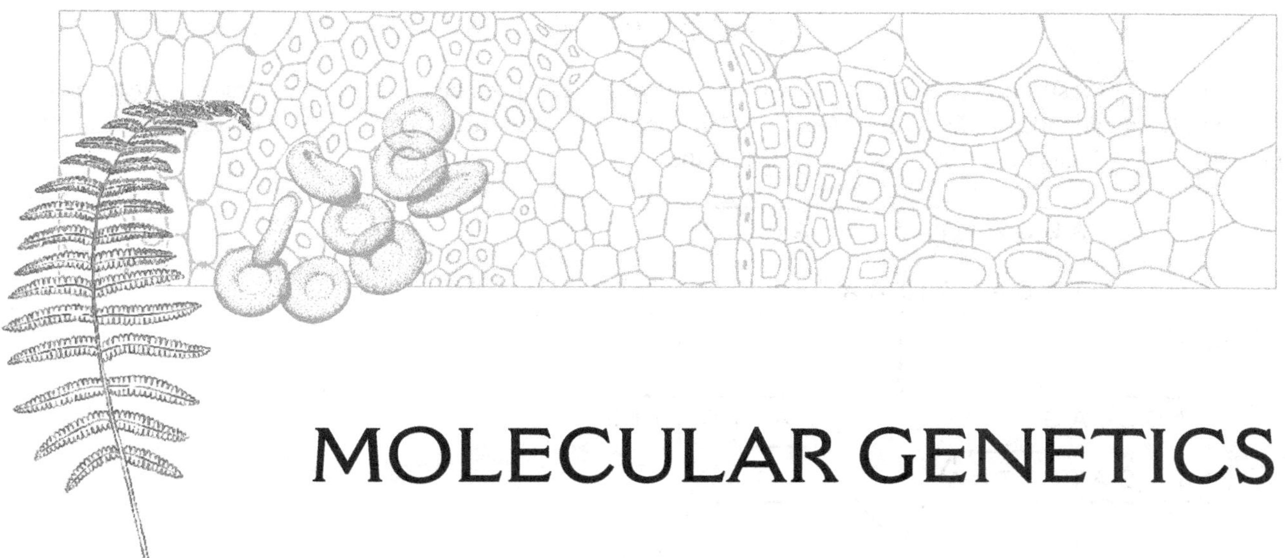

MOLECULAR GENETICS

INTRODUCTION:

Stanley Cohen and Herbert Boyer met by chance at a conference in Hawaii in 1972. This meeting turned out to be the beginning of a long and productive association that led to the birth of a new science, recombinant DNA technology. Stanley Cohen was studying **plasmids**, small circular pieces of DNA found in bacterial cells, and Herbert Boyer had discovered a class of enzymes, called **restriction endonucleases**, which recognize specific sequences of nitrogen bases in DNA and cut the DNA molecule at or near those sites. They envisioned the possibility of cutting and splicing together DNA from different organisms. From this vision, Genentech, Inc. was formed in 1976 and their first product, human insulin, was announced in 1978. The human insulin gene was isolated and combined with a plasmid. The plasmid was then used to transform bacteria cells that then began producing a human gene product. Becoming familiar with and using some of the techniques necessary for recombinant DNA technology is the subject of this lab.

Bacteria cells contain two different kinds of DNA, a circular chromosome and small circles of DNA called plasmids. Plasmids are easily and commonly transferred from one bacterial cell to another.

Since the 1950's microbiologists knew that viruses could grow in certain strains of bacteria but not in others. They began to look for the agent that protected some bacteria from viral infection and in 1968, the first restriction endonuclease was characterized. This is a class of enzymes that recognize DNA that is foreign to a bacterial cell and cuts it into fragments, thus protecting the cell from viruses. Since the effect of these enzymes is to restrict viral reproduction, they are called restriction enzymes or restriction endonucleases since they cut the DNA at specific internal **restriction sites**.

Hundreds of restriction enzymes have now been isolated and characterized. They are named for the bacteria from which they were isolated. EcoRI, for example was isolated from *Escherichia coli*, strain RY 13. "I" indicates that it was the first restriction endonuclease isolated from that strain of *E. coli*. Other restriction endonucleases that are used in this lab include HindIII, isolated from *Haemophilus influenzae*, strain Rd; AvaII, isolated from *Anabaena variabilis*; and PvuII, isolated from *Proteus vulgaris*.

One class of restriction enzymes cuts double stranded DNA in a zigzag pattern that leaves overhangs of single stranded nucleotides called sticky ends. For example, EcoRI recognizes a 6 nitrogen base restriction site: 5' GAATTC 3' and cuts the DNA between the G and the A.

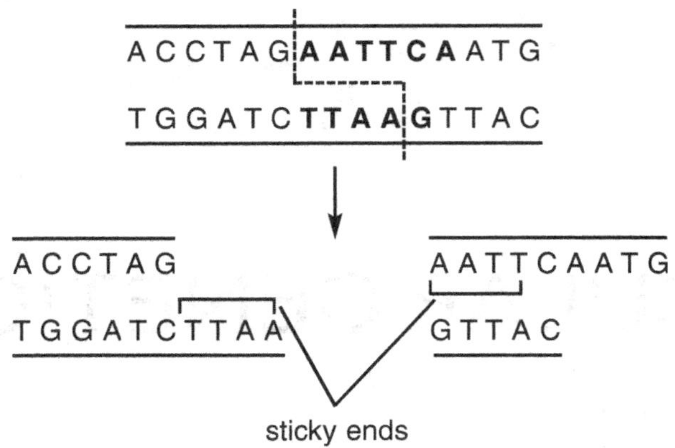

If DNA from two different sources are cut with the same restriction enzyme they will have complimentary sticky ends and will spontaneously hydrogen bond to each other when mixed together. If ligase is added to the mixture, phosphodiester bonds form between the two different DNA's and a recombinant molecule is formed. For example, the human gene for insulin can be combined with a bacterial plasmid. In a process called transformation, the plasmid inserts into a bacterial cell. The bacteria then uses the information encoded in the human gene to produce insulin.

One of the most basic techniques to recombinant DNA technology is mapping the restriction sites for common restriction endonucleases. In order to do this, a DNA molecule is cut with a restriction enzyme and the size of the resulting fragments is determined by **gel electrophoresis**. When placed in an electric field, DNA molecules are attracted toward the positive pole (anode) and repelled by the negative pole (cathode). It is the actual length of the DNA molecules that determines how fast they migrate. The medium through which the DNA moves is either polyacrylamide gel or agarose gel. We will be using agarose which is a natural polysaccharide of galactose and 3,6-anhydrogalactose derived from agar, which in turn is obtained from certain marine red algae. It acts like a sieve. Small molecules of DNA can move more rapidly through this sieve than the larger ones so the DNA fragments separate by size.

The DNA that you will be working with is the plasmid pUC19. This is a synthetic or man-made plasmid. It was developed by Joachim Messing at the Waksman Institute of Rutgers University and is widely used in recombinant DNA technology. This plasmid was previously digested with two different restriction enzymes, AvaII and PvuII, and with a combination of both enzymes (called a double digest). The goal is to determine how many restriction sites there are for these enzymes and where they are located on pUC19.

OBJECTIVES:

During this lab students will:

1. Develop an understanding of restriction enzymes and gel electrophoresis
2. Develop skills in micropipetting, and casting and loading gels
3. Determine the size of DNA fragments produced by gel electrophoresis
4. Map restriction sites on DNA

MATERIALS:

gel form
gel comb
masking tape
0.5 – 1 mL micropipettors
tips for micropipettors
discard beaker
solutions of food coloring
microfuge tubes
microcentrifuge
electrophoresis chambers
power supplies
agarose
TBE buffer
loading dye
uncut pUC19
AvaII digest of pUC19
PvuII digest of pUC19
double digest of pUC19
HindIII digest of λ DNA
ethidium bromide
transilluminator
camera
film
semi-log graph paper
rulers

PROCEDURES:

A. Casting a Gel

1. Use masking tape to form the two sides of the gel form. Press the tape securely to the gel form so the hot agarose will not leak out after it's poured into the form.
2. Place the gel comb in the slots by the black line on the gel form.
3. Pour the agarose slowly and steadily into the gel form until it covers about the length of the teeth of the gel comb. **Caution: the agarose is very warm. Use a folded paper towel to hold the flask.** Carefully check the gel for bubbles and debris floating on the gel. These can be gently pushed to the side of the gel with a micropipette tip if necessary. Do not disturb the gel as it cools and solidifies. As the gel solidifies, the color will change from clear to opaque.

B. Micropipetting

Micropipettes are very expensive precision instruments designed to transfer very small quantities of liquid. With the advent of recombinant DNA technology, micropipettes have become as common and important to a biologist as the microscope. Therefore, learning the correct use and care of a micropipette is very important and with practice, you will become as proficient in its use as you are with a microscope.

At the top of the micropipettor is a knob that is both a plunger and the volume adjustor. Rotating this knob will adjust the volume of liquid delivered by the pipette. The volume is displayed in a window near the top of the pipette.

0
1
5

There are two numbers in a row, then a white line followed by another number. The white line indicates a decimal point. The volume displayed on the left is 1.5 µL.

There are three different size micropipettors and the upper and lower limits of the volume that each pipette can deliver is printed on the pipette. **DO NOT ROTATE THE VOLUME ADJUSTOR ABOVE OR BELOW THOSE LIMITS.**

1. Turn the volume adjustor to deliver the desired amount of solution.
2. Put a tip on the micropipettor by firmly pushing the bottom of the pipette into a tip.
3. Depress the plunger to the **first stop**. Insert the tip into the solution that you wish to transfer and slowly release the plunger.

   ***TIP:** You will have the best control (and therefore accuracy) if you grasp the pipette by wrapping your palm around the pipette and use your thumb to work the plunger. You should hold the microfuge tube with the solution you wish to transfer at eye level in your other hand. Do not attempt to transfer a solution from a tube that someone else is holding or that is sitting in a rack on your desk. Check the tip to be sure there is no air space at the tip of the pipette or bubbles in the solution. If there is, expel the liquid and try again. The trick to accurate pipetting is to work the plunger slowly and smoothly.*

4. Put the tip of the pipette into the tube receiving the solution and depress the plunger to the **second stop**. Remove the pipette with the plunger still depressed so you don't suck the solution back into the pipette.

   ***TIP:** Hold the tip along the side wall of the tube receiving the solution. This allows capillarity to help draw the solution out of the pipette. Remember to depress the plunger slowly.*

5. Eject the tip into the discard beaker. Most micropipettors have an ejection button near the plunger on top of the pipette that you work with your thumb. (Some older model micropipettors have a third stop on the plunger for ejecting tips.)

   TIP:

- *Always change tips between transfers to avoid contamination.*
- *Hold the micropipettor upright at all times to prevent the solution from flowing into the piston and damaging the pipette.*
- *Never lay the pipette down on the desk with fluid in the tip.*
- *Never let the plunger snap back after withdrawing or delivering fluid. It can damage the piston.*
- *Never immerse the barrel of the micropipettor into a liquid. Make sure there is a tip in place.*

Practice Exercise

1. Deliver the following volumes of solution into a clean microfuge tube:

   2 μL of the red solution

   4 μL of the blue solution

   3 μL of the yellow solution

   1 μL of the green solution

2. "Touch spin" the microfuge tube in the microcentrifuge to draw all the solutions to the bottom of the tube. (Touch spin means to centrifuge the tube for only a few seconds) **Caution: Be sure to place the microfuge tubes in a balanced formation in the rotor of the microcentrifuge.**

3. Set the volume on the micropipettor to 10 μL and pick up the solution that you just transferred. If there is some solution still left in the microfuge tube you over-pipetted the four solutions. If there is an air space in the tip of the pipette, you under-pipetted the four solutions. Practice this technique until you can consistently pipette volumes accurately.

C. Preparing the DNA Samples

1. Obtain 6 microfuge tubes containing:

- HindIII marker
- uncut pUC
- loading dye •
- pUC19 digested with both AvaII and PvuII (double digest)
- pUC19 digested with AvaII
- pUC19 digested with PvuII

2. Transfer 2 μL of loading dye into each of the DNA samples.

   This dye has a two-fold purpose. It is denser than the buffer, so it will help the DNA go into the wells on the gel rather than floating away in the buffer. It is also used to track the progress of the DNA as it moves through the gel. The loading dye consists of two different dyes. Bromthymol blue runs through the gel at about the same rate as a 900 kb fragment of DNA. Xylene cyanol is a lighter aqua color and runs through the gel at about the same rate as a 300 kb fragment of DNA. These dyes do not bond to the DNA and are used for tracking purposes only.

3. Touch spin the DNA samples to mix the loading dye with the DNA.

D. Loading the Gels

1. Carefully remove the tape from the sides of the gel form.

2. Place the gel form into the electrophoresis chamber. Be sure to orient the black line on the gel form with the black dot on the electrophoresis chamber. This will insure that the DNA will migrate through the gel toward the anode.

3. Carefully pour the TBE buffer into the chambers on either side of the gel. There should be enough buffer to cover the gel.

   The most common buffer is Tris-borate (TBE) buffer which is composed of Tris-borate, boric acid, and EDTA. The buffer is necessary because during electrophoresis, the anode side becomes alkaline and the cathode side of the electrophoresis becomes acidic.

4. Carefully remove the comb from the gel by pulling it straight up. The comb formed 8 wells in the gel.
5. Deliver 10 μL of each DNA sample to a well using Figure 1 as a guide.

Figure 1 Diag am for Loading the Gel

E. Electrophoresis of the DNA Samples

1. Slide the cover onto the electrophoresis chamber.
2. Connect the electrodes to the power supply.
3. Turn on the power supply and set the voltage to 100 mV.
4. Observe the bubbles by both electrodes in the chamber. Within a few minutes, the dye will begin moving out of the wells and migrating toward the anode (red line). At this point the voltage can be increased to 125 mV.
5. Run the electrophoresis until the light blue dye crosses the red line on the gel form. This usually takes 30 – 45 minutes.

F. Staining the Gels

In order to visualize the fragments of DNA, they are usually stained with a fluorescent dye, ethidium bromide. The dye enters the gel and binds to the DNA by intercalating or fitting between the stacked bases in the DNA molecule. Ethidium bromide that is bound to the DNA will fluoresce an intense red-orange color (560 nm) when illuminated with ultraviolet (UV) light (260 to 360 nm).

Ethidium bromide is very toxic because it binds tightly to DNA. It is a powerful mutagen and may cause cancer. **Always wear gloves when handling gels or solutions containing the dye.** Ultraviolet light also causes skin cancer and can cause permanent blindness by damaging the retina. **UV transilluminators should be on for less than one minute and special UV protective goggles should always be worn over the eyes.**

Because of these dangers, it is much safer and also easier to detect the DNA if a picture is taken and the gel discarded.

1. **Turn off the power to the electrophoresis chamber.**
2. Slide off the lid and gently lift the gel form out of the chamber.
3. Write your group number or name on the lip of a weighing boat. Slide the gel off the gel form into a weighing boat that will be used for staining.
4. Give the gel to your lab instructor for staining and photographing.

G. Graphing the Size Standard

Once the gel is photographed, you can analyze it and determine the size of the DNA fragments. This is accomplished by running DNA fragments of known size in at least one of the lanes in each gel. A typical standard is the plasmid pBR322 digested with BstNI. BstNI is a restriction endonuclease isolated from *Bacillus stearothermophilis*, strain N. The plasmid pBR322 is an E. coli plasmid that is 4361 bp in size.

Below is a restriction map showing the restriction sites for BstNI on the pBR322 plasmid. The number at each restriction site indicates the location of the restriction site in base pairs from the origin. The origin is labeled as 0/4361. BstNI does not cut the pBR322 plasmid at this location.

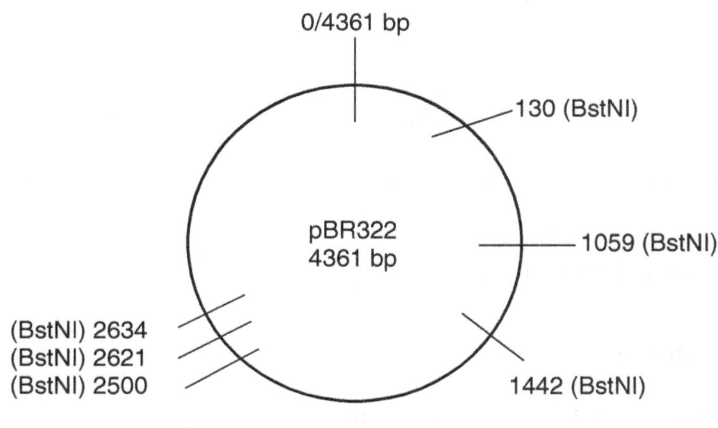

BstNI digest of pBR322

The size of each fragment is determined by subtracting the location of 2 adjacent restriction sites. For example the fragment between the restriction sites 130 and 1059 is 929 bp in size (1059 - 130 = 929).

How many fragments are formed when BstNI digests pBR322? (answer: 6)

What is the size of each of the fragments? (answer: 929 bp, 383 bp, 1058 bp, 121 bp, 13 bp, and 1857 bp)

1. Using the photograph of your gel, measure the distance that the standard DNA fragments have migrated from the well. (Measure from the leading edge of the well to the leading edge of the band of DNA. The size of each fragment is already known and is usually represented as kilobase pairs or kb.

2. The log10 of the molecular length of each DNA fragment in kb is then graphed against the distance migrated in the gel (cm):

   a. Set up the graph with Size (kb) on the Y axis and distance migrated (cm) on the X axis.

   b. Since you are using 2-cycle semi-log graph paper, label the first cycle in tenths (0.1, 0.2, 0.3.....kb) and the second cycle in units (1, 2, 3...kb).

   c. Graph the distance of migration for each DNA fragment vs. its size

3. Measure the distance of migration of the bands of unknown size from the AvaII, PvuII, Ava + Pvu digests and the uncut DNA.

4. Estimate the size of these unknown fragments using the standard curve of the HindIII size standard. For example, if an unknown fragment migrated 3.0 cm, find where 3.0 cm intersects your standard curve and read across to the size. See the diagram below.

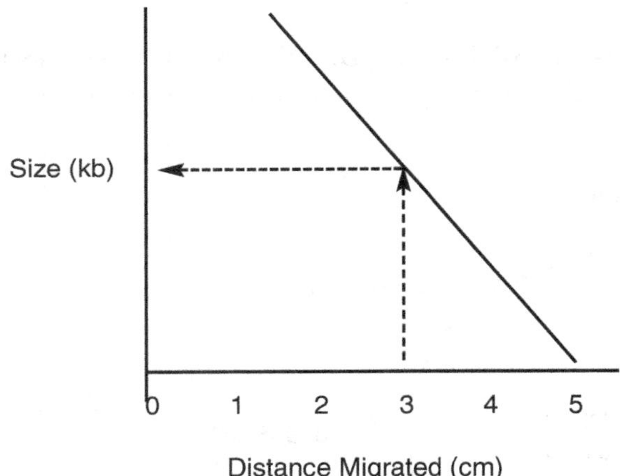

H. Mapping Restriction Sites

1. Determine whether the DNA is circular or linear.

2. Determine the number of restriction sites for each enzyme by examining the number of fragments produced. With linear DNA the number of fragments is always 1 more than the number of restriction sites; with circular DNA, the number of fragments equals the number of restriction sites.

3. Add up the total length of the DNA for each of the digests. This should reveal any "masked" fragments. Masked fragments are two similar sized fragments of DNA with different nitrogen base sequences. They will appear as one band on a gel because they are the same size.

4. Look for fragments in one enzyme's pattern that appear to be cut by the alternative enzyme. Do this by comparing the single digest of a particular enzyme with the double digest. Any fragments present in the single digest that are not present in the double digest were cut by the second enzyme. It is often good to start with the frequent cutter's fragments and then look for those that are cut by the less frequent cutter enzyme.
5. Draw pictures to test various hypotheses.

Sample Problem

As part of an undergraduate research project, a student was attempting to construct a restriction map for the plasmid pUC23 using the restriction enzymes EcoRI and BamHI. After carrying out both single and double enzyme digests and electrophoresis the picture below is obtained, showing the number of DNA fragments produced in each digest, along with the sizes of each fragment.

From this information, construct a restriction map of the pUC23 plasmid for enzymes EcoRI and BamHI.

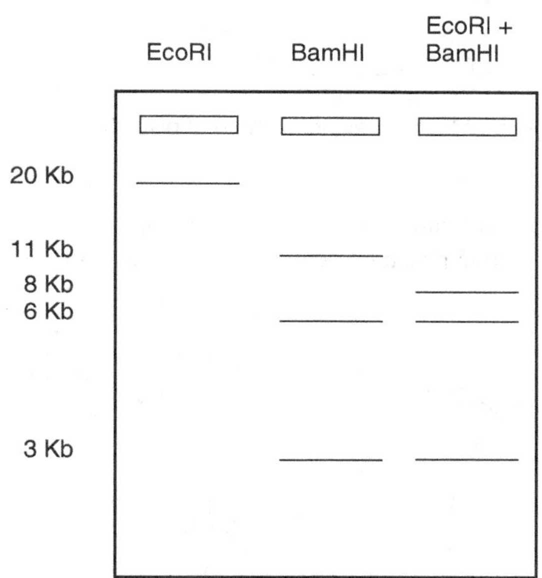

Diagram of gel with BamHI and EcoRI digests

Step 1:
We know that this DNA is circular since it is a plasmid.

Step 2:
EcoR1 digest produces one fragment, therefore there is one restriction site for EcoRI (GAATTC). BamHI digest produces three fragments therefore there are three restriction sites for BamHI.

Step 3:
The fragment produced by the EcoRI digest is 20 kb, therefore the pUC23 plasmid is 20 kb. The fragments from all the other digests must equal 20 kb. The BamHI fragments are 11 kb, 6 kb, and 3 kb which total 20 kb. The fragments from the double digest with EcoRI and BamHI total 17 kb (8 + 6 + 3 kb). This indicates that there is another 3 kb fragment which is masked.

Step 4:
The 11 kb fragment in the BamHI digest is not present in the double digest. This means that EcoRI cuts inside this fragment. (EcoRI cuts the 11 kb fragment into 8 kb and 3 kb segments.)

Step 5:
Draw a restriction map of the frequent cutter (in this example, that is BamHI).

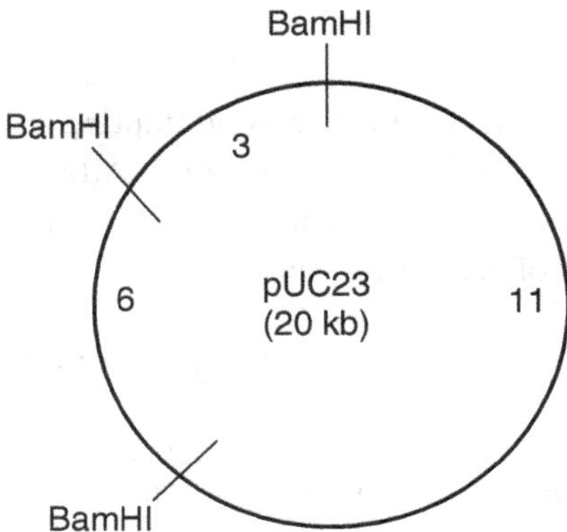

Diagram of BamHI restriction map of pUC23

Step 6:
Draw the restriction site for the less frequent cutter on the restriction map. EcoRI cuts the 11 kb fragment into two fragments (8 kb and 3 kb). There are two possible locations for this EcoRI restriction site:

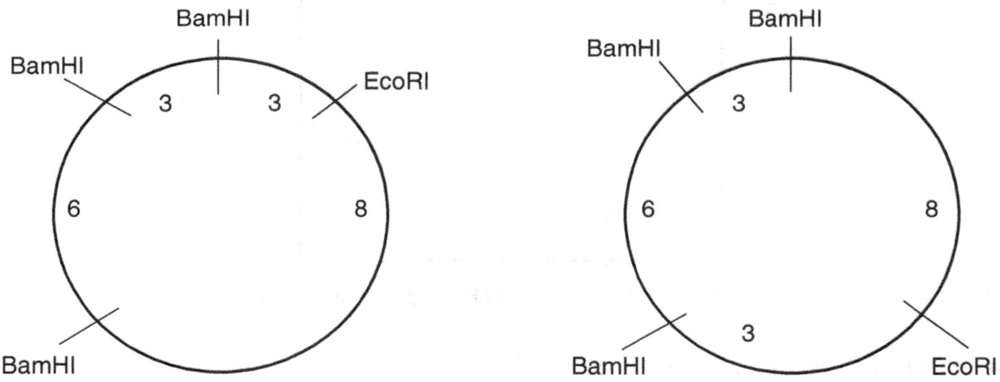

Diagram of BamHI and EcoRI restriction maps of pUC23

Step 7:
Make sure your restriction map agrees with all of the data from the restriction digest.

Mitosis and Meiosis

Laboratory Objectives

After completing this lab topic, you should be able to:

1. Describe the activities of chromosomes, centrioles, and microtubules in the cell cycle, including all phases of mitosis and meiosis.
2. Recognize human chromosomes in leukocytes.
3. Identify the phases of mitosis in root tip and whitefish blastula cells.
4. Describe differences in mitosis and cytokinesis in plant and animal cells.
5. Describe differences in mitosis and meiosis.
6. Explain crossing over, and describe how this can bring about particular arrangements of ascospores in the fungus *Sordaria*.

Introduction

The nuclei in cells of eukaryotic organisms contain chromosomes with clusters of **genes,** discrete units of hereditary information consisting of double-stranded deoxyribonucleic acid (DNA). Structural proteins in the chromosomes organize the DNA and participate in DNA folding and condensation. When cells divide, chromosomes and genes are duplicated and passed on to daughter cells. Single-celled organisms divide for reproduction. Multicellular organisms have reproductive cells (eggs or sperm), but they also have somatic (body) cells that divide for growth or replacement.

In somatic cells and single-celled organisms, the nucleus divides by **mitosis** into two daughter nuclei, which have the same number of chromosomes and the same genes as the parent cell. In multicellular organisms, in preparation for sexual reproduction, a type of nuclear division called **meiosis** takes place. In meiosis, nuclei of certain cells in ovaries or testes (or sporangia in plants) divide twice, but the chromosomes replicate only once. This process results in four daughter nuclei with differing alleles on the chromosomes. Eggs or sperm (or spores in plants) are eventually formed. Generally, in both mitosis and meiosis, after nuclear division the cytoplasm divides, a process called **cytokinesis.**

Events from the beginning of one cell division to the beginning of the next are collectively called the **cell cycle.** The cell cycle is divided into two major phases: interphase and mitotic phase (M). The M phase represents the division of the nucleus and cytoplasm (Figure 1).

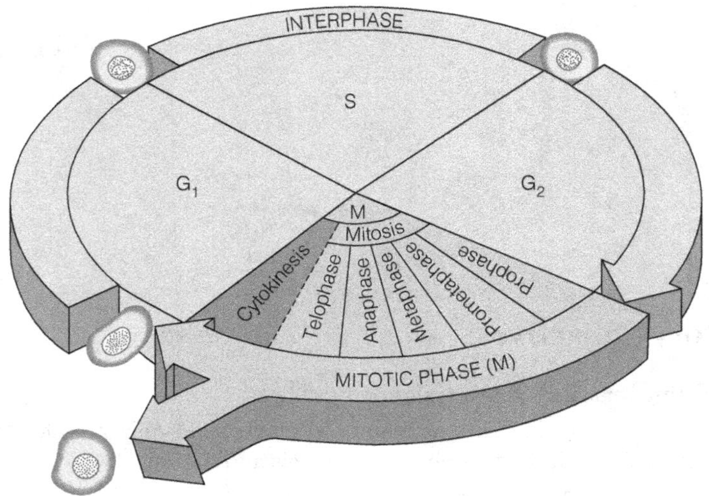

Figure 1.
The cell cycle. In interphase (G_1, S, G_2), DNA replication and most of the cell's growth and biochemical activity take place. In the M phase, the nucleus divides in mitosis, and the cytoplasm divides in cytokinesis.

EXERCISE 1

Modeling the Cell Cycle and Mitosis in an Animal Cell

Materials

60 pop beads of one color
60 pop beads of another color
4 magnetic centromeres
4 centrioles

Introduction

Scientists use models to represent natural structures and processes that are too small, too large, or too complex to investigate directly. Scientists develop their models from observations and experimental data, usually accumulated from a variety of sources. Building a model can represent the culmination of a body of scientific work, but most models represent a well-developed hypothesis that can then be tested against the natural system and modified.

Linus Pauling's novel and successful technique of building a physical model of hemoglobin was based on available chemical data. This technique was later adopted by Francis Crick and James Watson to elucidate the nature of the hereditary material, DNA. Watson and Crick built a wire model utilizing evidence collected by many scientists. They presented their conclusions about the structure of the DNA helix in the journal *Nature* in April 1953 and were awarded the Nobel Prize for their discovery in 1962.

Today in lab you will work with a partner to build models of cell division: mitosis and meiosis. Using these models will enhance your understanding of the behavior of chromosomes, centrioles, membranes, and microtubules during the cell cycle. After completing your model, you will consider ways in which it is and is not an appropriate model for the cell cycle. You and your partner should discuss activities in each stage of the cell cycle as you build your model. After going through the exercise once together, you will demonstrate the model to each other to reinforce your understanding.

In the model of mitosis that you will build, your cell will be a **diploid** cell ($2n$) with four chromosomes. This means that you will have two homologous pairs of chromosomes. One pair will be long chromosomes, the other pair, short chromosomes. (**Haploid** cells have only one of each homologous pair of chromosomes, denoted n.)

Lab Study A. Interphase

During interphase, a cell performs its specific functions: Liver cells produce bile; intestinal cells absorb nutrients; pancreatic cells secrete enzymes; skin cells produce keratin. Interphase consists of three subphases, G_1, S, and G_2, which begin as a cell division ends. As interphase begins, there is approximately half as much cytoplasm in each cell as there was before division. Each new cell has a nucleus that is surrounded by a **nuclear envelope** and that contains chromosomes in an uncoiled, or decondensed, state. In this uncoiled state, the mass of DNA and protein is called **chromatin.**

Procedure

1. Build a homologous pair of single-stranded chromosomes using 10 beads of one color for one member of the long pair and 10 beads of the other color for the other member of the pair. Place the centromere at any position in the chromosome, but note that it must be in the same position on homologous chromosomes. Build the short pair with the same two different colors, but use fewer beads. You should have enough beads left over to duplicate each chromosome.
2. Model **interphase** of the cell cycle:
   a. Pile all the assembled chromosomes in the center of your work area to represent the decondensed chromosomes as a mass of chromatin in **G_1 (gap 1).**

   b. Position two centrioles as a pair just outside your nucleus. Have the two members of the centriole pair at right angles to each other. (Recall, however, that most plant cells do not have centrioles.)

   In the G_1 phase, the cytoplasmic mass increases and will continue to do so throughout interphase. Proteins are synthesized, new organelles are formed, and some organelles such as mitochondria and chloroplasts grow and divide in two. Throughout interphase one or more dark, round bodies, called **nucleoli** (singular, **nucleolus**), are visible in the nucleus.

   c. Duplicate the centrioles: Add a second pair of centrioles to your model; again, have the two centrioles at right angles to each other.

   Centriole duplication begins in late G_1 or early S phase.

   d. Duplicate the chromosomes in your model cell to represent DNA replication in the **S (synthesis) phase:** Make a second strand that is identical to the first strand of each chromosome. In replicating chromosomes, you will use two magnets to form the new centromere. Recall, however, that the centromere in a cell is a single unit until it splits in metaphase. In your model, consider the pair of magnets to be the single centromere.

Unique activities taking place during the S phase of the cell cycle are the replication of chromosomal DNA and the synthesis of chromosomal proteins. DNA synthesis continues until chromosomes have been duplicated. Each chromosome is now described as **double-stranded,** and each strand is called a **sister chromatid.** Sister chromatids are identical to each other.

e. Do not disturb the chromosomes to represent **G_2 (gap 2).**

During the G_2 phase, in addition to continuing cell activities, cells prepare for mitosis. Enzymes and other proteins necessary for cell division are synthesized during this phase.

f. Separate your centriole pairs, moving them toward opposite poles of the nucleus to represent that the G_2 phase is coming to an end and mitosis is about to begin.

How many pairs of homologous chromosomes are present in your cell during this stage of the cell cycle?

Lab Study B. M Phase (Mitosis and Cytokinesis)

In the M phase, the nucleus and cytoplasm divide. Nuclear division is called *mitosis.* Cytoplasmic division is called *cytokinesis.* Mitosis is divided into five subphases: prophase, prometaphase, metaphase, anaphase, and telophase.

Procedure

1. To represent **prophase,** leave the chromosomes piled in the center of the work area.

   Prophase begins when chromosomes begin to coil and condense. At this time they become visible in the light microscope. Centrioles continue to move to opposite poles of the nucleus, and as they do so, a fibrous, rounded structure tapering toward each end, called a **spindle,** begins to form between them. Nucleoli begin to disappear.

   What structures make up the fibers of the spindle? (Check text if necessary.)

2. At **prometaphase,** the centrioles are at the poles of the cell. To represent prometaphase, move the centromeres of your chromosomes to lie on an imaginary plane (the equator) midway between the two poles established by the centrioles.

   During prometaphase chromosomes continue to condense. The nuclear envelope breaks down as the spindle continues to form. Some spindle fibers become associated with chromosomes, and the push and pull of spindle fibers on the chromosomes ultimately leads to their movement to the equator. When the centromeres lie on the equator, prometaphase ends and the next phase begins.

Describe the association of chromosomes and spindle fibers (check your text).

How many double-stranded chromosomes are present in your prophase/prometaphase nucleus?

Students often find it confusing to distinguish between chromosome number and chromatid number. To simplify this problem, count the number of centromeres. The number of centromeres represents the number of chromosomes.

3. To represent **metaphase,** a relatively static phase, leave the chromosomes with centromeres lying on the equator.

   In metaphase, double-stranded chromosomes lie on the equator (also called the metaphase plate). The two sister chromatids are held together by the centromere. Metaphase ends as the centromere splits.

   Label Figure 2 with *chromosome, sister chromatids, spindle fibers, centromere, centrioles.*

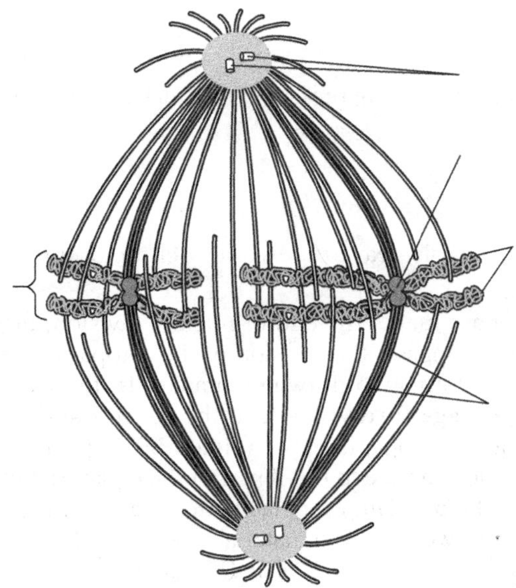

Figure 2.
The mitotic spindle at metaphase.

4. Holding on to the centromeres, pull the magnetic centromeres apart and move them toward opposite poles. This action represents **anaphase.**

   After the centromere splits, sister chromatids separate and begin to move toward opposite poles. Chromatids are now called **chromosomes.** Anaphase ends as the chromosomes reach the poles.

   Describe the movement of the chromosome arms as you move the centromeres to the poles.

   Certain biologists are currently investigating the role played by spindle fibers in chromosome movement toward the poles. Check your text for a discussion of one hypothesis, and briefly summarize it here.

5. Pile your chromosomes at the poles to represent **telophase.**

   As chromosomes reach the poles, anaphase ends and telophase begins. The spindle begins to break down. Chromosomes begin to uncoil, and nucleoli reappear. A nuclear envelope forms around each new cluster of chromosomes. Telophase ends when the nuclear envelopes are complete.

   How many chromosomes are in each new nucleus?

   How many chromosomes were present in the nucleus when the process began?

6. To represent cytokinesis, leave the two new chromosome masses at the poles.

   The end of telophase marks the end of nuclear division, or mitosis. Sometime during telophase, the division of the cytoplasm, or cytokinesis, results in the formation of two separate cells. In cytokinesis in animal cells, a **cleavage furrow** forms at the equator and eventually pinches the parent cell cytoplasm in two (Figure 3a). In plant cells membrane-bound vesicles migrate to the center of the equatorial plane and fuse to form the **cell plate.** This eventually extends across the cell, dividing the cytoplasm in two. Cell wall materials are secreted into the space between the membranes of the cell plate (Figure 3b, c).

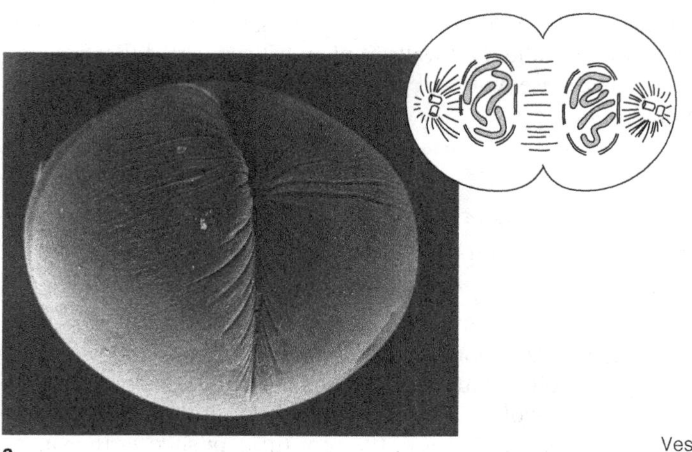

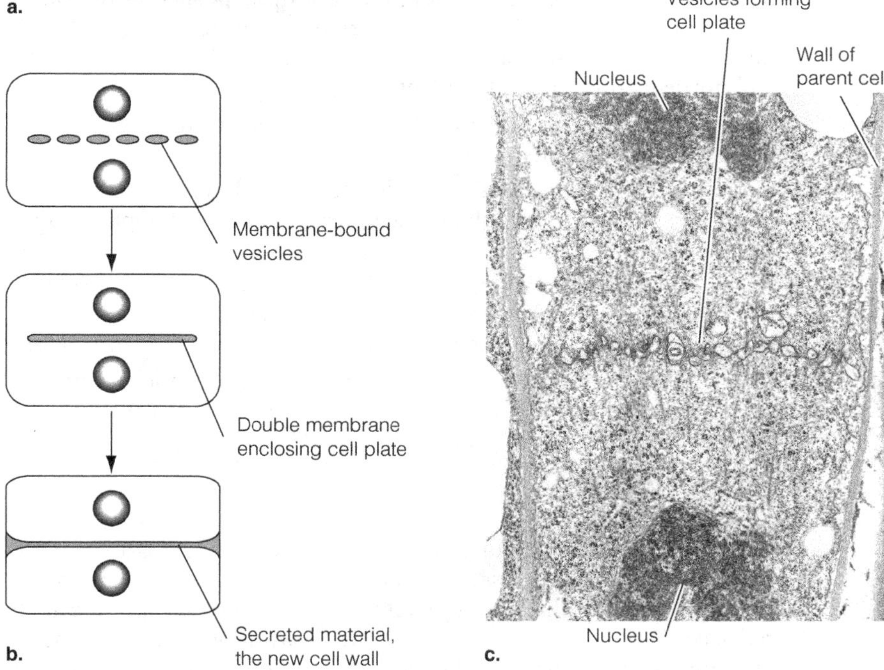

Figure 3.
Cytokinesis in animal and plant cells. (a) In animal cells, a cleavage furrow forms at the equator and pinches the cytoplasm in two.
(b) In plants, a cell plate forms in the center of the cell and grows until it divides the cytoplasm in two.
(c) Photomicrograph of cytokinesis in a plant cell.

EXERCISE 2
Observing Mitosis and Cytokinesis in Plant Cells

Materials

prepared slide of onion root tip
compound microscope

Introduction

The behavior of chromosomes during the cell cycle is similar in animal and plant cells. However, differences in cell division do exist. Plant cells have no

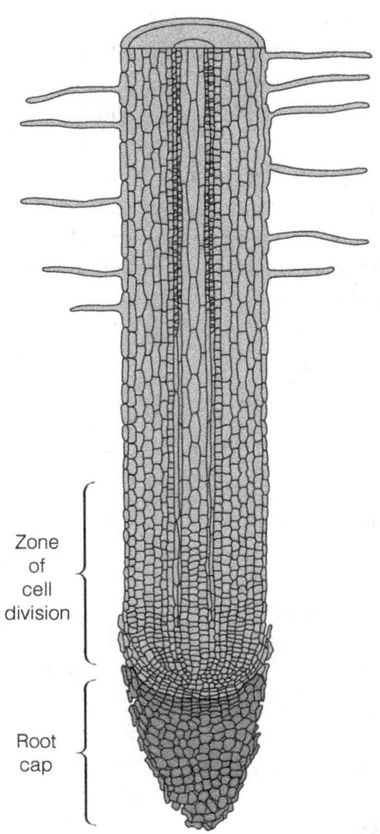

Figure 4.
Longitudinal section through a root tip. Cells are dividing in the zone of cell division just behind the root cap.

centrioles, yet they have bundles of microtubules that converge toward the poles at the ends of a spindle. Cell walls in plant cells dictate differences in cytokinesis. In this exercise, you will observe dividing cells in the zone of cell division of a root tip.

Procedure

1. Examine a prepared slide of a longitudinal section through an onion root tip using low power on the compound microscope.
2. Locate the region most likely to have dividing cells, just behind the root cap (Figure 4).

   At the tip of the root is a root cap that protects the tender root tip as it grows through the soil. Just behind the root cap is the zone of cell division. Notice that rows of cells extend upward from this zone. As cells divide in the zone of cell division, the root tip is pushed farther into the soil. Cells produced by division begin to mature, elongating and differentiating into specialized cells, such as those that conduct water and nutrients throughout the plant.
3. Focus on the zone of cell division. Then switch to the intermediate power, focus, and switch to high power.
4. Survey the zone of cell division and locate stages of the cell cycle: interphase, prophase, prometaphase, metaphase, anaphase, telophase, and cytokinesis.
5. As you find a dividing cell, speculate about its stage of division, read the following descriptions given of each stage to verify that your guess is correct, and, if necessary, confirm your conclusion with the instructor.
6. Draw the cell in the appropriate boxes provided. Label nucleus, nucleolus, chromosome, chromatin, mitotic spindle, and cell plate when appropriate.

Interphase (G_1, S, G_2)

Nuclear material is surrounded by a nuclear envelope. Dark-staining bodies, nucleoli, are visible. Chromosomes appear only as dark granules within the nucleus. Collectively, the chromosome mass is called *chromatin*. The chromosomes are not individually distinguishable because they are uncoiled into long, thin strands. Chromosomes are replicated during this phase.

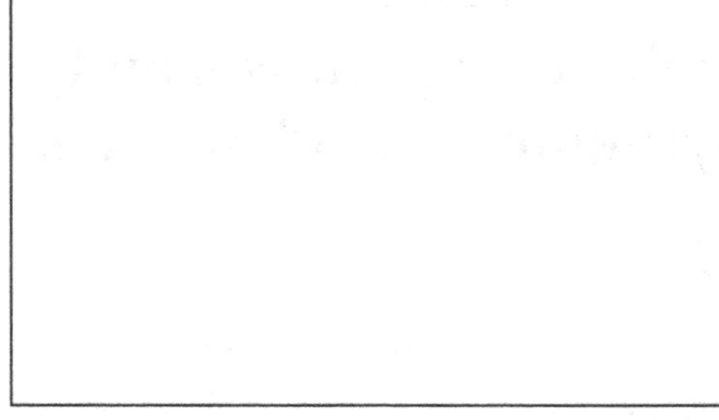

Prophase

Chromosomes begin to coil and become distinguishable thin, thread-like structures, widely dispersed in the nucleus during prophase. Although there are no centrioles in plant cells, a spindle begins to form. Nucleoli begin to disappear. The nuclear envelope is still intact.

Prometaphase

By prometaphase, the chromosomes are thick and short. Each chromosome is double-stranded, consisting of two chromatids held together by a centromere. The nuclear membrane breaks down in prometaphase. Chromosomes move toward the equator.

Metaphase

Metaphase begins when the centromeres of the chromosomes lie on the equator of the cell. The arms of the chromatids extend randomly in all directions. A spindle may be apparent. Spindle fibers are attached to centromeres and extend to the poles of the cell. As metaphase ends and anaphase begins, the centromeres split.

Anaphase

The splitting of centromeres marks the beginning of anaphase. Each former chromatid is now a new single-stranded chromosome. These chromosomes are drawn apart toward opposite poles of the cell. Anaphase ends when the migrating chromosomes reach their respective poles.

Telophase and Cytokinesis

Chromosomes have now reached the poles. The nuclear envelope re-forms around each compact mass of chromosomes. Nucleoli reappear. Chromosomes begin to uncoil and become indistinct. Cytokinesis is accomplished by the formation of a cell plate that begins in the center of the equatorial plane and grows outward to the cell wall.

EXERCISE 3
Observing Chromosomes, Mitosis, and Cytokinesis in Animal Cells

In this exercise, you will look at the general shape and form of human chromosomes and observe chromosomes and the stages of mitotic division in the whitefish. You will also compare these chromosomes with the plant chromosomes studied in Exercise 2. Chromosome structure in animals and plants is basically the same in that both have centromeres and arms. However, plant chromosomes are generally larger than animal chromosomes.

Lab Study A. Human Chromosomes in Dividing Leukocytes

Materials

slides of human leukocytes (white blood cells) on demonstration with compound microscopes

Introduction

Cytogeneticists examining dividing cells of humans can frequently detect chromosome abnormalities that lead to severe mental retardation. To examine human chromosomes, leukocytes are isolated from a small sample of the patient's blood and cultured in a medium that inhibits spindle formation during mitosis. As cells begin mitosis, chromosomes condense and become distinct, but in the absence of a spindle they cannot move to the poles in anaphase. You will observe a slide in which many cells have chromosomes condensed as in prometaphase or metaphase, but they are not aligned on a spindle equator.

Procedure

1. Attempt to count the chromosomes in one cell in the field of view. Normally, humans have 46 chromosomes. Persons with trisomy 21, or Down syndrome, have 47 chromosomes. Are the cells on this slide from a person with a normal chromosome number?

2. Notice that each chromosome is double-stranded, being made up of two sister chromatids held together by a single centromere. In very high magnifications, bands can be seen on the chromosomes. Abnormalities in banding patterns can also be an indication of severe mental retardation.

Lab Study B. Mitosis in Whitefish Blastula Cells

Materials

prepared slide of sections of whitefish blastulas
compound microscope

Introduction

The most convenient source of actively dividing cells in animals is the early embryo, where cells are large and divide rapidly with a short interphase. In blastulas (an early embryonic stage), a large percentage of cells will be dividing at any given time. By examining cross sections of whitefish blastulas, you should be able to locate many dividing cells in various stages of mitosis and cytokinesis.

Procedure

1. Examine a prepared slide of whitefish blastula cross sections. Find a blastula section on the lowest power, focus, switch to intermediate power, focus, and switch to high power.
2. As you locate a dividing cell, identify the stage of mitosis. Be able to recognize all stages of mitosis in these cells.
3. Identify the following in several cells:

   nucleus, nuclear envelope, and **nucleolus**

   chromosomes

   mitotic spindle

   asters—an array of microtubules surrounding each centriole pair at the poles of the spindle

   centrioles—small dots seen at the poles around which the microtubules of the spindle and asters appear to radiate

   cleavage furrow

Results

1. List several major differences you have observed between mitosis in animal cells and mitosis in plant cells:

2. Locate, draw, and label in the space provided a blastula cell in metaphase and a cell in telophase/cytokinesis to illustrate these differences.

Metaphase

Telophase/Cytokinesis

EXERCISE 4
Modeling Meiosis

Materials

60 pop beads of one color
60 pop beads of another color
8 magnetic centromeres
4 centrioles
letters *B, D, b,* and *d* printed on mailing labels

Introduction

Meiosis takes place in all organisms that reproduce sexually. In animals, meiosis occurs in special cells of the gonads; in plants, in special cells of the sporangia. Meiosis consists of *two* nuclear divisions, **meiosis I** and **II**, with an atypical interphase between the divisions during which cells do not grow and synthesis of DNA does not take place. This means that meiosis I and II result in four cells from each parent cell, each containing half the number of chromosomes, one from each homologous pair. Recall that cells with only one of each homologous pair of chromosomes are haploid (n) cells. The parent cells, with pairs of homologous chromosomes, are diploid ($2n$). The haploid cells become sperm (in males), eggs (in females), or spores (in plants). One advantage of meiosis in sexually reproducing organisms is that it prevents the chromosome number from doubling with every generation when fertilization occurs.

What would be the consequences in successive generations of offspring if the chromosome number were not reduced during meiosis?

Lab Study A. Interphase

Working with another student, you will build a model of the nucleus of a cell in interphase before meiosis. Nuclear and chromosome activities are similar to those in mitosis. You and your partner should discuss activities in the nucleus and chromosomes in each stage. Go through the exercise once together, and then demonstrate the model to each other to reinforce your understanding. Compare activities in meiosis with those in mitosis as you build your model.

Procedure

1. Build the premeiotic interphase nucleus much as you did the mitotic interphase nucleus. Have two pairs of chromosomes ($2n = 4$) of distinctly different sizes and different centromere positions. Have one member of each pair of homologues be one color, the other, a different color.

2. To represent G_1 (gap 1), pile your four chromosomes in the center of your work area. The chromosomes are decondensed.

   Cell activities in G_1 are similar to those activities in G_1 of the interphase before mitosis.

   In G_1, are chromosomes single-stranded or double-stranded?

3. Duplicate the chromosomes to represent DNA duplication in the S (synthesis) phase. Recall that in living cells, the centromeres remain single, but in your model you must use two magnets. What color should the sister chromatids be for each pair?

4. Duplicate the centriole pair.
5. Leave the chromosomes piled in the center of the work area to represent G_2 (gap 2).

   As in mitosis, in G_2 the cell prepares for meiosis by synthesizing proteins and enzymes necessary for nuclear division.

Lab Study B. Meiosis I

Meiosis consists of two consecutive nuclear divisions, called *meiosis I* and *meiosis II*. As the first division begins, the chromosomes coil and condense, as in mitosis. Meiosis I is radically different from mitosis, however, and the differences immediately become apparent. In your modeling, as you detect the differences, make notes in the margin of your lab manual.

Procedure

1. Meiosis I begins with the chromosomes piled in the center of your work area.

   As chromosomes begin to coil and condense, prophase I begins. Each chromosome is double-stranded, made up of two sister chromatids. Two pairs of centrioles are located outside the nucleus.
2. Separate the two centriole pairs and move them to opposite poles of the nucleus.

   The nuclear envelope breaks down and the spindle begins to form as in mitosis.
3. Move each homologous chromosome to pair with its partner. You should have four strands together.

   Early in prophase I, each chromosome finds its homologue and pairs in a tight association. The process of pairing is called **synapsis.** Because the chromosomes are double-stranded, this means that each paired doubled chromosome complex is made of four strands. This complex is called a **tetrad.**

   How many tetrad complexes do you have in your cell, which is $2n = 4$?

4. Represent the phenomenon of **crossing over** by detaching and exchanging identical segments of any two nonsister chromatids in a tetrad.

   Crossing over takes place between nonsister chromatids in the tetrad. In this process, a segment from one chromatid will break and exchange with the exact same segment on a nonsister chromatid in the tetrad. The crossover site forms a **chiasma** (plural, **chiasmata**).

5. Return the exchanged segments of chromosome to their original chromosomes before performing the crossing-over activity in the next step.

   Genes (traits) are often expressed in different forms. For example, when the gene for seed color is expressed in pea plants, the seed may be green or yellow. Alternative forms of genes are called **alleles.** Green and yellow are alleles of the seed-color gene. It is significant that crossing over produces new allelic combinations among genes along a chromatid. To see how new allelic combinations are produced, proceed to step 6.

6. Using the letters printed on mailing labels, label one bead (gene locus) on each chromatid of one chromosome *B* for brown hair color. Label the beads in the same position on the two chromatids of the other member of the homologous pair *b* for blond hair color.

   The *B* and *b* represent alleles, or alternate forms of the gene for hair color.

   On the chromatids with the *B* allele, label another gene *D* for dark eye color. On the other member of the homologous pair of chromosomes, label the same gene *d* for pale eyes. In other words, one chromosome will have *BD*, the other chromosome, *bd* (Figure 5).

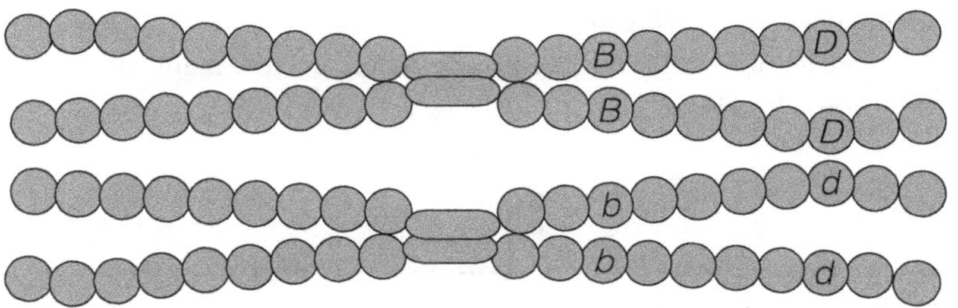

Figure 5.
Arrangement of alleles *B*, *b*, *D*, and *d* on chromosome models. One double homologous chromosome has *B* alleles and *D* alleles on each chromatid. The other has *b* and *d* alleles on each chromatid.

7. Have a crossover take place between the loci for hair color and eye color. Remember, the crossover must take place between nonsister chromatids.

   What combinations of alleles are now present on the chromatids?

8. Confirm your results with your laboratory instructor.

If you are having difficulty envisioning the activities of chromosomes in prophase I and understanding their significance, discuss these events with your lab partner and, if needed, ask questions of your lab instructor before proceeding to the next stage of meiosis I.

9. Move your tetrads to the equator, midway between the two poles.

   Late in prophase I, tetrads move to the equator.

10. To represent metaphase I, leave the tetrads lying at the equator.

    During this phase, tetrads lie on the equatorial plane. *Centromeres do not split as they do in mitosis.*

11. To represent anaphase I, separate each double-stranded chromosome from its homologue, and move one homologue toward each pole. In our model, the two magnets in sister chromatids represent one centromere holding together the two sister chromatids of the chromosome.

    How does the structure of chromosomes in anaphase I differ from that in anaphase in mitosis?

12. To represent telophase I, place the chromosomes at the poles. You should have one long and one short chromosome at each pole, representing a homologue from each pair.

    Two nuclei now form, followed by cytokinesis. How many chromosomes are in each nucleus?

The number of chromosomes is equal to the number of centromeres. In this model, two magnets represent one centromere in double-stranded chromosomes.

Would you describe the new nuclei as being diploid ($2n$) or haploid (n)?

13. To represent meiotic interphase, leave the chromosomes in the two piles formed at the end of meiosis I.

    The interphase between meiosis I and meiosis II is usually short. There is little cell growth and no synthesis of DNA. All the machinery for a second nuclear division is synthesized, however.

14. Duplicate the centriole pairs.

Lab Study C. Meiosis II

The events that take place in meiosis II are similar to the events of mitosis. Meiosis I results in two nuclei with half the number of chromosomes as the parent cell, but the chromosomes are double-stranded (made of two chromatids), just as they are at the beginning of mitosis. The events in meiosis II must change double-stranded chromosomes into single-stranded chromosomes. As meiosis II begins, two new spindles begin to form, establishing the axes for the dispersal of chromosomes to each new nucleus.

Procedure

1. To represent prophase II, separate the centrioles and set up the axes of the two new spindles. Pile the chromosomes in the center of each spindle.

   The events that take place in each of the nuclei in prophase II are similar to those of a mitosis prophase. In each new cell the centrioles move to the poles, nucleoli break down, the nuclear envelope breaks down, and a new spindle forms. The new spindle forms at a right angle to the axis of the spindle in meiosis I.

2. Align the chromosomes at the equator of their respective spindles.

   As the chromosomes reach the equator, prophase II ends and metaphase II begins.

3. Leave the chromosomes on the equator to represent metaphase II.

4. Pull the two magnets of each double-stranded chromosome apart.

   As metaphase II ends, the centromeres finally split and anaphase II begins.

5. Separate sister chromatids (now chromosomes) and move them to opposite poles.

   In anaphase II, single-stranded chromosomes move to the poles.

6. Pile the chromosomes at the poles.

   As telophase II begins, chromosomes arrive at the poles. Spindles break down. Nucleoli reappear. Nuclear envelopes form around each bunch of chromosomes as the chromosomes uncoil. Cytokinesis follows meiosis II.

   a. What is the total number of nuclei and cells now present?

b. How many chromosomes are in each?

c. How many cells were present when the entire process began?

d. How many chromosomes were present per cell when the entire process began?

e. How many of the cells formed by the meiotic division just modeled are genetically identical? (Assume that alternate forms of genes exist on homologues.)

Results

Summarize the major differences between mitosis and meiosis in Table 1.

Table 1
Comparing Nuclear and Chromosomal Activities in Mitosis and Meiosis

	Mitosis	**Meiosis**
Synapsis		
Crossing over		
When centromeres split		
Chromosome structure and movement during anaphase		
No. of divisions		
No. of cells resulting		
No. of chromosomes in daughter cells		
Genetic similarity of daughter cells to parent cells		

EXERCISE 5
Meiosis in *Sordaria fimicola:* A Study of Crossing Over

Materials

petri dish containing mycelia resulting from a cross between *Sordaria* with black and tan spores
slides and coverslips
dropper bottles of water
matches
wire bacterial transfer loop
alcohol lamp

Introduction

In the study of meiosis, you demonstrated that genetic recombination may occur as a result of the exchange of genetic material between homologous chromosomes in the process of crossing over. Crossing over occurs during prophase I, when homologous chromosomes synapse. While they are joined in this complex, nonsister chromatids may break at corresponding points and exchange parts. A point at which they appear temporarily joined as a result of this exchange is called a **chiasma** (Figure 6).

Sordaria fimicola is a fungus that spends most of its life as a haploid **mycelium,** a mass of cells arranged in filaments. When conditions are favorable, cells of filaments from two different mating types fuse (see Figures 7a and b); ultimately, the nuclei fuse (Figure 7c) and $2n$ zygotes are produced, each inside a structure called an **ascus** (plural, **asci**) (Figure 7d). Asci are protected within a **perithecium.** Each $2n$ zygote undergoes meiosis, and the resulting cells (ascospores) remain aligned, the position of an ascospore within the ascus depending on the orientation of separating chromosomes on the equatorial plane of meiosis I. After meiosis, each resulting ascospore divides once by mitosis (Figure 7e), resulting in eight ascospores per ascus (Figure 7f). This unique sequence of events means that it is easy to detect the occurrence of crossing over involving chromatids carrying alleles that encode for color of spores and mycelia.

If two mating types of *Sordaria,* one with black spores and the other with tan spores, are grown on the same petri dish, mycelia from the two may

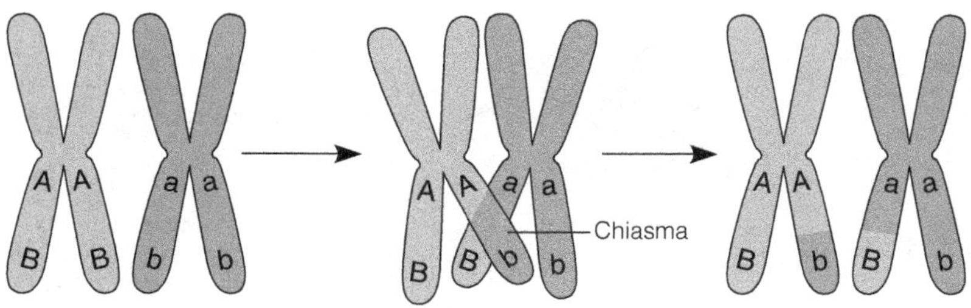

Figure 6.
Crossing over. Chromatid arms break and rejoin with a nonsister member of the tetrad, forming a chiasma between nonsister chromatids. This process results in the exchange of genetic material.

Figure 7.
Abbreviated diagram of the life cycle of *Sordaria fimicola.*
(a) Cells from filaments of two different mating types fuse.
(b) One cell with two nuclei is formed.
(c) The two nuclei fuse, forming a 2*n* zygote. (d) The zygote nucleus begins meiosis, and an ascus begins to form in a perithecium. (e) Meiosis continues, followed by mitosis.
(f) The mature ascus contains eight ascospores. (g) Micrograph of crushed perithecium with asci containing ascospores.

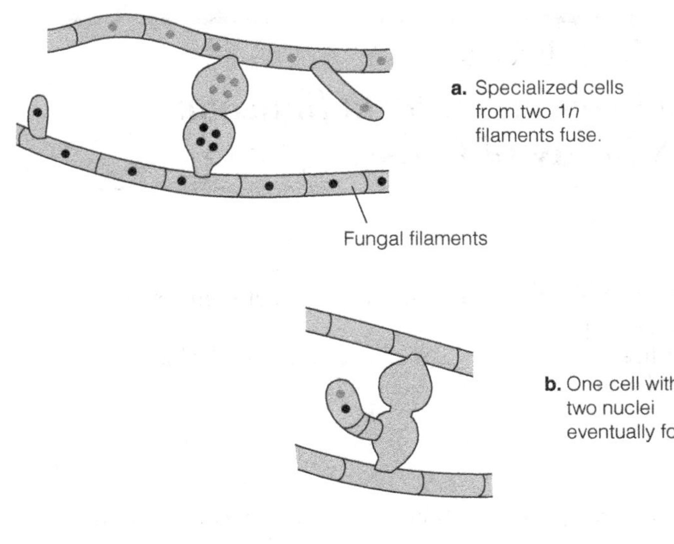

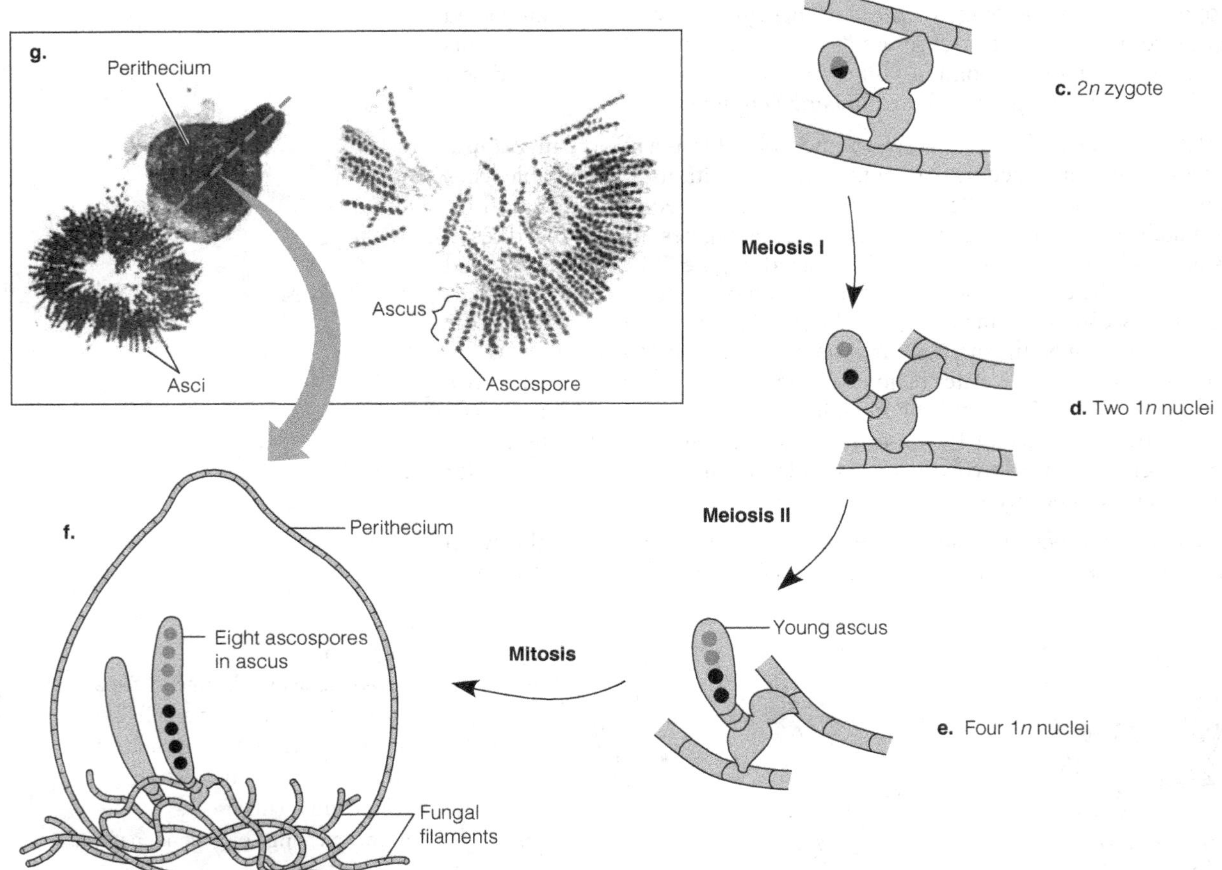

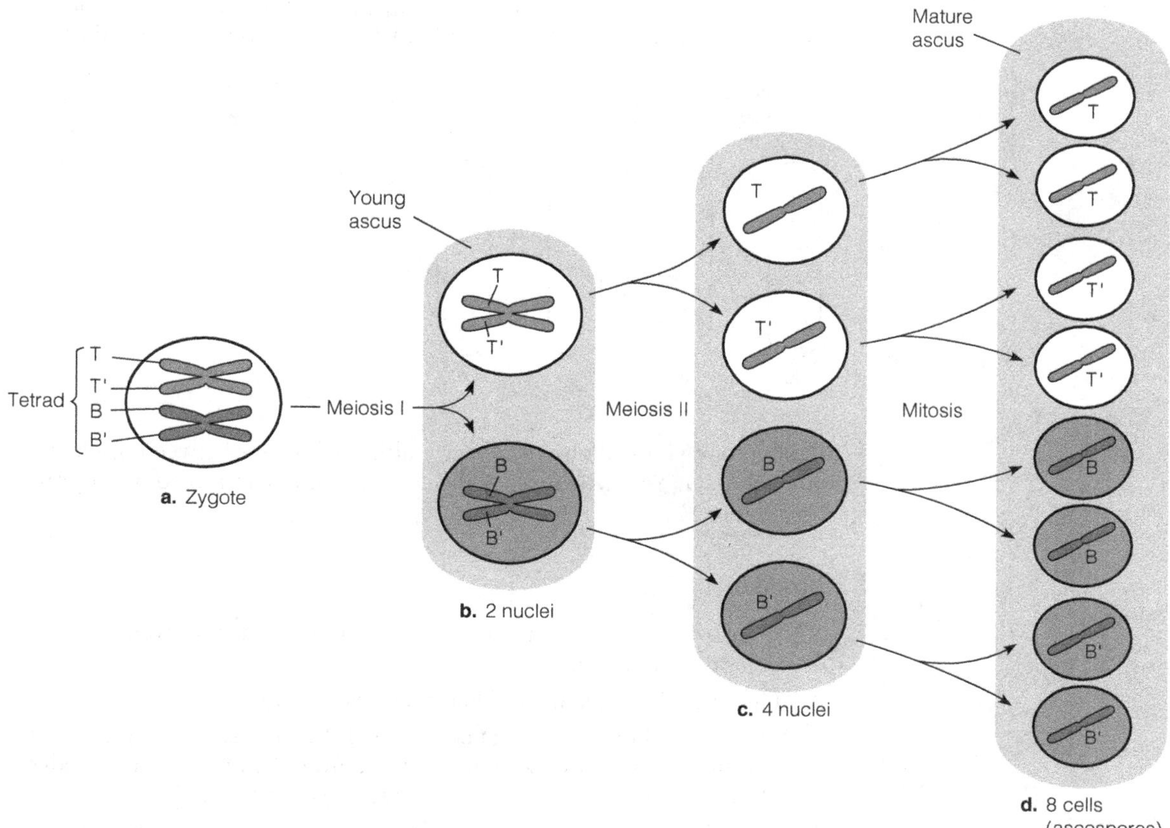

Figure 8.
Arrangement of spores in asci resulting from a cross between fungi with black spores and fungi with tan spores when no crossing over takes place. (a) In the zygote nucleus, the light homologous chromosome has chromatids labeled T and T′. Each chromatid has identical tan alleles for spore color. The dark homologous chromosome (chromatids labeled B and B′) has black alleles. (b) During meiosis I, the two homologous chromosomes separate into two different nuclei retained in one developing ascus. (c) Meiosis II produces four nuclei, two containing a chromosome with the tan allele and two containing a chromosome with the black allele, still within the one ascus. (d) Now each nucleus divides by mitosis, followed by cytokinesis, resulting in eight cells, called ascospores. The ascus now contains eight ascospores. Four of the spores have the tan allele in their nuclei and appear tan-colored. Four ascospores have the black allele and appear black.

grow together, and certain cells may fuse. Nuclei from two fused cells then fuse, and the resulting zygote contains one chromosome carrying the allele for black spores and another carrying the allele for tan spores. After meiosis takes place, one mitosis follows, and the result is eight ascospores in one ascus: four black spores and four tan spores. If no crossing over has taken place, the arrangement of spores will appear as in Figure 8.

If crossing over does take place, the arrangement of spores will differ. In the spaces provided, using Figure 8 as a reference, draw diagrams that illustrate the *predicted* arrangement of spores in the ascus when crossing over takes place between the following chromatids and the alleles for color are exchanged: (a) T and B, (b) T and B′, (c) T′ and B, and (d) T′ and B′.

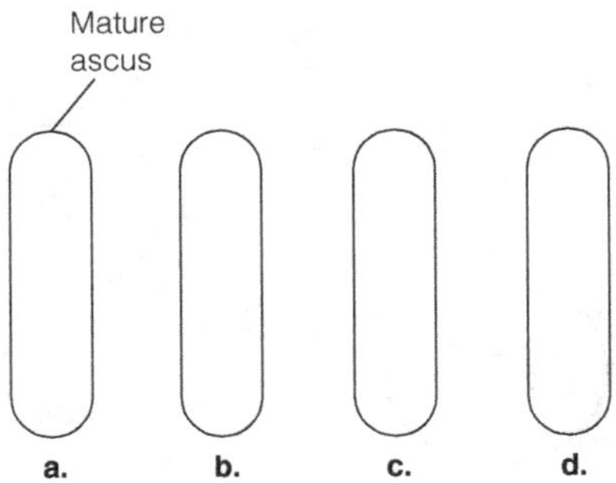

In lab today, you will observe living cultures of crosses between black and tan *Sordaria*. You will look for asci with spores arranged as in your predictions.

Procedure

1. Place a drop of water on a clean slide, and carry it and a coverslip to the demonstration table.
2. Light the alcohol lamp and flame a transfer loop.
3. Open the lid of the *Sordaria* culture slightly, and use the loop or other instrument to remove several perithecia from the region near the edge of the dish where the two strains have grown together (Figure 9).
4. Place the perithecia in the drop of water on your slide, and cover it with the coverslip.
5. Return to your work area.
6. Using the eraser end of a pencil, tap lightly on the coverslip to break open and flatten out the perithecia.
7. Systematically scan back and forth across the slide using the intermediate power of the compound microscope. When you locate clusters of asci, focus, switch to high power, count the asci, and determine if crossing over has taken place. Record your numbers in Table 2.

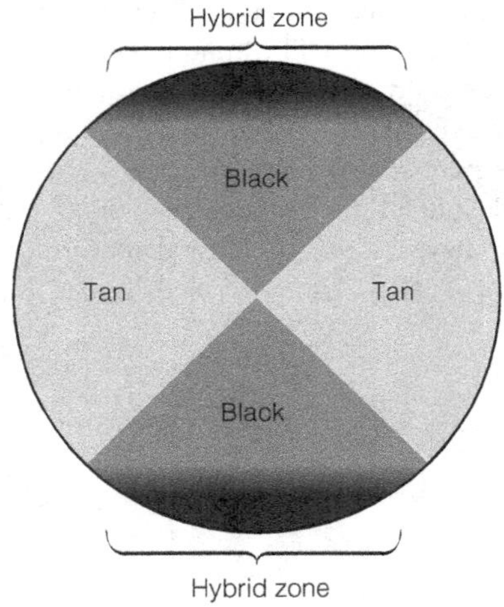

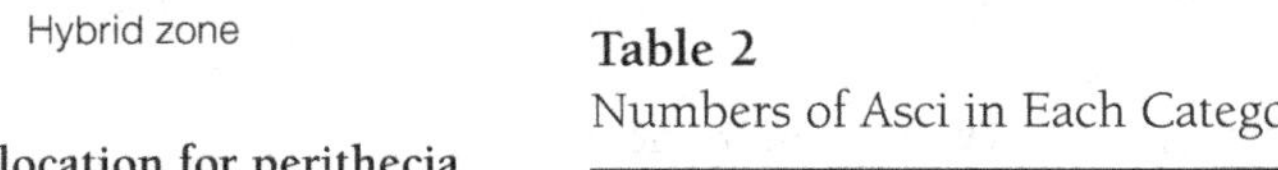

Figure 9.
Most likely location for perithecia containing asci with hybrid spores. Following the procedure, collect dark, round perithecia from zones of hybridization along the petri dish perimeter as indicated.

Results

In Table 2, record the numbers of asci with (a) spores all of one color (indicating that the zygote was formed by fusion of cells of the same strain), (b) black and tan spores with no crossover, and (c) black and tan spores with a crossover.

Table 2
Numbers of Asci in Each Category

Spores all one color	
Crossover absent	
Crossover present	

Discussion

1. What percentage of asci observed resulted from the fusion of cells from different strains?

2. What percentage of those asci resulting from the fusion of different strains demonstrates crossovers?

Questions for Review

1. Define the following terms and use each in a meaningful sentence. Give examples when appropriate.

   mitosis, meiosis, cytokinesis, chromosome, chromatin, centromere, centriole, spindle, aster, homologous chromosome, synaptonemal complex, synapsis, tetrad, chiasma, sister chromatid, nucleolus, mitotic spindle, cell plate, cleavage furrow, diploid, haploid, mycelium, perithecium, ascus

2. Describe the activity of chromosomes in each stage of mitosis.

3. In the photomicrograph of dividing root cells at right, identify interphase and the following phases of mitosis: prophase, metaphase, anaphase, telophase, and cytokinesis.

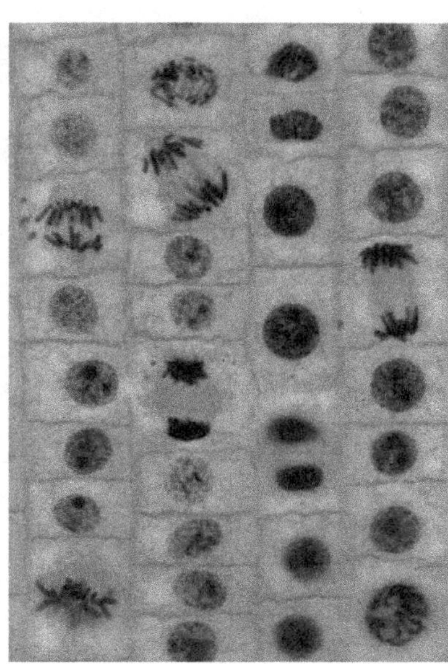

4. Describe the activity of chromosomes in each stage of meiosis I.

5. Describe the activity of chromosomes in each stage of meiosis II.

6. Provide examples of plant and animal cells that typically undergo mitosis. Provide examples for meiosis.

Applying Your Knowledge

1. Self-fertilization frequently takes place in fungi. Discuss the adaptive advantages of different strains mating.

2. What advantage does the process of crossing over bring to reproduction?

3. Can you think of any way in which new gene combinations resulting from crossovers might be disadvantageous?

4. Explain why models are important to scientific study of biological systems. Provide two examples of models other than those described in the exercises.

5. Why would the method of cytokinesis in animal cells not work in plant cells?

6. Biologists have hypothesized that centrioles in animal cells play a role in the organization of the mitotic spindle. Most plant cells, on the other hand, have no centrioles but are able to form spindles. Use your text or other sources and write a paragraph discussing hypotheses that explain this observation.

7. Identical twins Jan and Fran were very close sisters. So, when Jan died suddenly, Fran moved in to help take care of Jan's daughter (her niece), Millie. Some time later Fran married her brother-in-law and became Millie's stepmother. When Fran announced that she was pregnant, poor Millie became confused and curious. "So," Millie asked, "who is this baby? Will she be my twin? Will she be my sister, my stepsister, my cousin?" Can you answer her questions? What is the genetic relationship between Millie and the baby? What processes are involved in the formation of gametes and how do they affect genetic variation?

References

Becker, W. M., L. Kleinsmith, and J. Hardin. *The World of the Cell,* 4th ed. Redwood City, CA: Benjamin/Cummings, 2000.

Bold, H. C., C. J. Alexopoulos, and T. Delevoryas. *Morphology of Plants and Fungi.* New York: Harper & Row, 1980.

Websites

The following are websites dealing with the cell cycle and mitosis:

http://www.cellsalive.com/cellcycle.html
http://www.cellsalive.com/mitosis.html
http://www.biology.arizona.edu/cell_bio/tutorials/cell_cycle/cells2.html

Animation of meiosis and independent assortment:

http://www.csuchico.edu/~Bio/207/animations/assortment.html

Photo Credits

3a: ©David M. Phillips/Visuals Unlimited. 3c: Micrograph by B. A. Palevitz. Courtesy of E. H. Newcomb, University of Wisconsin. 7: From Bold, Alexopoulos, and Delevoryas, *Morphology of Plants and Fungi*, 5th ed., Harper Collins, 1980, p. 677.

Art Credits

2: Adapted from Neil Campbell, Jane Reece, and Larry Mitchell, *Biology,* 5th ed. (Menlo Park, CA: Benjamin/Cummings, 1999), ©1999 The Benjamin/Cummings Publishing Company. 4: Adapted from Neil Campbell, *Biology,* 3rd ed. (Redwood City, CA: Benjamin/Cummings, 1993), ©1993 The Benjamin/Cummings Publishing Company.

Mendelian Genetics: *Drosophila*

Laboratory Objectives

After completing this lab topic, you should be able to:

1. Discuss why *Drosophila* is one of the most important organisms used in eukaryotic genetics.
2. Explain how a biochemical assay can be used as an indication of biochemical phenotypes.
3. Describe the inheritance pattern of the gene for aldehyde oxidase.
4. Name genes using the convention recommended in *Drosophila* genetics.
5. Determine parental genotypes by investigating offspring.
6. Use the chi-square test to evaluate experimental results.
7. Describe gene mapping.

Introduction

The exercises in this lab topic exemplify some of the classic areas of genetic research that led to an understanding of the principles governing the inheritance of specific traits. Initial experiments were concerned with the transmission of hereditary factors from generation to generation and led to the discovery of Mendel's laws, which define the pattern of inheritance of individual genes. Later experiments identified chromosomes as the physical structures wherein the units of heredity reside and provided firm cytological evidence for the theorems of Mendelian genetics. More recent investigations have addressed the biochemical and molecular basis of gene expression.

One of the classic tools of genetic research is the fruit fly, *Drosophila melanogaster.* This organism has been used in genetic studies for nearly 80 years and has played an important role in the development of our knowledge of heredity. *Drosophila melanogaster* has been important in such studies because this organism has a very low chromosome number. The haploid (n) number of chromosomes is 4, and the chromosomes are designated X(1), 2, 3, and 4 (Figure 1). The 2, 3, and 4 chromosomes are the same in both sexes and are referred to as **autosomes** to distinguish them from the X and Y **sex chromosomes.** *Drosophila* females are characterized by two X chromosomes while *Drosophila* males have an X and a Y chromosome. Chromosome 4 and the Y chromosome contain so few genes that, for all practical purposes, they can be ignored. Thus, almost the entire genetic content of the *Drosophila* genome resides on only three chromosomes: X, 2, and 3.

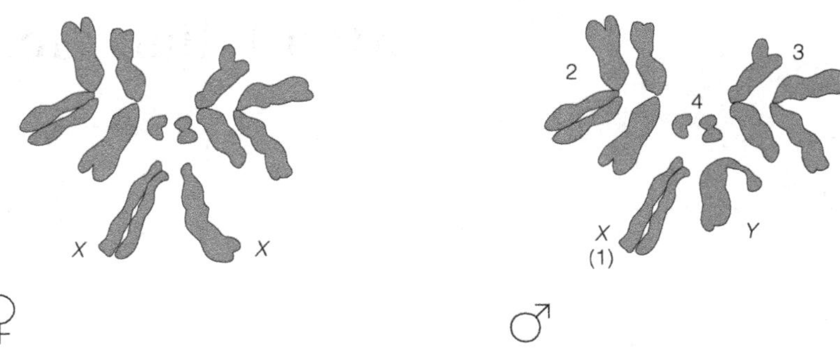

Figure 1.
Metaphase chromosomes from a dividing cell in *Drosophila melanogaster*. The haploid number of chromosomes is 4. Females have two X chromosomes while males have an X and a Y chromosome.

Another characteristic of *Drosophila* that makes it an excellent genetic research tool is its short generation time. At 25°C, a *Drosophila* culture will produce a new generation in 10 days: 1 day in the egg (embryo) stage, 5 days in the larval stage, and 4 days in the pupal stage (Figure 2).

You will use *Drosophila melanogaster* in each of the following exercises. You will be asked to investigate the inheritance of a gene called *aldox,* and you will determine the position of this gene on its chromosome; that is, you will map the gene.

EXERCISE 1
Establishing the Enzyme Reaction Controls

Materials

stereoscopic microscope
vials 1a and 1b
ether dropper bottles or FlyNap
re-etherizer
2 spot assay plates
large and small white index cards
toothpicks
pestle
Kimwipes®
assay mixture dropper bottles
water bottle

Introduction

The trait to be studied in each exercise of this lab topic is the presence or absence of the enzyme **aldehyde oxidase (AO),** which catalyzes the oxidation of a number of aldehydes, including acetaldehyde and benzaldehyde. AO activity is controlled by one gene, the **aldox** gene. Although *Drosophila* flies possess AO activity, its physiological importance to the organism is not well understood. Mutant strains that exhibit no AO activity are available, and their viability and fertility are normal. This latter observation indicates that AO activity is not a vital enzyme activity for a fly that is reared in a laboratory setting.

To test for AO activity, you will use an **enzyme spot test,** or **spot assay.** This test works on the following principle: In the presence of AO, the substrate benzaldehyde, when mixed with the color indicator nitroblue-tetrazoliun (NBT)–phenazine methylsulfate (PMS), will oxidize to form ben-

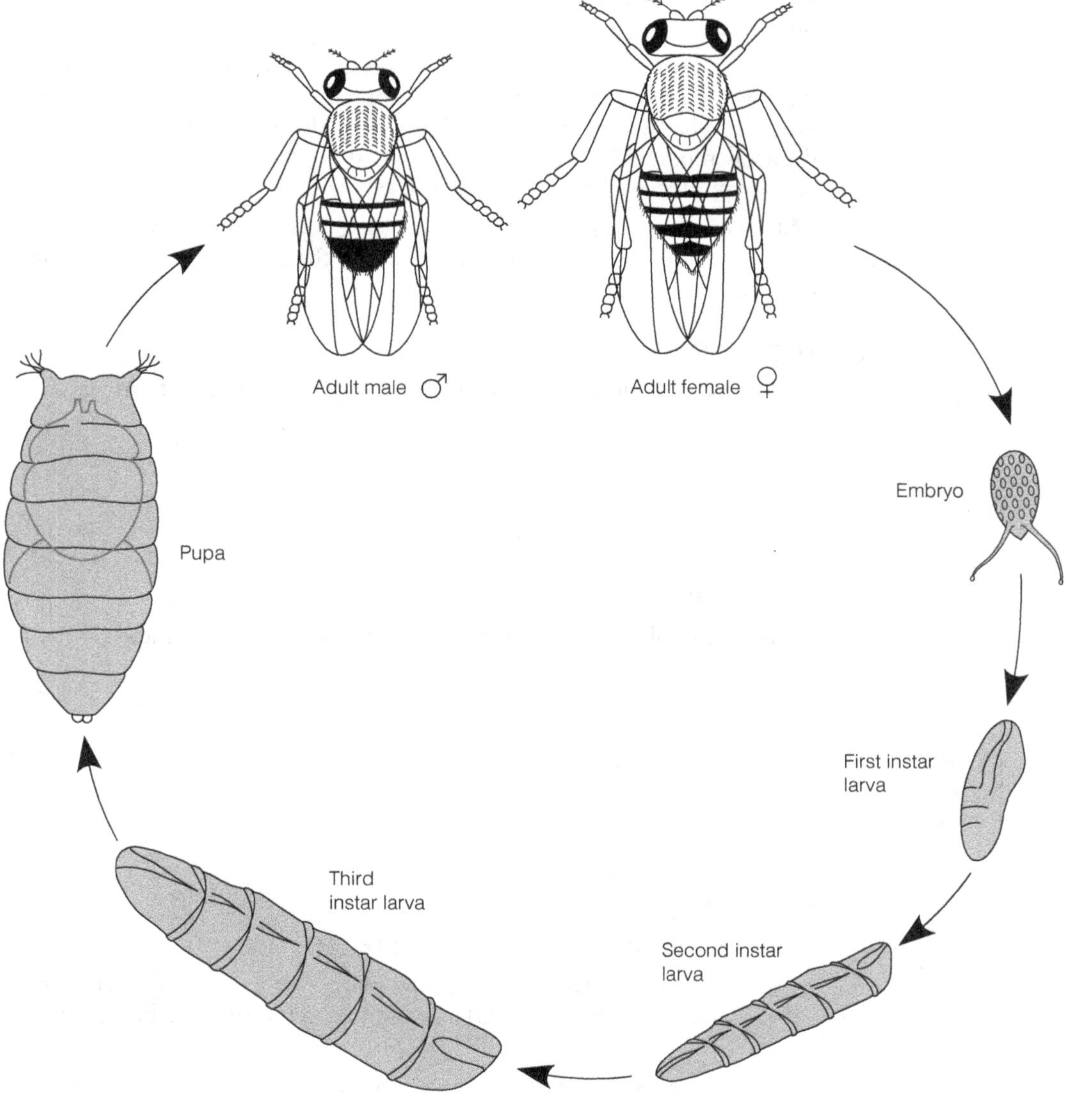

Figure 2.
Developmental stages of *Drosophila melanogaster.* An embryo hatches to a larva, which undergoes two molts and then pupates. The pupae develop into adult winged flies.

zoic acid and a blue color. The blue color indicates that the enzyme is present and active.

This reaction can be diagrammed as follows:

Substrate	**Enzyme AO**	**Product**
benzaldehyde + NBT + PMS (assay mixture)	⟶	benzoic acid + blue products

Without AO, the reaction will not proceed, and no blue color will be produced.

This first exercise will demonstrate the positive and negative enzyme reactions as seen in the spot assay. Vial 1a contains flies that have the enzyme present. What will be the results if flies from this vial are homogenized in the assay mixture? Will they demonstrate AO activity? (Remember that AO activity produces a blue color with the assay.)

Vial 1b contains flies that do not have the enzyme present. What will be the results if these flies are homogenized in the assay mixture? Will they demonstrate AO activity?

Hypothesis

Hypothesize about AO activity in flies from vial 1a and flies from vial 1b.

Prediction

Predict the results of the experiment (test) based on your hypothesis (if/then).

Procedure

1. Anesthetize the flies in vials 1a and 1b as follows:
   a. From your ether dropper bottle, place 2 or 3 drops of ether on the cotton plug of your vial. Be sure to recap the ether bottle tightly.

Remember that ethyl ether fumes are explosive. Use in a well-ventilated room. No flames or sparks! If a spill occurs, call an instructor.

   b. Invert your vial so that the adult flies will fall asleep on the cotton plug rather than on the culture medium.
   c. When flies have become immobilized on the cotton plug, remove them for examination.
   d. Using the stereoscopic microscope, examine the flies on a white card using a toothpick to turn them.
   e. A fly "re-etherizer" petri dish with a gauze pad taped in the lid is provided in case the adults begin to awaken before phenotype classifi-

cation is concluded. Place the lid/gauze pad saturated with ether over the flies when needed.

2. From each vial, identify two or three females and two or three males, and return the rest to their appropriate vial. (Vial 1a will be used again in later experiments.) Use the following criteria to distinguish adult males and females (Figure 3).
   a. *Size.* The female is generally larger than the male.
   b. *Shape of abdomen.* The female abdomen is larger and more pointed than the male abdomen.
   c. *Abdominal pigmentation.* In dorsal view, the alternating dark and light bands on the entire rear portion of the female abdomen are visible; the last few segments of the male are uniformly pigmented.

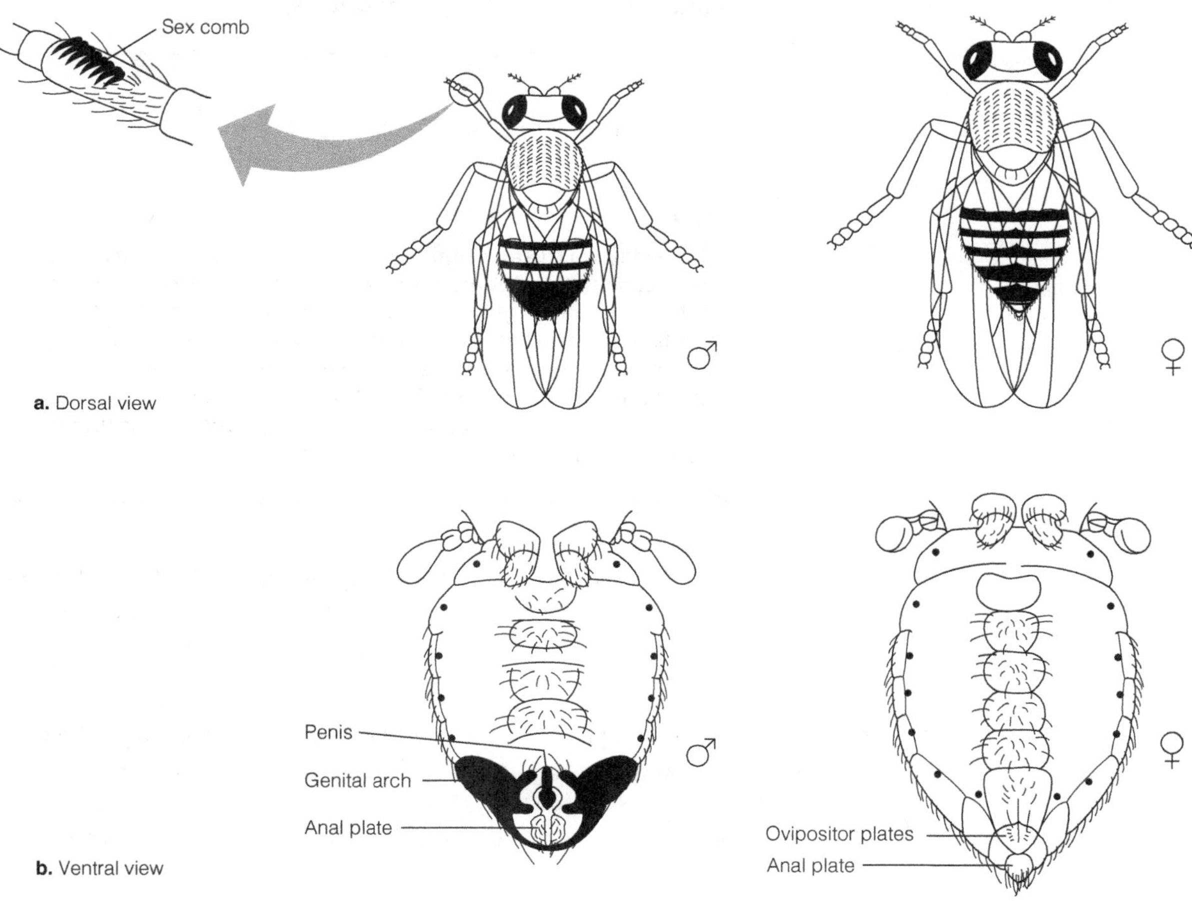

Figure 3.
Characteristics of male and female *Drosophila melanogaster*. The female is larger and has alternating dark and light dorsal bands on the abdomen. The dorsal abdomen of the male is uniformly pigmented. Conspicuous sex combs are visible on each foreleg of the male. In ventral view, the male's darkly pigmented genital arch and penis are visible.

d. *Sex comb.* On males, there is a tiny brushlike tuft of hairs on the basal tarsal segment of each foreleg. This is the most reliable characteristic for sexing males accurately.

e. *External genitalia.* On the ventral portion of the abdomen, the female has anal plates and lightly pigmented ovipositor plates. The male has anal plates and a darkly pigmented genital arch and penis.

3. Keeping track of the sexes, place the flies from vial 1a in one row of a spot assay plate, one fly per well.
4. Place the flies from vial 1b in a different row.

The next two steps need to be done quickly, since the assay mixture is light sensitive. Cover the spot plate with an index card if there is any delay between steps.

5. Add 1 drop of assay mixture to each well.

The assay mixture contains carcinogens. Do not allow it to contact skin. Wash hands thoroughly after performing the tests. Disposable gloves may be provided for your use. Notify an instructor if a spill occurs. If an instructor is unavailable, wipe up the spill wearing disposable gloves and using dry paper towels. Follow dry towels with towels soaked in soap and water. Dispose of all towels and gloves in a plastic bag in the trash.

6. Homogenize the flies with a pestle. Wipe off the pestle after each fly to avoid contamination. Why is it necessary to homogenize the flies?

7. Place the spot plate in a place away from light, such as a desk drawer.
8. After 5 minutes, check the reactions, and record your results in Table 1 in the Results section.
9. Thoroughly rinse your spot plate, and shake off the excess water.

Results

Complete Table 1 on the next page as the results of the assay tests are determined.

Table 1
AO Activity in Male and Female Flies from Vials 1a and 1b

Vial 1a (AO Present)			Vial 1b (AO Absent)		
Fly No.	Sex (F, M)	AO Activity (+/–)	Fly No.	Sex (F, M)	AO Activity (+/–)
1			1		
2			2		
3			3		
4			4		
5			5		
6			6		

Discussion

1. Do your results match your predictions?

2. Does the sex of the fly appear to have an impact on the results of the assay test?

3. Which two characteristics are most useful to your group in determining the sex of flies?

EXERCISE 2

Determining the Pattern of Inheritance of the Aldox Gene

Materials

vial 1a
vial 2
remaining materials from Exercise 1

Introduction

This exercise initiates our study of the pattern of inheritance of the aldox gene, which determines the activity of aldehyde oxidase (AO).

The gene is called the *aldox gene;* the enzyme produced by this gene is *aldehyde oxidase* and is abbreviated AO.

In this exercise, you will determine which **allele** (form of the gene) is dominant: enzyme-present or enzyme-absent. In addition, you will determine if the gene is **autosomal** or **sex-linked.** A sex-linked gene is located on one sex chromosome but not on the other. An autosomal gene is located on any chromosome *except* a sex chromosome. Finally, you will use this information to name the gene according to conventional naming procedures used by *Drosophila* geneticists.

The organisms you will use are in vial 2, which contains the offspring (called *F_1 progeny*) from a mating between a female that *lacks the enzyme* and a male that *has the enzyme.* For now, name the enzyme-present allele *AO-present* and the enzyme-absent allele *AO-absent.* The female is from a stock of flies that, when inbred, *consistently* lacks the enzyme from generation to generation. We say that this stock **breeds true** for AO-absent. The male is from a stock that *consistently* has the enzyme from generation to generation; that is, it breeds true for AO-present. This stock, which has the enzyme, is genetically like flies most commonly found in nature and is called the **wild type.**

It is necessary to understand this background information to be able to predict the outcome of this cross. To help you in your predictions, answer the following questions.

1. What is the genotype of the female (maternal parent—lacks the enzyme) in our cross?

2. What would be the genotype of the male (paternal parent—has the enzyme) in our cross if the gene is *not* sex-linked?

3. What would be the genotype of the male if the gene *is* sex-linked?

4. What would be the genotypes of the F_1 progeny if the gene is *not* sex-linked?

5. What would be the genotype if the gene *is* sex-linked?

Hypothesis

Hypothesize about the inheritance of this gene. Is it sex-linked? According to your hypothesis, what will be the genotypes of the parents?

Prediction

Predict the offspring from the hypothesized parents. *(Hint:* Set up a Punnett square.)

Procedure

1. Anesthetize the flies in vial 2.
2. Count out ten males and ten females. Keep track of the sexes of flies as you place them in the spot plate. Record the sex of each fly in Table 2.

It is easier to keep accurate records if you put all males in one row of the spot plate and all females in another row. Do not write on the spot plates!

3. Perform the spot assay as described in Exercise 1 with the following addition: From vial 1a, select a single fly and assay it with this and all following experiments. This will provide you with a *positive control* to compare with your unknown assays.

The assay mixture is light sensitive. Cover the spot plate with an index card between steps.

4. When you see that the positive control has turned blue, indicating that the assay is working, record the results in Table 2.
5. Rinse out the spot plate carefully.

Results

Record the sex of each fly and the results of the spot assay tests in Table 2.

Table 2

Data Sheet for Exercise 2: Results of Spot Assay Tests on F_1 Progeny from a Female That Lacks AO Activity and a Male That Has AO Activity

Fly No.	Sex (F, M)	AO Activity (+/–)	Fly No.	Sex (F, M)	AO Activity (+/–)
1			11		
2			12		
3			13		
4			14		
5			15		
6			16		
7			17		
8			18		
9			19		
10			20		
Positive control:					

Discussion

1. What allele appears to be dominant?

2. What evidence of your results in Table 2 supports your answer?

3. Determine the conventional way to name this gene. The following information will assist you. For any gene with two alleles, there exists the wild type and the mutation. Recall that the wild type is the allele most commonly found in nature. In this case, the wild type is AO-present. AO-absent is considered a **mutation,** a change in the DNA of the gene. In naming genes and alleles, give the gene an appropriate name. (In this case, the gene is named *aldox* because the enzyme that it produces catalyzes the oxidation of aldehydes.) If the mutation is dominant, capitalize the first letter in the name. If the mutation is recessive, do not capitalize. Based on the results of your experiment (see question 1), should the aldox gene be written beginning with a capital or a lower-case letter?

4. Correctly write the names of the wild-type and mutant alleles. By convention, wild-type alleles are designated by a superscript + after the name.

5. Did you hypothesize that the gene was sex-linked (on a sex chromosome) or autosomal (not on a sex chromosome)?

6. Describe how your results either support or falsify your hypothesis.

7. Write a statement describing your conclusions from this experiment.

EXERCISE 3

Determining Parental Genotypes Using Evidence from Progeny

Materials

vial 1a
vial 3
remaining materials from Exercise 1

Introduction

Once the pattern of inheritance has been determined, this information can be used to predict genotypes and phenotypes of individuals by observing parents, siblings, and offspring. Vial 3 contains the first-generation (F_1) progeny from a mating between unknown parents. The objective of this exercise is to determine the genotypes of the parents. At this stage in the investigation, you have no data from observations on which to base a hypothesis. The following procedure will allow you to collect preliminary data, then, using this data, to propose and test a hypothesis about the genotypes of the parents.

Procedure, Preliminary Observations

1. Anesthetize the flies in vial 3.
2. Count out 24 flies and place them in individual spot plate wells.
3. Perform the spot assay, including a positive control, a fly from vial 1a.
4. Record the results on *two* data sheets, Table 3, and the data sheet for the total class (provided by the instructor).

Results, Preliminary Observations

1. Record results of assay tests on progeny of the unknown parents in Table 3 on the next page.
2. Total the number of offspring in each phenotype category.

	Your Totals	Class Totals
AO-present	___________	___________
AO-absent	___________	___________

3. Review observations made in previous experiments.
   a. Is the trait sex-linked?

   b. Which allele is dominant?

Table 3
Data Sheet for Exercise 3: Results of Assay Tests on Progeny of Unknown Parents

Fly No.	AO Activity (+/–)	Fly No.	AO Activity (+/–)
1		13	
2		14	
3		15	
4		16	
5		17	
6		18	
7		19	
8		20	
9		21	
10		22	
11		23	
12		24	
Positive control:			

Hypothesis

Using all observations, hypothesize the genotypes of the parent flies, making sure to name the alleles correctly.

Prediction

Predict the results of the experiment (if/then).

Procedure—Testing Your Hypothesis

Using the total class data and Table 4, perform the chi-square test to determine if the results of the exercise support or falsify your hypothesis. Calculate the expected values for each trait based on the total number of flies counted in your class.

Results

Complete the chi-square calculations in Table 4.

Table 4
Chi-Square Calculations to Evaluate Results of Exercise 3
(Observed value represents total class data.)

	AO Activity (+)	AO Activity (–)
Observed value (o)		
Expected value (e)		
Deviation ($o - e$) or d		
Deviation^2 (d^2)		
d^2/e		
Chi-square (χ^2) $= \Sigma d^2/e$		
Degrees of freedom (df)		
Probability (p) (see a χ^2 table)		

Discussion

1. Do the class results support or falsify your hypothesis?

2. Does this experiment support or contradict your conclusions concerning the pattern of inheritance derived from Experiment 2?

EXERCISE 4
Mapping Genes

Materials

vial 1a
vial 4
remaining materials from Exercise 1

Introduction

In this exercise, you will investigate the inheritance of two genes in *Drosophila:* the aldox gene and a gene that influences eye color named **sepia.** In the wild-type fly (sepia⁺), eye color is red. In the mutant fly, eye color is dark brown. The wild-type allele is dominant over the mutant. The flies you will be studying are the offspring from a cross in which the parents differ in these two genes: a **dihybrid cross.** You will ask if these two genes are transmitted from parent to offspring *linked* together or if each gene is inherited independently of the other. If genes are transmitted from parent to offspring linked together, this means that they are located on the same chromosome. Then if the location of one gene is known, the pattern of inheritance can provide evidence that will allow you to determine the location of the second gene. With this information, you can construct a map showing gene locations.

Vial 4 contains the F_1 progeny from a mating between parents having the following genotypes:

Parent 1		Parent 2
$\frac{\text{sepia}^{+}\ \text{aldox}^{+}}{\text{sepia aldox}}$	↔	$\frac{\text{sepia aldox}}{\text{sepia aldox}}$

where sepia⁺ represents the dominant, wild-type eye color allele that produces red eye color and sepia represents the mutant, recessive allele that produces a dark-brown eye color.

Hypothesis

Hypothesize about the inheritance of these two genes. Are they inherited linked together or independently of each other?

Prediction

Predict the ratios of phenotypic classes of offspring resulting from the mating described above.

Use a Punnett square to illustrate your prediction.

Procedure

1. Anesthetize the flies in vial 4.
2. Count out 50 flies, and classify them on the basis of eye color (red or sepia).
3. Keeping the eye colors separate, perform the spot assay, including a positive control from vial 1a.
4. Record the results in Table 5 on the next page.
5. Rinse out the spot plate.

Results

1. Record the results of the eye color classification and the spot test for each fly in Table 5. Total your results below. Add your results to the total class data sheet provided by the instructor. Total the class data and record below.

	Your Totals	Class Totals
red eyes, AO-present	__________	__________
red eyes, AO-absent	__________	__________
sepia eyes, AO-present	__________	__________
sepia eyes, AO-absent	__________	__________

2. What phenotypic classes were observed in the total class data, and in what approximate ratio?

3. On separate paper, using class totals, perform the chi-square test to determine if the results support or falsify your hypothesis.

Table 5
Data Sheet for Exercise 4: Mapping Genes, Recording Eye Color and AO Activity for 50 Flies

Fly No.	Eye Color	AO (+/–)	Fly No.	Eye Color	AO (+/–)
1			26		
2			27		
3			28		
4			29		
5			30		
6			31		
7			32		
8			33		
9			34		
10			35		
11			36		
12			37		
13			38		
14			39		
15			40		
16			41		
17			42		
18			43		
19			44		
20			45		
21			46		
22			47		
23			48		
24			49		
25			50		

Discussion

1. Do the data support your predicted results?

2. If the results differ from what was expected, can you suggest an explanation for these differences?

3. Suppose that the aldox gene and the sepia gene are located on the same chromosome. This means that when meiosis takes place, the two genes will *not* assort independently but will be linked together, moving into the same gamete *unless crossing over has taken place*. Only if crossing over takes place will **recombinant classes** of phenotypes be observed. A **recombinant chromosome** is one emerging from meiosis with a combination of alleles not present on the chromosomes entering meiosis.

   What are the recombinant classes of phenotypes for this cross?

4. The distance between two genes is related to the frequency of recombinants produced during meiosis. The closer two genes are, the fewer recombinants. Geneticists use an arbitrary measure, or map unit, to represent the distance between two genes. The specific relationship between map units and recombinants is

$$\text{Map units} = \frac{\text{number of recombinants}}{\text{total}} \leftrightarrow 100$$

5. In your experiment, did recombinant classes exist? If they did, how frequent were they?

6. Do your data suggest that aldox and sepia are on the same chromosome, and if so, how far is the aldox locus from the sepia locus?

7. What would be the exact map position of the aldox locus if the sepia locus is 26.0? Are you sure?

Questions for Review

1. List the most obvious characteristics used to determine the sex of a fruit fly.

2. In *Drosophila,* crosses between male flies with normal bristles on their bodies (the wild type) and female flies with short, stubby bristles result in an F_1 generation with all flies having short, stubby bristles. Which allele, normal or mutant, is dominant?

   Using *Drosophila* convention, suggest an appropriate name or designation for this gene.

Applying Your Knowledge

1. In a testcross between a heterozygous tomato plant with round fruit shape and smooth fruit skin and a homozygous recessive plant with elongated fruit shape and fuzzy skin, the following numbers of offspring were counted: smooth, round = 246; smooth, long = 24; fuzzy, round = 24; fuzzy, long = 266.

   Do these results deviate from expected results of a testcross? Explain fully.

2. Explain why we cannot use a testcross to detect linkage between two genes located on the same chromosome 50 map units apart.

References

This lab topic was first published as J. G. Morgan and V. Finnerty, "Inheritance of Aldehyde Oxidase in *Drosophila melanogaster*" in *Tested Studies for Laboratory Teaching* (Volume 12), Proceedings of the 12th Workshop/Conference of the Association for Biology Laboratory Education (ABLE), Corey A. Goldman, Editor. Used by permission.

Manning, Gerard. The *Drosophila* Virtual Library. [online] available at http://www.ceolas.org/fly/, 2001.

Website

Interactive fruitfly genetics lab, requires registration:
http://biologylab.awlonline.com/Flylab/

Art Credits

2, 3: From Demerec and Kaufman, *Drosophila Guide*, 9th ed. (Washington, DC: Carnegie Institution of Washington, 1986), ©1986 Carnegie Institution of Washington. Reprinted by permission.

Text Credits

First published as Morgan, J. G., and V. Finnerty, "Inheritance of aldehyde oxidase in *Drosophila melanogaster*" in *Tested Studies for Laboratory Teaching*, Volume 12, Proceedings of the 12th Workshop/Conference of the Association for Biology Laboratory Education (ABLE), Corey A. Goldman, Editor. Used by permission.

APPENDIX

Scientific Writing

For the scientific enterprise to be successful, scientists must communicate their work. Major scientific findings are never kept secret. Instead, scientists share their ideas and results with other scientists, encouraging critical review and alternative interpretations from colleagues and the entire scientific community. Communication, both verbal and written, occurs at every step along the research path. While working on projects, scientists present their preliminary results for comments from their coworkers at laboratory group meetings and in written research reports. At a later stage, scientists report the results of their research activities as a poster or oral presentation at a scientific meeting. Then the final report is prepared in a rather standard scientific paper format and submitted for publication in an appropriate scientific journal. At each stage in this process, scientists encourage and require critical review of their work and ideas by their peers. The final publication in a peer-reviewed journal generally promotes additional research and establishes this contribution to current knowledge.

One of the objectives of every lab topic in this manual is to develop your writing skills. You will generate and write hypotheses, results, observations, answers to questions, and more, as one way of learning biology. Also, you will practice writing in a scientific paper format and style to communicate the results of your investigations. By the time you have completed the lab topics in this manual, you will have written the equivalent of at least two complete scientific papers.

As you investigate the different lab topics, you will make observations, ask questions, and propose hypotheses. You will design and conduct experiments using procedures of your own design or following procedures in the manual. You will record results, designing tables and graphs to present your data in a logical and organized format. You will then interpret results and come to conclusions based on your hypotheses. This process is reflected in the design of a scientific paper and the format you will use for your laboratory papers. Each paper will be divided into sections that reflect these activities.

A scientific paper usually includes the following parts: a **Title** (statement of the question or problem), an **Abstract** (short summary of the paper), an **Introduction** (background and significance of the problem), a **Materials and Methods** section (report of exactly what you did), a **Results** section (presentation of data), a **Discussion** section (interpretation and discussion of results), and **References Cited** (books and periodicals used). A **Conclusion** (concise restatement of conclusions) and **Acknowledgments** (recognition of assistance) may also be included.

We propose that you practice writing throughout the biology laboratory program by submitting individual sections of a scientific paper. Although your instructor will determine which sections you will write for a given lab topic, we outline a sample writing program below.

Scientific Writing Program

Examples of Individual Sections of a Scientific Paper for Suggested Lab Topics:

Title Page and Materials and Methods for Lab Topic Scientific Investigation

Results for Lab Topic Enzymes

Discussion for Lab Topic Diffusion and Osmosis

Results plus Discussion for Lab Topic Cellular Respiration and Fermentation

Introduction and References Cited for Lab Topic, Photosynthesis

Your instructor will evaluate each of these sections, pointing out areas of weakness and suggesting improvements. By the time you have completed these assignments, you will have submitted the equivalent of one scientific paper.

Having practiced writing each section of a scientific paper in the first half of the laboratory program, you will then write one or two complete laboratory papers in scientific paper format during the second half of the laboratory program, reporting the results of experiments, preferably those that you and your research team have designed and performed. Because performing the experiment will be a collaborative effort, you and your teammates will share information for the Materials and Methods and Results sections of your reports. However, the Introduction, Discussion, and References Cited (or References) sections must be the product of your own personal library research and creative thinking. If you are not certain about the level of independence and what constitutes plagiarism in this laboratory program, ask your instructor to clarify the class policy. *In the most extreme case of plagiarism, a student presents another student's report as his or her own. However, representing another person's ideas as your own without giving that person credit is also plagiarism and is a serious offense.*

A more detailed description of each section of a scientific paper follows. As you write your paper, clearly label each section (except the title page), placing the title of the section against the left margin on a separate line.

Title Page and Title

The title page is the first page of the paper and includes the title of the paper, your name, the course title, your lab time or section, your instructor's name, and the due date for the paper. *The title should be as short as possible and as long as necessary to communicate to the reader the question being answered in the paper.* For example, if you are asking a question about the inheritance patterns of the gene for aldehyde oxidase production in *Drosophila melanogaster,* a possible title might be "Inheritance of the Gene for Aldehyde Oxidase in *Drosophila melanogaster.*" Something like "Inheritance in Fruit Flies" is too general, and "A Study of the Inheritance of the Enzyme Aldehyde Oxidase in the Fruit Fly *Drosophila melanogaster*" is too wordy. The words "A Study of the" are superfluous, and "Enzyme" and "Fruit Fly" are redundant. The suffix *-ase* indicates that aldehyde oxidase is an enzyme, and most scientists know that *Drosophila melanogaster* is the scientific name of a common fruit fly species. However, it is appropriate to include in the title both common and scientific names of lesser known species.

Place the title about 7 cm from the top of the title page. Place "by" and your name in the center of the page, and place the course name, lab section, instructor's name, and due date, each on a separate centered line, at the bottom of the page. Leave about 5 cm below this information.

Abstract

The abstract, if one is requested by the instructor, is placed at the beginning of the second page of the paper, after the title page. *The abstract concisely summarizes the question being investigated in the paper, the methods used in the experiment, the results, and the conclusions drawn.* The reader should be able to determine the major topics in the paper without reading the entire paper. The abstract should be no more than 250 words, and fewer if possible. Compose the abstract after the paper is completed.

Introduction

The introduction has two functions: (1) to provide the context for your investigation and (2) to state the question asked and the hypothesis tested in the study. Begin the introduction by reviewing background information that will enable the reader to understand the objective of the study and the significance of the problem, relating the problem to the larger issues in the field. Include only information that directly prepares the reader to understand the question investigated. Most ideas in the introduction will come from outside sources, such as scientific journals or books dealing with the topic you are investigating. All sources of information must be referenced and included in the References Cited (or References) section of the paper, but the introduction must be in your own words. Refer to the references when appropriate. Unless otherwise instructed, place the author of the reference cited and the year of publication in parentheses at the end of the sentence or paragraph relating the idea; for example, "(Finnerty, 1992)." Additional information on citing references is provided on p. 756, References Cited. Do not use citation forms utilized in other disciplines. Do not use footnotes and avoid the use of direct quotes.

As you describe your investigation, include only the question and hypothesis that you finally investigated. Briefly describe the experiment performed and the outcome predicted for the experiment. Although these items are usually presented after the background information near the end of the introduction, you should have each clearly in mind before you begin writing the introduction. It is a good idea to write down each item (question, hypothesis, prediction) before you begin to write your introduction.

Write the introduction in the past tense when referring to your experiment; but when relating the background information, use the present tense as you refer to another investigator's published work. Previously published work is considered established in the present body of knowledge.

Throughout your paper, we encourage you to use the active voice whenever possible. Doing so makes the paper easier to read and more understandable. In biology, editors of scientific journals are now suggesting or requiring use of the active voice.

In general, the Introduction is written before the Discussion; however, some authors prefer to write the Introduction last. Remember to revise the Introduction after completing your paper.

Materials and Methods

The Materials and Methods section describes your experiment in such a way that it can be repeated. This section should be a narrative description that integrates the materials with the procedures used in the investigation. Do not list the materials and do not list the steps of the procedure. Rather, write the Materials and Methods section concisely in paragraph form in the past tense. Be sure to include levels of treatment, numbers of replications, and controls. If you are working with living organisms, include the scientific name and the sex of the organism if that information is relevant to the experiment. If you used computer software or any statistical analyses, include these in the Materials and Methods section.

The difficulty in writing this section comes as you decide the level of detail to include in your paragraphs. You must determine which details are essential for another investigator to repeat the experiment. For example, if in your experiment you incubated potato pieces in different concentrations of sucrose solution, it would not be necessary to explain that the pieces were incubated in plastic cups labeled with a wax marking pencil or to provide the numbers of the cups. In this case, the molarity of the sucrose solutions, the size of the potato pieces and how they were obtained, and the amount of incubation solution are the important items to include. Do not include failed attempts unless the technique used may be tried by other investigators. Do not try to justify your procedures in this section.

The Materials and Methods section is often the best place to begin writing your paper. The writing is straightforward and concise, and you will be reminded of the details of the work.

Results

The Results section consists of at least four components: (1) one or two sentences reminding the reader about the nature of the research, (2) one or more paragraphs that describe the results, (3) figures (graphs, diagrams, pictures), and (4) tables. *The Results is the central section of a scientific paper.* Therefore, you should think carefully about the best way to present your results to the reader. The data included in tables and graphs should be summarized and emphasized in the narrative paragraph. Draw the reader's attention to the results that are important. Describe trends in your data and provide evidence to support your claims. This section also is written in the past tense.

Before writing the Results section, prepare the tables and figures. Remember to number figures and tables consecutively throughout the paper (*see Scientific Investigation for instructions on creating figures and tables and their presenta-*

tion). Refer to figures and tables within the paragraph as you describe your results, using the word Figure or Table, followed by its number; for example, "(Figure 1)." If possible, place each figure or table at the end of the paragraph in which it is cited.

If you have performed a statistical analysis of your data, such as chi-square, include the results in this section.

Report your data as accurately as possible. Do not report what you expected to happen in the experiment nor whether your data supported your hypothesis. Do not discuss the meaning of your results in this section. Do not critique the results. Any data you plan to include in the Discussion section must be presented in the Results. Conversely, do not include data in the Results that you do not mention in the Discussion.

Write the Results section before attempting the Discussion section. This will ensure that the results of your investigation are clearly organized, logically presented, and thoroughly understood before they are discussed. For this reason, some scientists begin with the Results section when writing a paper.

Discussion

In the Discussion section, you will analyze and interpret the results of your experiment. Simply restating the results is not interpretation. The Discussion must provide a context for understanding the significance of the results. Explain why you observed these results and how these results contribute to our knowledge. Your results either will support or confirm your hypothesis or will negate, refute, or contradict your hypothesis; but the word *prove is* not appropriate in scientific writing. If your results do not support your hypothesis, you must still state why you think this occurred. Support your ideas from other work (books, lectures or outside reading of scientific literature). State your conclusions in this section.

Complete your Introduction and Results sections before you begin writing the Discussion. The figures and tables in the Results section will be particularly important as you begin to think about your discussion. The tables allow you to present your results clearly to the reader, and graphs allow you to visualize the effects that the independent variable has had on the dependent variables in your experiment. Studying these data will be one of the first steps in interpreting your results. As you study the information in the Introduction section and your data in the Results section, write down relationships and integrate these relationships into a rough draft of your discussion.

The following steps, modified from Gray, Dickey, and Kosinski (1988), may be helpful to you as you begin to organize your discussion and before you write the narrative:

1. Restate your question, hypothesis, and prediction.
2. Answer the question.
3. Write down the specific data, including results of statistical tests.
4. State whether your results did or did not confirm your prediction and support or negate your hypothesis.
5. Write down what you know about the biology involved in your experiment. How do your results fit in with what you know? What is the significance of your results?

6. How do your results support or conflict with previous work? Include references to this work.
7. Clearly state your conclusions.
8. List weaknesses you have identified in your experimental design that affected your results. List any problems that arose during the experiment itself that affected your results. The weaknesses of the experiment should not dominate the Discussion. Include one or two sentences only if these problems affected the results. Remember the focus of the Discussion is to convey the significance of the results.
9. You are now ready to write the narrative for the Discussion. Integrate all of the information into several simple, clear, concise paragraphs. Discuss the results; do not simply restate the data. Refer to other work to support your ideas.

References Cited (or References)

A References Cited section lists only those references cited in the paper. A References section (bibliography), on the other hand, is a more inclusive list of all references used in producing the paper, including books and papers used to obtain background knowledge that may not be cited in the paper. For your paper you should have a References Cited section that includes only those references cited in the paper. The format for the References Cited section differs slightly from one scientific journal to the next. How does an author know which format to use? Every scientific journal provides "Instructions to Authors" that describe specific requirements for this important section and all other aspects of the paper. You may use the format used in this lab manual and provided in the examples below, select the format in a scientific journal provided by your instructor, or use another accepted format for listing your references. Your instructor may provide additional instructions. Be sure to read the references that you cite in your paper.

Examples of Reference Citations

Journal article, one author:

Whittaker, R. H. "New Concepts of Kingdoms of Organisms." *Science,* 1969, vol. 163, pp. 150–160.

Journal article, two or more authors:

Watson, J. D., and F. H. Crick. "Molecular Structure of Nucleic Acids: A Structure for Deoxyribose Nucleic Acid." *Nature,* 1953, vol. 171, pp. 737–738.

Book:

Darwin, C. R. *On the Origin of Species.* London: John Murray, 1859.

Chapter or article in an edited book:

Baker, H. G. "Characteristics and Modes of Origin of Weeds" in *Genetics and Colonizing Species,* eds. H. G. Baker and G. L. Stebbins. New York: Academic Press, 1965, pp. 147–152.

Government publication:

Office of Technology Assessment. *Harmful Non-indigenous Species in the United States*. Publication no. OTA-F-565. Washington, D.C.: U.S. Government Printing Office, 1993.

In the text of the paper, cite the references using the author's name and the year. For example: "The innate agonistic behavior of the male Siamese fighting fish has been widely studied (Simpson, 1968)." "Simpson (1968) has described the agonistic behavior of the male Siamese fighting fish." If there are more than two authors, use the first author's name followed by *et al.* (and others). For example: (Simpson *et al.*, 1968).

Using Information Sources from the Web

The Web can provide access to online reference resources including *Biological Abstracts, Current Contents, Medline,* and *Annual Reviews* among many others. These search tools provide access to a wide range of published papers, some of which may be available online as full text journals. For suggestions and examples of how to locate sources using the Web, see Pechenik (2001). Scientific papers published in professional journals have gone through an extensive review process by other scientists in the same field. Most scientific articles have been revised based on comments by the reviewers and the editors. Sources of information that lack this critical review process do not have the same validity and authority.

The World Wide Web (WWW) is an exciting, immediate, and easily accessible source of information. However, unlike traditional bibliographic resources in the sciences, the WWW includes websites with material that has not been critically reviewed. Your instructor may prefer that you use the WWW only for locating peer-reviewed resources or as a starting point to promote your interest and ideas. You may not be allowed to use WWW sources at all. Consult your instructor concerning use of online information.

If you do use the WWW to locate information, you should be prepared to evaluate these sites critically. Remember always to record the online address for any site you use as a reference. Tate and Alexander (1996) suggest the following five criteria for evaluating WWW sources:

1. **Authority.** Determine the author and sponsor for the WWW site. What is the professional affiliation of the author? Are phone numbers and addresses included? Is there a link to the sponsor's home page? Does the author list his or her qualifications? If the material is copyrighted, who owns the copyright?
2. **Accuracy.** Look for indications of professional standards for writing, citations, figures, and tables. Are there typographical, spelling, and grammatical errors? Are sources of information cited? Are the data presented or simply summarized?
3. **Objectivity.** Is the site provided as a public service, free of advertising? If advertising is present, is it clearly separate from the information? Does the site present only the view of the sponsor or advertiser?

4. **Currency.** Determine the date of the site and whether it is regularly revised. How long has the site existed? When was it last updated? Are figures and tables dated? Some WWW sites disappear overnight. Always record the date that you visited the site and retrieved information.
5. **Coverage.** Is the information offered in a complete form or as an abstract or summary of information published elsewhere? Is the site under construction? When was the site last revised?

We have included one suggested format for citing online information in the References Cited section of your paper. Also see the examples at the end of many lab topics in this manual. Other formats may be suggested by your instructor or librarian.

Author. *Title.* [online] available http://www.address, date accessed.

For example: Manning, G. *The Drosophila Virtual Library.* [online] available http://www.ceolas.org/fly/, 1998.

Reminders

Scientific writing should be clear and concise. This requires critical thinking and repeated revision. You should read background information carefully and critically in preparation for designing your investigation and to provide a context for your work. As you complete your investigation, you must think critically about your results and the best way to present your results. Scientific writing involves using evidence from your work and that of others to make a clear and logical argument. To be successful you must plan time for researching your topic, analyzing your results, and then revising your writing. For suggestions and examples of how to revise your work, see Chapter 5, "Revising," in Pechnik (2001).

As you begin writing your paper, refer to the following list for hints on how to make your writing stronger:

1. Write clearly in short and logical, but not choppy, sentences.
2. Use the past tense in the Abstract, Materials and Methods, and Results sections. Also use the past tense in the Introduction and Discussion sections when referring to your experiment.
3. Write in grammatically correct English.
4. When referring to the scientific name of an organism, the genus and species should be in italics or underlined. The first letter of the genus is capitalized, but the species is written in all lowercase letters; for example, *Drosophila melanogaster.*
5. Use metric units. Use numerals when reporting measurements, percentages, decimals, and magnifications. When beginning a sentence, write the number as a word. Numbers of ten or less, that are not measurements, are written. Numbers greater than ten are given as numerals.
6. The word "data" is plural.
7. Record the citation information for any references, including online sources, at the time you read the information. Refer to the citation format to record the complete citation.
8. Save a copy of your work on a disk and print a copy of your paper before turning in the original.

9. Begin writing early to allow time for revision. Simplify your writing. Delete unnecessary words. Adjectives and adverbs have limited use in describing your work.
10. Carefully proofread your work, even if your word processor has checked for grammatical and spelling errors. These programs cannot distinguish between your and you're, for example.

References

The following sources are recommended to give additional help and examples in scientific writing:

Gray, L. S., J. Dickey, and R. Kosinski. *Writing Guide.* Clemson, SC: Clemson University, 1988.

McMillan, V. E. *Writing Papers in the Biological Sciences.* New York, NY: St. Martin's Press, 1988.

Moore, R. *Writing to Learn Biology.* New York, NY: Saunders College Publishing, 1992.

Pechenik, J. A. *A Short Guide to Writing about Biology,* 4th ed., New York, NY: Addison Wesley, 2001.

Tate, M., and J. Alexander. "Teaching Critical Evaluation Skills for World Wide Web Resources." *Computers in Libraries,* Nov/Dec 1996, pp. 49–55.

Websites

Bibliography on Evaluating Internet Resources: http://refserver.lib.vt.edu/libinst/critTHINK.HTM, 1998.

Biologist's Guide to Library Resources: www.ase.tufts.edu/biology/bguide/, 2000.

Text Credits

Adapted from L. S. Gray, J. Dickey, and R. Kosinski, *Writing Guide* (Clemson, SC: Clemson University, 1988), by permission.

APPENDIX

Chi-Square Test

Chi-square is a statistical test commonly used to compare observed data with data we would expect to obtain according to a specific scientific hypothesis. For example, if according to Mendel's laws, you expect 10 of 20 offspring from a cross to be male and the actual observed number is 8 males out of 20 offspring, then you might want to know about the "goodness of fit" between the observed and the expected. Were the deviations (differences between observed and expected) the result of chance, or were they due to other factors? How much deviation can occur before the investigator must conclude that something other than chance is at work, causing the observed to differ from the expected? The chi-square test can help in making that decision. The chi-square test is always testing what scientists call the **null hypothesis,** which states that there is no significant difference between the expected and the observed result.

The formula for calculating chi-square (χ^2) is:

$$\chi^2 = \Sigma(o - e)^2 / e$$

That is, chi-square is the sum of the squared difference between observed (o) and expected (e) data (or the deviation, d), divided by the expected data in all possible categories.

For example, suppose that a cross between two pea plants yields a population of 880 plants, 639 with green seeds and 241 with yellow seeds. You are asked to propose the genotypes of the parents. Your scientific hypothesis is that the allele for green is dominant to the allele for yellow and that the parent plants were both heterozygous for this trait. If your scientific hypothesis is true, then the predicted ratio of offspring from this cross would be 3:1 (based on Mendel's laws), as predicted from the results of the Punnett square (Figure B.1). The related null hypothesis is that there is no significant difference between your observed pea offspring and offspring produced according to Mendel's laws. To determine if this null hypothesis is rejected or not rejected, a χ^2 value is computed.

To calculate χ^2, first determine the number expected in each category. If the ratio is 3:1 and the total number of observed individuals is 880, then the expected numerical values should be 660 green and 220 yellow ($^3/_4 \times 880 = 660$; $^1/_4 \times 880 = 220$).

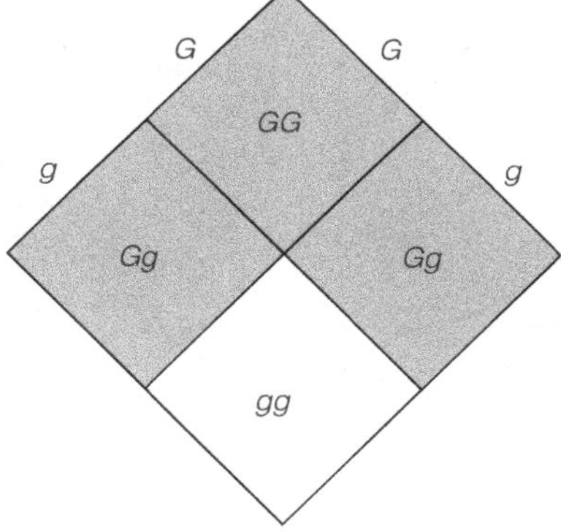

Figure 1.
Punnett square. Predicted offspring from cross between green- and yellow-seeded plants. Green (G) is dominant (3/4 green; 1/4 yellow).

Chi-square analysis requires that you use numerical values, not percentages or ratios.

Then calculate χ^2 using the formula, as shown in Table 1. Note that we get a value of 2.673 for χ^2. But what does this number mean? Here's how to interpret the χ^2 value:

1. Determine **degrees of freedom** (df). Degrees of freedom can be calculated as the number of categories in the problem minus 1. For example, if we had four categories, then the degrees of freedom would be 3. In our example, there are two categories (green and yellow); therefore, there is 1 degree of freedom.
2. Determine a relative standard to serve as the basis for rejecting the hypothesis. Scientists allow some level of error in their decision making for testing their hypotheses. The relative standard commonly used in biological research is $p < 0.05$. The ***p* value** is the *probability* of rejecting the null hypothesis (that there is no difference between observed and expected), when the null hypothesis is true. In other words, the p value gives an approximate value for the error of falsely stating that there is a significant difference between your observed numbers and the expected numbers, when there is *not* a significant difference. *When we pick $p < 0.05$, we state that there is less than a 5% chance of error of stating that there is a difference when, in fact, there is no significant difference.* Although scientists and statisticians sometimes select a lower significance value, in this manual we will assume a value of 0.05.
3. Refer to a chi-square distribution table (Table 2). Using the appropriate degrees of freedom, locate the value corresponding to the p value of 0.05, the error probability that you selected. If your χ^2 value is *greater* than the value corresponding to the p value of 0.05, then you reject the null hypothesis. You conclude that the observed numbers are significantly different from the expected. In this example your calculated value, $\chi^2 = 2.673$, is not larger than the table χ^2 value of 3.84 (df = 1, $p = 0.05$). *Therefore, your observed distribution of plants with green and yellow seeds is not significantly different from the distribution that would be expected under Mendel's laws. Any minor differences between your offspring distribution and the expected Mendelian distribution can be attributed to chance or sampling error.*

Step-by-Step Procedure for Testing Your Hypothesis and Calculating Chi-Square

1. State the hypothesis being tested and the predicted results.
2. Gather the data by conducting the relevant experiment (or, if working genetics problems, use the data provided in the problem).
3. Determine the expected numbers for each observational class. Remember to use numbers, not percentages.

Chi-square should *not* be calculated if the expected value in any category is less than 5.

4. Calculate χ^2 using the formula. Complete all calculations to three significant digits.

Table 1
Calculating Chi-Square

	Green	**Yellow**
Observed (*o*)	639	241
Expected (*e*)	660	220
Deviation ($o - e$)	–21	21
Deviation² (d^2)	441	441
d^2/e	0.668	2.005
$\chi^2 = \Sigma d^2/e = 2.673$		

Table 2
Chi-Square Distribution

Degrees of Freedom (df)	**Probability (*p*)**										
	0.95	**0.90**	**0.80**	**0.70**	**0.50**	**0.30**	**0.20**	**0.10**	**0.05**	**0.01**	**0.001**
1	0.004	0.02	0.06	0.15	0.46	1.07	1.64	2.71	3.84	6.64	10.83
2	0.10	0.21	0.45	0.71	1.39	2.41	3.22	4.60	5.99	9.21	13.82
3	0.35	0.58	1.01	1.42	2.37	3.66	4.64	6.25	7.82	11.34	16.27
4	0.71	1.06	1.65	2.20	3.36	4.88	5.99	7.78	9.49	13.28	18.47
5	1.14	1.61	2.34	3.00	4.35	6.06	7.29	9.24	11.07	15.09	20.52
6	1.63	2.20	3.07	3.83	5.35	7.23	8.56	10.64	12.59	16.81	22.46
7	2.17	2.83	3.82	4.67	6.35	8.38	9.80	12.02	14.07	18.48	24.32
8	2.73	3.49	4.59	5.53	7.34	9.52	11.03	13.36	15.51	20.09	26.12
9	3.32	4.17	5.38	6.39	8.34	10.66	12.24	14.68	16.92	21.67	27.88
10	3.94	4.86	6.18	7.27	9.34	11.78	13.44	15.99	18.31	23.21	29.59
	Nonsignificant								Significant		

Source: R. A. Fisher and F. Yates, *Statistical Tables for Biological, Agricultural, and Medical Research*, 6th ed., Table IV, Longman Group UK Ltd., 1974.

5. Use the chi-square distribution table to determine the significance of the value.
   a. Determine the degrees of freedom, one less than the number of categories. Locate that value in the appropriate column.
   b. Locate the χ^2 value for your significance level ($p = 0.05$ or less).
   c. Compare this χ^2 value (from the table) with your calculated χ^2.
6. State your conclusion in terms of your hypothesis.
   a. If your calculated χ^2 value is greater than the χ^2 value for your particular degrees of freedom and p value (0.05), then *reject the null hypothesis* of no difference between expected and observed results. *You can conclude that there is a significant difference between your observed distribution and the theoretical expected distribution* (for example, under Mendel's laws).
   b. If your calculated χ^2 value is less than the χ^2 value for your particular degrees of freedom and p value (0.05), then *fail to reject the null hypothesis* of no difference between observed and expected results. *You can conclude that there does not seem to be a significant difference between your observed distribution and the theoretical expected distribution* (for example, under Mendel's laws). *You can conclude that any differences between your observed results and the expected results can be attributed to chance or sampling error.* (Note: It is incorrect to say that you "accept" the null hypothesis. Statisticians either "reject" or "fail to reject" the null hypothesis.)

The chi-square test will be used to test for the goodness of fit between observed and expected data from several laboratory investigations in this lab manual.

Reference

Motulsky, M. *Intuitive Biostatistics.* New York: Oxford University Press, 1995.

Text Credits

Table 2: From R. A. Fisher and F. Yates, *Statistical Tables for Biological, Agricultural and Medical Research*, 6th ed, Table IV. Reprinted by permission of Addison Wesley Longman Ltd.